In prison I often ████████████████████
scriptions of saints ███████████ *not falter*
under whips and hot iron: there was, for instance, the
excellent and in many ways realistic Italian film, The
Open City, *in which the Resistance hero spat in the*
face of his cruel interrogator, the Gestapo officer.
This is just the scene which in such circumstances
cannot happen. The Resistance hero, or his opposite
number in A.V.H. custody, by the time he faces the
demands of his interrogator, is physically unable to
show pride. The Gestapo or A.V.H. sees to that. To
be proud and dignified while cigarette ends are
stamped out on one's skin is surely more difficult than
cinema-goers would think. But it can be tried. To be
proud and dignified after being forbidden to go to the
lavatory for twenty-four hours cannot even be tried.
—from Chapter 6, "Why Did We All Confess?"

Paul Ignotus, *who came to London as a refugee
from the Nazis in 1939, returned there in 1956 after
his ordeal in Hungarian prisons was ended. He now
lives in* "an unluxurious, but comfortable flat, facing
Battersea Park, London" *with his wife and small son.
He has contributed articles to* Encounter, *the* New
Statesman, *and other English periodicals.*

PAUL IGNOTUS

POLITICAL

PRISONER

With an Epilogue by the Author

Bringing His Story Up to Date

COLLIER BOOKS
NEW YORK, N.Y.

Acknowledgement

I am indebted to innumerable friends and acquaintances both for surviving those chapters of my life described in this book, and for being able to describe them. Many helped me with their hospitality in exile, and many with their knowledge of English; many in filling the gaps in my memory while I was putting down my recollections; and many, even from among people whom I had never met, by standing up for me while the Hungarian authorities intended that I should "rot alive" in prison. The list of such friends is too long to be printed. But I ask them all, if they ever come across these pages, to be assured of my profound gratitude.

Contents

Foreword

I should like to think that my narrative speaks for itself. But a word of explanation may be required for what I skipped in it—mainly the detailed background of the Hungarian Revolution of October, 1956, and the reasons for its failure. It was too great a subject to be included, and too recent to be seen with detachment. This anyway, was how I felt while I wrote this book. Now I feel the time approaching when it will be possible to deal with the subject outspokenly and as an eye-witness; and, in fact, I am planning to do this in a future book.

About the spelling of Hungarian Christian names in this book: I have kept to the Hungarian version except for anyone whose name may be familiar in other versions among non-Hungarian readers. But I have kept the Indo-European way of putting the Christian name before the surname; in Hungarian, as in most oriental languages, it is the other way round.

P.I.

Chapter 1

First Time in London

I CAME to England for the first time in the winter of
1938–9, on false pretences. I called myself a journalist.
Indeed I had always been a journalist and tried to carry
on in London, after taking refuge from the Nazi terror
which was beginning to grip Hungary. But in London the
terror was a thing to be ignored. My status as a refugee
had to be forgotten. A movement to ignore obvious facts
was current all over Europe.

The country from which I came, and the one in which I
was to settle, and the two which allowed me to cross their
territories could all assume that Hungary was an independent and constitutional monarchy, though in fact she
was already a German satellite. Her ruling oligarchy was
appropriately headed by an admiral of the old Habsburg
Monarchy, a handsome old gentleman who spoke several
languages but read none. His name was Miklós (Nicholas)
vitéz ("the brave") Horthy de Nagybánya. Social snob-
bery turned his admiration towards the old Hungarian and
Austrian aristocracies, and also towards England which
had the oldest aristocracy and most powerful navy. But
the people he really trusted were small noblemen, the
landed gentry and privileged bureaucrats. They disliked
and imitated the Nazis. The parliamentary façade of Hungarian life with all its commercial and humanitarian benefits had to be kept up. Except for the Communists, no
political party was outlawed. The legal fiction of Hungary
left no reason for anyone to leave the country on account
of race, creed or political leanings; but the cleavage between law and facts widened day by day. A growing number of refugees left the country, pretending they went for
health, business or a holiday. One of the common pretexts
was journalism, and I chose that. It was natural for my
Government to pretend to believe me.

As a refugee, I had to accept the strange attitudes I

found. In a way it was comfortable. I could call at the Hungarian Legation with the politeness of an accredited newspaper correspondent and share the friendly feeling many of the staff there had towards the West. I was able to maintain regular correspondence with my relatives and friends in Budapest. On the other hand, this meant a lower status than the declared refugees enjoyed. Jews from Germany, democrats from Italy, Republicans from Spain and all the rest had their relief centres. They had a legal right to live as beggars in political exile. Crypto-refugees were merely unauthorized beggars.

The Hungary which I had left behind was a false but enchanting country. Her independence, her Constitution and her tax returns were all false. It was a Paradise for spivs, as they would later have been called in London. But the national genius allowed even decent people to live quite merrily in Hungary. Statisticians might show that a great part of the population, chiefly the landless peasantry, was practically starving. This was roughly true, but they had their own ways of managing. The county magistrates and police, known for their harshness, did not much bother about minor offences so long as their own authority was not challenged. Life was often humiliating rather than unpleasant, and it had a certain bucolic appeal.

The capital, my native city, Budapest, was false on a more splendid and enlightened scale. Its situation, with its fine bridges over the broad River Danube, and the proud Gothic monuments from the end of the last century, made it one of the most spectacular spots of Europe. It was a city which struck every visitor at first as extremely beautiful; but the impression changed after a few days; a more intimate knowledge of its people and surroundings was needed to find that it was permeated with charm. Its cafés, night clubs and restaurants were excellent. Apricot brandy in the restaurants and night clubs was appreciated by the Duke of Windsor, then Prince of Wales. The cafés had different merits. They were the fountain of illicit trading, adultery, puns, gossip and poetry. They were also the origin of Hungarian liberty. In 1848 a group led by the twenty-six year old poet, Petőfi, set out from the café Pilvax to march against the bastions of absolutism and feudalism and succeeded for a while in overthrowing them. In a less rhetorical way the cafés had been since then the meeting places for the intellectuals and those who opposed oppression. When there was a Free Press they were almost its editorial offices, and when there was no Free Press they made up for it. In the inter-war period, a limited number of Government and Opposition newspapers and magazines could be published. Ten times a year, however, and with various obstacles, magazines without any official backing could also be published. It was a corrupt and happy-go-lucky society, vulgar in some respects, sophisticated, often astoundingly naïve.

In the late thirties, Hungary had become a chaos of ideas and sentiments. Impressed by Mussolini and Hitler, many people became thoroughly reactionary and believed themselves to be revolutionary. On the criss-cross map of muddled slogans and competing trends, any social vision had its proper place. Even Communism, arch-enemy of the existing régime, was allowed among the revolutionary currents in mid-stream. Only one point of view received no sympathy—the "old-fashioned Left-wing." No young man with an eye to his career would hold such out-dated views as the Liberals, Radicals or Social Democrats.

I was an old-fashioned Social Democrat, a liberal and Bourgeois Radical. I was an editor of the unrecognized, unregistered journal Szép Szó which had undertaken the impertinent task of opposing the slogans of Nazis and of Horthy's anti-Nazis equally. We kept an old-fashioned Left Wing flag flying, and made our appeal chiefly to the young men. The importance of my position in Hungary was negligible; yet I can boast of having been, for a few months in the late thirties, the most unpopular person in my country. When my name was mentioned at Nazi meetings, it had longer and louder *boos* than any other. The Government's anti-Nazis disliked me no less. I was in their view the Great Nuisance. I had always kept away from Communism, which I truly disliked; and so my person had to be protected, so long as the legal fiction was preserved. The only thing they could want me to do was disappear from the country.

I enjoyed neither high income nor high social status, but I had a special gift for irritating people. The reader must forgive my conceit, but I have rare ability in making people angry. What Baudelaire called "the aristocratic pleasure of displeasing" had always appealed to me no less than the democratic virtue of standing up for conventional ideals. On top of this, I was of Jewish extraction and therefore an object for "Turanian" as well as "Aryan" racial attacks.

My farewell was typical. I did not travel as a refugee, so there was no trouble in getting a passport and even, as a journalist, a free First Class ticket to the frontier. Except for aristocrats and very wealthy people, only those who had free tickets used to travel First Class: members of Parliament, senior civil servants, and journalists. The guard gave a soldier's salute to First Class passengers when he came into their carriage. As far as the frontier I had noble treatment. At the frontier an official looked at my passport and noticed by my name the symbol marked on the documents of people suspected of Communism or other subversive activities: the year of issue stamped after the name. Everyone knew what that meant, but the police had never explained why this could be found in some passports and not others. The official buffeted me out of the train. In a dark place I was stripped and searched, and all my luggage thrown to pieces. As nothing "illegal" was found, the frustrated guard shouted at me angrily to hurry up . . . I thought it better not to argue. I was glad it was over. It was fortunate that he had not troubled to read my notes. One dependable merit in a police state is that the police hate reading. I had ample opportunity to discover this later, in another and even more stupid police state, as a prisoner of Stalin and Rákosi.

Clearly I had to leave Hungary, but why choose England? I thought of France as my second home and it would have been natural for me to stay there. I knew French fluently and had a number of friends there. It had always attracted me more than any country except my own; but at that moment this made me the more disappointed with it. Paris seemed to suffer already from a spirit of defeat. All that I admired there seemed to be falling to pieces. I hardly knew a word of English, and no more of England than did any tolerably educated man in my country. I had an admiration for her traditions and social achievements, but no acquaintance with particular qualities I witnessed later. My decision to settle there was partly from a wish to try something of which I knew nothing. For that matter I could have tried the North Pole. A North Pole with central heating would have been perfect, I thought. It did not turn out that way. But for all the strangeness and despite my thoroughly continental taste and character, I found myself at ease among English people.

Even in my humble position it was reassuring to find that people did not tell lies. When I tried to get work as a hotel porter, or an invitation to write a book about Hungary, "I am afraid I can't encourage you" was the unvarying reply. In other countries I would have been rudely turned away or greeted with enthusiasm but no commitment. I found it a blessing to live among people on whose word I could rely. It would not be easy, I felt, to get them to do something; but once they had agreed, they would not abandon me. "There is no need to despair about them," I said to my father, Hugo Ignotus, who was also by then a crypto-refugee in London. Thirty years before, he had been the leading essayist and editor in the Hungarian intellectual renaissance; politically, one would have called him an advanced Liberal. He, too, had felt he could no longer risk living in Hungary. Brought up in the Victorian age, he could not help being more worried about our insecurity than I was. "No doubt the English do not tell you lies," he answered sadly; "they promise nothing but they do keep their promise."

I lived by the Thames in South East London, facing the City, on the ground floor. From my window I saw cranes, boats, lorries, St. Paul's, smoke and sky. Next to me stood the cottage from which Sir Christopher Wren used to watch the workmen carrying out his plans on the other side of the river. I was surrounded by wharves, breweries, and historical remains. This was Southwark, the most provincial quarter of metropolitan London. It is a working-class district so ancient as to seem exclusive, almost aristocratic. Its intruders, its parvenus, were the handful of gentlefolk, attracted by its romantic atmosphere or proletarian smell, who chose to live there.

I tried to make friends with as many of the indigenous residents as possible, partly in order to learn English. "For Heaven's sake," a friend told me, "don't do that; you'll pick up a Cockney accent and be lost." More lost, I asked, than if I stuck to my Magyar accent? "Far more," my friend replied; "there is nothing wrong in not knowing English in England; but to know it in the way of an English navvy is shocking." I appreciated the wisdom of his advice but trusted the virulence of my Magyar accent. The small boys and girls playing on the embankment knew me, and on fine summer evenings a few would gather under my window. I gave them sweets, which made me more popular than I had hoped; they would talk to me for hours. This was too much of an evening lesson in children's Cockney. "Well, goodbye now, I'll go and have my dinner." They stared at one another; "'e means 'is *supper*," a boy explained. He was right; my meal could not be called a dinner. Except when I was asked out, my rule was never to have a square meal. I lived on scrambled eggs, which I concocted myself, and on mild-and-bitter and cold meat pie. Half consciously I knew I chose this diet because I did like scrambled eggs and found mild-and-bitter with cold pie stylish; three-course hot meals at the A.B.C. might have cost less but I had a happy instinct which stopped me from adding it up.

The little three-storey house in which we lived has since been destroyed by the Blitz. Its arrangements showed a somewhat archaic taste; the bathtub stood in the kitchen, and the lavatory in a tiny courtyard. I found it most attractive. It had fair proportions, and a modest but respectable air. I suspected it had been a brothel or gambling house once; not the actual building perhaps, erected only about one hundred and fifty years before, but its predecessor from which it inherited narrow passages leading from surprising corners in surprising directions. In Puritanical days, Southwark used to be a centre for crime, art and gaiety; the merchants of the City of London used to cross the river, as they would cross the Channel in Victorian decades, to indulge a love for beauty, or for making love, forbidden in their own business and family surroundings. The secret passages served as emergency exits when the houses were raided.

I knew I had hard times to face. I was already 38; it is not easy for a man to start a new life at that age. Besides, I had always been incompetent in money matters and non-technically minded. The only possible prospect was to remain a parasite until I knew English well enough to experiment in journalism.

My only comfort in this gloomy position was the delight of irresponsibility. Since childhood I had wished, at least for a while, to be an orphan or tramp with no commitments. I could never afford that: though a bachelor, I had relatives and felt certain links with respectability. The approaching victory of Nazism had convinced me that in Hungary I could no longer help my family. So a plague had liberated me, but liberty it was and I enjoyed it. My beggar's life was full of illuminating adventures.

These started with the charming people whose hospitality I was enjoying in Southwark. They were an old English upper-middle-class family whose interests lay in business, socialism and books. Many of them married foreign girls, a ravishing Hungarian among them; hence my friendship with her husband. When I had to leave Hungary I asked her in an embarrassed letter whether I could count on their friendship if I were to make an excursion to London. "We cannot offer you much," the reply was, "but if you have use for a little room, empty at the moment, which I should be glad to furnish by the time you move in . . ." Indeed I had use for it.

I was their third lodger. The first floor was inhabited by a slim pretty girl who was always dressed in slacks and whose enthusiasm was divided among mushrooms, beer and men. In her rooms I first met Mr. Zilliacus, and in her rattling little car I first saw the East End docks. She wanted to show me slums but did not find any. Then we entered a pub where she was sure she would find revolutionaries but there was none of them either. But we found shuv'ha'penny—a great discovery after my limited experience of darts in the *Anchor* on Bankside.

On the second floor, or garret, Michael lived. He was about my age, the brother of my friend who rented the house. Michael was the black sheep of his family, except that it was a family where black sheep were unimaginable, because of their high liberalism under which the blacker a sheep the more sympathetic he might be. The rest had some leanings towards Communism; he was a Communist, very pure and simple. He had fought in the International Brigade. He was anti-*bourgeois,* body and soul. He ran about naked in the house because, "why not?"; he had no prejudices. He liked meat and vegetables for breakfast, always dressed shabbily, and had a boyish face.

"Hello Paul, come and have a pint of mild-and-bitter with me." This was my first invitation from him, as spokesman of the English working-class revolution, to explore proletarian life. It was he who first took me to the *Anchor.* This Public House is now polished and carefully maintained as a historical monument. Then it was more humble, though the proprietor knew its connexions with Dr. Johnson. Young workmen in caps lingered by the bar, talking about football pools, singing occasionally and playing darts. Michael was on Christian-name terms with them. "Why not have a shot at it Paul: great fun," he told me. I tried to throw darts, and was clumsy even for a beginner. Michael's clumsiness was second only to mine but we enjoyed it. "Pleasant fellows, these workmen," I whispered to him, "do you know them well?" He smiled proudly. "Very well indeed. All good comrades." He said good-bye to them with a clenched fist according to Popular Front ritual. They did not seem to mind it; nor did they think of reciprocating it.

I remember only one occasion when Michael talked

politics at the *Anchor*. This was with a good-humoured
Merchant Navy seaman, whose racy expressions and
sharp features might have qualified him for a part in a
film. He turned out to be a staunch Tory. "It's a free
country Michael, that's what I say; now have one on me.
Mild-and-bitter? And you sir?"

I never concealed from Michael my scepticism about
Russian socialism. I agreed we should support the idea of
a Popular Front, and an alliance between the Western
Powers and the U.S.S.R. This allowed him to treat me too
as a good comrade, chiefly because he liked to treat as
comrades the people he liked; and he was happier greeting people with clenched fists than arguing with them.
What I liked in Michael and his family was their liberalism—a quality which in Russia would have been impossible, and which they were about to bury with shouts of
triumph. Knowing I was a progressive writer and a refugee from Fascism they assumed I must share their sympathetic interest for the Russian way of life. Now and then I
felt I should say how much I preferred them to their
ideals. But I felt it would be too rude and I kept quiet.

One night I was struck by Michael's voice as he chatted
vigorously with a woman under my window. Later, as my
light was still on, he came in, excited as I had seldom
seen him. "Good God, Paul, such idiots," he panted,
"those chaps in the Foreign Office; imagine *me* having
Cassado in this house! That traitor!" I do not know
whether the English reader remembers the name. Colonel
Cassado was an officer in the Spanish Republican army
who contrived, with some support from the British and
the French, to turn out Negrin's Popular Front Government towards the end of the Civil War. His aim was a
compromise agreement with Franco. The approach was
rejected, and Cassado had to go into exile. Now he was in
London. I could not understand at first from Michael's excited narrative just what the lady had said, but he repeated it in detail. A woman from the Foreign Office, who
knew Michael as a fellow resident in Southwark, had
greeted him. "You fought in Spain and you're a good anti-

Fascist, aren't you," she began. She wondered whether a refugee from Franco's Spain could be taken into his house. She had an excellent candidate for it, a Colonel Cassado.

"I hope you weren't rude to that good soul," I told Michael.

"Well, I lost my temper but I don't think I was rude. I just told her there was no question of having a traitor to live among honest people. If there were any genuine Republicans needing to be helped, we would do what we could. Some workers or something of that sort. She understood and didn't seem hurt. She said she would let me know if there were."

About a week later the good comrades arrived, an enchanting couple. The man was Pedro, a tailor whose right hand had been crippled in the fighting. He could not be a tailor again, but would learn English in London and then find work on a farm. He was a short and vivid man, with broad gestures and glittering eyes, a satisfactory socialist for Michael. On May Day when he saw how few London workers marched under the red flag he felt embittered. After a Fascist gathering at the street corner he came home quite pale, unable to understand how British workers could tolerate the impertinence of tyrants. When he found from a newspaper that H.M. Government was about to recognize Franco he cried that life was *merda*. Neither he nor his wife was impressed by freedom in Britain; what is all this freedom worth if you aren't allowed to kill Fascists? I tried cautiously to explain the British way. "Don't you really like anything in this country?" I asked them.

"We do. Chocolate."

Michael was delighted with Pedro. He brushed up his Spanish by congratulating him on his fighting spirit at all times of the day. I joined the discussion with my brand of Spanish, made up from French, Latin and whatever I could glean from their own talk.

Pedro's wife was called Maria. She was a tall, tired-looking woman with beautiful features; a long dark face, half Madonna, half Gipsy. She sang Spanish songs delightfully, especially Flamenco. In spite of my agnosticism I wanted to hear her sing some religious songs. I was careless enough to suggest this, and to add coyly that Catholicism suited women. I got a sharp protest from the two of them. No such nonsense among Spanish workpeople. Women, Pedro explained, were by nature *materialista*, and religion, which was but a collection of superstitions inherited from the Middle Ages, suited them even less than men. I was out-voted.

They had a room next to mine on the ground floor. There was no difficulty in putting them up; but Maria took the kitchen under her care and it had to be quickly revolutionized, or rather counter-revolutionized. Until then nobody had much cared who might be taking a bath there while someone else was at the stove—"why not," we were untroubled by *bourgeois* prejudices. But some came in with the good comrades from Spain. A curtain was drawn round the bath-tub. While Michael bathed inside, and Maria prepared the meal outside, Pedro would anxiously watch the curtain and pull it now and then, nervous of gaps.

Then we would sit down in the kitchen to our common meal, *tortilla* or something of the kind; the girl from the first floor in slacks, Pedro, Michael and myself. Maria would stand by and wait on us, and eat when we had finished. "Why not join us?" the three of us asked. O no, that was impossible. *Sothialista, materialista,* a decent woman would not sit down with men. Of course, we also continued our excursions to the *Anchor*. Maria came with us as far as the threshold and then ran home. We could never persuade her to enter.

Co-existence based upon charity is likely to be irritating. We could not but feel aware that the lady on the first floor, and Michael in the garret, were our aristocrats. Not that they stuck together, far from it. Two aristocrats were too many for such a small community. Irritable scenes would break out between them, and I tried occasionally to make peace; then they both started disliking me. In the end, despite ignorance of the language, the Spanish couple and I discovered that we were linked more intimately to each other than to our hosts.

In our Southwark Spanish we could talk, though more with our hands than our tongues. I would sit and chat with Pedro in the kitchen, Maria standing next to his chair, through evenings when the others were out. On one occasion I happened to mention Cassado as a traitor. Pedro pressed my hand and asked in a tone of serious intimacy, "Pablo, truly why do you think Cassado is a traitor?" I had never thought carefully about it; it seemed to be assumed among Republicans. "Listen, at a time when everything was lost he tried to save lives. Is that treachery?" Maria joined in, leaning over her husband's shoulder. She described, or rather recalled by acting, what the end of the Civil War had been like. *Boom-boom,* she said, bombs had been falling everywhere. "Negrin?" With her slim fingers she showed on the table how he had run away. "Del Vayo?" The same performance with her fingers on the table. "Pasionara?" Again, the same. *"Pedro y io?"* She showed with gestures how helplessly she and her husband had just stared up at the sky. Cassado had not managed to save much but still a handful of people owed their lives to him. Maria and Pedro were among them. Was it wicked to be grateful for it? I agreed it was not.

Pedro had been advised to say he was a Communist in this house. Pedro had tried to explain to the Foreign Office people that he was *sothialista* but no *communista.* The answer was he must not be so fussy. Was there really much difference between the two?

I was sorry my vocabulary in Southwark Spanish was not rich enough to let me tell Pedro and Maria what I felt. Despite differences of social background and nationality, and also of approach, I felt they were really my best comrades.

By the outbreak of the war Pedro and Maria had already got their permanent abode on a farm, and the lady in slacks from the first floor and Michael from the garret had also moved elsewhere. The lease of the house was nearly at an end but I stayed on there for a while. I could not afford labour to black out the windows, and was incompetent to do the job myself; so I spent some of the autumn evenings strolling in the streets, or trying to read in the pubs, or sitting and staring from the window of my unlighted room. A lady who lived near discovered my loneliness and invited me to tea. I gladly accepted and we became good friends. She was a middle-aged spinster, with a pleasant house on the embankment and a factory job which she liked. She was an old Southwark resident and knew much about the people round about. Her middle-class pride was fascinating. She held strong opinions and would add, "everybody thinks so: thinking people, I mean, not working people, of course." She was very frank. "Your friends . . ." and she shook her head, "playing the fighters for freedom and then letting you down like that. Shocking." "But why do you say they let me down?" I asked. "They were very kind to me while they were living here, and I am grateful. Why should it be their duty to look after me when they are busy somewhere else?" I was unable to convince her. She also confessed that she had viewed me at first with suspicion for being mixed up with them, but had later discovered that I was not so bad after all. A foreigner, no doubt; but at least one of the thinking people, and a decent fellow as far as she could see. Again, I intervened on behalf of my vanished friends. Weren't they decent English people? She jumped. "Those, *English?* Those, *decent?* My God, their behaviour. A woman running about in slacks. A man calling everybody by his Christian name after seeing him for no more than a minute. Everybody was shocked."

"The thinking people, you mean? Not the working people?"

"O, they didn't differ about *that.* Charwomen and all would complain about them. No one could understand what made them think of coming to this district. They should go to Bloomsbury with those habits. But behave like that here! The workmen and their wives were simply disgusted. Thank God we've got rid of them. Now at last we feel we are among ourselves."

Amongst working people, she meant, as well as thinking people.

Chapter 2

At Home in the British Isles

I TRIED to volunteer for the forces but had no qualification as an officer and was not allowed to serve in the ranks. In the early spring of 1940 I was given work with the B.B.C., where I stayed until the autumn of 1947; first as a translator-typist, later as Hungarian Intelligence Assistant, and after the war as a Hungarian Programme Assistant.

I look back on this time in the B.B.C. quite affectionately, though much of my energy was wasted in criticizing the programmes which were broadcast to Hungary. The European Intelligence Department, directed by Jonathan Griffin, was an interesting miscellany of people of various nationalities, concerned to form a picture of the reactions of the audience. We relied mainly on letters from listeners, and later also, after the collapse of France, on hostile comments and hidden compliments in the continental Press and radio services.

I am much indebted to the B.B.C., and not least for having had Miss Margaret Lambert, at that time South-East Europe Intelligence Officer, as my chief. She shared much of my political concern and suggested I should talk with one or two political writers or members of Parliament. "Why not talk to Professor Seton-Watson?" And she rang him. "I wonder whether I could ask you to see my Hungarian assistant, Paul Ignotus . . ."—"I shall be delighted," the late Professor replied; "I know his father who is a very distinguished writer." Miss Lambert was impressed. Shortly afterwards, when I was with her in Oxford, she rang

Mr. Wickham Steed who had his country house in the vicinity. "I wonder whether I could come and see you and bring with me my Hungarian assistant, Paul Ignotus? You may know his father . . ." "His father?" Wickham Steed exclaimed. "His *grandfather*!* He wrote the most beautiful German." Miss Lambert, again, was most impressed and amused. In her approach she was, if she will forgive me, a pugnacious and revolutionary Whig; combining a passion for the rights of every human with a playful belief in tribal heredity. She is the daughter of Lord Lambert, at that time the *doyen* of the Commons, the last remnant of the guard once referred to as "Mr. Gladstone's young men." Her confidence in me was enhanced by an assumption that I too had acquired a sense of politics and liberal tradition in the nursery.

Professor Seton-Watson and Mr. Wickham Steed were fine men but I cannot say that my acquaintance with them took me very far. They were the Great Friends of Czechoslovakia. Thanks to the Masaryk heritage, this implied a more liberal approach to human problems than the conventional sort of sympathy at that time for my own country. But it was outdated liberalism; they were almost as easily ready to condone Little Entente nationalism as the Great Friends of Hungary were to exonerate Hungarian nationalists.

Through Miss Lambert I got in touch with the *New Statesman* circle and the Union of Democratic Control. She was far from seeing eye to eye with them about everything. As a Whig, of course, she could not. "But you see," she would say, "they are still the ones who understand most of what it is about. You must talk to them." I started contributing to the *New Statesman*, first with short anonymous notes, during the war. In the series of documents published by the U.D.C. on various foreign policy subjects, the Hungarian one was based on my draft. In my eagerness to put my sentences in good English I called the *Cordon Sanitaire*, in my original manuscript, "Sanitary Belt." This was received with cheers by the Committee discussing my sug-

* My grandfather, Leo Veigelsberg, who died in 1908, was editor and leader writer of *Pester Lloyd*.

gestions but deleted from the final version, along with some other East-European mental sparks of mine which were not reckoned suitable for the purpose.

In this way I first met Kingsley Martin, Richard Crossman, John Freeman, Norman Mackenzie, Dorothy Woodman who was then the Secretary of the U.D.C., and dear old Mr. Brailsford and others whose friendship I have had every reason to cherish—though I have often felt that in its policies the *New Statesman* can be oddly adolescent.

Among all my *New Stateman* friends it is with Kingsley that I felt the most long-lasting and most inarticulate link. Really it was he who, probably without realizing it, set me rolling on the tracks of English journalistic and literary life. I felt he was full of understanding and sympathy for me; but not for my point of view, particularly in the course of personal talks. I had and have a tremendous admiration for him but could chat with most of his associates and lieutenants more easily than with him. I often wondered why. I suspect that for all his passionate internationalism and his willingness to criticize his own country he is more English than anyone I knew, not only in Bloomsbury but even in Yorkshire or Somerset. His approach is insular and global. He is interested in his garden, and the people in the local pub, and the misery-stricken areas in India and Congo, and the survival of the human race. I do not think he is much interested in Europe. He is a good European only because he writes well. It struck me as typical that those of his writings which impressed me most deeply were obituaries on personalities almost as thoroughly English as himself—Mrs. Webb and Mr. Chamberlain. With tact and grace and tender irony, he depicted on such occasions the genius and idiosyncrasies of what was perhaps most overwhelmingly British in Britain, the Victorian English upper middle-classes. When I congratulated him on this he made me think I had not properly understood his writings, and he may have been right. But this did not prevent us from being friends and working from time to time together. And with his introduction I first approached the *Manchester Guardian* to which I have several times contributed since the war.

Miss Lambert's associations were not confined to the Left. We sometimes had lunch with the most passionate spokesman of anti-Russian suspicions at that time, Mr. Voigt, editor of the *Nineteenth Century*, a man of deep intellect and deep bias who very much intrigued me. He struck me as Kingsley Martin's opposite: by conviction a passionate British nationalist, and by character Continental, even Teutonic.

Miss Lambert was very friendly with Veronica Wedgwood and introduced me to her house; Miss Wedgwood was also a Whig, but of a less aggressive kind. I had known her as an eminent historian and was fascinated by her as a person. As a Left wing Hungarian I felt I owed much to her name. It was the Committee led by her uncle, Colonel Josiah Wedgwood, which had issued the most brilliant (and depressing) document ever put out on the Hungarian White Terror in 1919–20, and on the shocking attitude taken at that time by the official British representatives in Budapest.

Hungarians in war-time Britain had their own public life which hardly penetrated either to the British or to the Hungarian public. There were various "Free Hungarian Movements," now competing and quarrelling, now uniting in a Front, and then splitting again. I made a solemn pledge not to be involved, a pledge which I myself did not take seriously. It could not be helped. Emigré politics may more often than not be waste of time, but to shirk one's responsibility in them may amount to treason.

The most outstanding personality among the Free Hungarians was Count Michael Károlyi, President of the short-lived Hungarian Republic of 1918. He had arrived in England with his wife on the eve of the war, and they went to live in a modest room in Oxford.

I first saw him there, at the time of the phoney War, when I was spending a few days with the writer Baron Lajos Hatvany, who had also crossed the Channel on the eve of the war and withdrawn to a boarding house in Wellington Square. On a sunny morning he was shouting, in his usual bantering way, through the window of his ground floor sitting-room: "This is how I have to see my President." Károlyi was just pushing a barrow loaded with suitcases and odd little pieces of furniture. He was moving from his room to another room. He was already in his sixties and impeded in his walk by a limp, the result of a cycling accident years before. Yet he performed the job in a cheerful spirit. His hat had slipped to his neck in the heat of toil but his eyes were glittering with self-satisfaction through his spectacles. "That's an excellent barrow," he shouted back, "a real treasure."

Before his exile, he had possessed other treasures. He used to be the second richest landlord in Hungary. His wife was also wealthy: she was the niece and foster daughter of the younger Count Jules Andrássy, and the granddaughter of Count Jules Andrássy who was Hungarian Prime Minister after the Compromise of 1867, later Foreign Minister of the Austro-Hungarian Monarchy and, as such, an associate of Bismarck.

Károlyi was a baldish tall man with expressive features which might equally have been taken as aristocratic or Jewish; he liked to tell stories about occasions when he had been mistaken for a Jew. His wife, much younger than he, had a figure of fair proportions with a noble presence and vivid face, dominated by large green eyes. They were an extremely elegant couple but now they were living in penury, and the first thing which impressed me was the way they accepted it. I never knew the details of their financial position. I could not tell whether some of their privations owed their origin to some strange intention of theirs. The Countess, in particular, felt tempted towards Puritan discipline. She always refused to travel by taxi, and I never knew whether to take this as a gesture against spendthrift *bourgeois* manners or indignation because she had no car of her own. At that time she made a rule to spend no more than (I think) 10*d.* a day, per person, on food. Even if they could have afforded more, they were certainly badly off and took it graciously. Their complaints were exclusively political, so were most of their interests. Madam Károlyi was in love with British institutions. Once I was given two tickets to a meeting of the Oxford Union, and asked the

Count's permission to invite her. "Very kind of you," he answered, "but really . . ." and he held out 1s. 2d. "Buy her a tin of sardines and tell her it was you who bought it. She loves them. . . ."

One of the Free Hungarian movements, which generally included the old anti-Horthy refugees, was represented by the Károlyis. Another, originally associated with the pro-British wing of the Hungarian Legation, had unofficial backing from the Foreign Office. In my heart I was with the Károlyis, but I saw that they would not be able to achieve anything alone. I thought they ought to combine with the other important Free Hungarian movement. The very idea made the Count angry.

Again and again, he repeated that everyone associated with the Horthy régime was a political whore. Each time I answered that everyone who had lived in Hungary during those years had to some extent been associated with the Horthy régime. It could not have been otherwise. "Believe me," I said, "no one opposed that régime more bitterly than I; but I made use of the tolerance or vanity of its rulers. Without that, I could not have managed even the journalism of opposition. Was I a political whore?"

"I suppose you were," the Countess intervened. She was a fascinating person. At that period she disliked me thoroughly, and made no attempt to conceal it. A man from left-wing literary circles in Hungary, unwilling to give her husband unqualified support—this was blasphemy. When the British declaration of war against Hungary was approaching, she told some of my friends quite openly that she expected Paul Ignotus would be interned as an enemy alien.

A day or two after that declaration of war I happened to enter Miss Lambert's room when she was discussing a subject with Countess Károlyi who had also come to see her. European Intelligence had been bombed out of its first offices and was then housed in Bedford College, Regent's Park. The Countess glared at me. "You—here?" "I am sorry to disappoint you," I said. Fortunately she was used to meeting people she disliked; they were too many to be ignored. After her talk with Miss Lambert she allowed

me to see her out to the gates. It was a mild winter afternoon, the sun shimmering on fallen dry leaves and the
melting snow. We walked for about an hour and forgot
about Free Hungary. We spoke of our grandfathers and
fathers who had worked together, and about mutual friends,
the family doctors of the Andrássys and their clever children. In spite of very different social backgrounds, we had
many common family recollections. We discussed English
novels and Hungarian poets. Many a year has passed, including times when we have certainly not seen eye to eye;
but since that day we have succeeded in agreeing at least to
disagree.

There was a strictly non-political social gathering of
Hungarians and Hungarian Czechs, called the London
Hungarian Club. They only wanted, they said, to serve
paprika chicken at reasonable prices to Hungarians, tormented by gastronomic nostalgia, and to have musical evenings and literary talks and so forth. After Hitler's attack
on Russia they suddenly wanted something else: they
wanted Unity. It was to be unity at any price, with everybody, unity to save Hungarian honour, unity to help our
admirable British hosts, unity to defeat the Fascist beasts.
They sang *God Save the King* and old Hungarian independence marches more enthusiastically, and avoided references to socialist demands more carefully, than any
other Movement. They were the Communists.

Towards the end of the war Unity among the three Free
Hungarian Movements came about, in the form of a Hungarian Council with Count Károlyi as its President. I was
one of its co-opted members. It did not achieve much; but
to the credit of those who took part in its work the Free
Hungarian community was saved from that torrent of mutual denunciation which so often ruins any kind of émigré
politics.

I began to know the British at the moment of their great
danger.

"It was magnificent," Mr. Eden reported in a broadcast
about what he had seen at Dunkirk. My British left-wing

friends were grimly humorous about his enthusiasm. Even Mr. Churchill thought it right to suggest some reserve about the triumphant mood with which the returning troops were greeted; it was not by evacuations, he emphasized, that wars were won. Military experts can decide how far it was magnificent on the French shores. What I witnessed in the British capital certainly struck me as magnificent.

Magnificence is not necessarily perfection. "The English," Napoleon said, "owe their ultimate triumph over me merely to their stupidity. They did not notice that I had beaten them." He may have been right; apart from his failure to see what great wisdom this kind of stupidity contained. After the collapse of France, this became obvious. The cartoonist, Low, who invented Colonel Blimp, did not mind accepting the sort of single-track rhetoric which any Colonel Blimp would indulge in his patriotic fervour. His cartoon in the *Evening Standard*, luckily devoid of humour at the moment, showed a British Tommy in ragged trousers and with bulging chest. "Well, then alone . . ." was the caption. I listened carefully to the talk in the tube trains. "Finished, you know," one Londoner said to another, gloomily looking up from his paper. "In France, of course," the other nodded, no less unhappily. That it was still going in Britain could not be questioned. It was, at that moment, determination to death. It was the sole thing common sense could suggest.

Common sense is a very misleading word, meaning often the most uncommon of virtues. Surely the British own it to quite a rare extent. But I would not deny that the way in which it rules them is not always reassuring. Unimaginativeness doubtless contributes to it. In people of rare political insight—like Low, for instance—common sense and uncommon awareness may work in harmony. Whether the same could be expected from the average of any nation, I cannot tell. There were aspects of British behaviour in those days which worried and irritated me. Others amused me. Most of them made me admire and love the British.

The wholesale internment of Germans as "enemy aliens" at the time of the Fifth Column scare was idiotic. To take precautions was of course necessary. But to lock up on these grounds such fighters against Nazism as Rudolf Olden* was obviously a service to Hitler, apart from being unkind.

Ignorance of the issues involved, and courtesy towards the enemy, were the oddest features of the moment. The interned Germans were huddled together in their makeshift barracks, Jews and political refugees, wretched and exhausted, with their worn-out nerves, terrified all the time about the prospects of invasion, haunted by fear of the Gestapo, and anxious about British plans concerning them. In came the Intelligence Officer one day, fresh and smart, greeting them politely. They asked him nervously whether there was any news. "O," he answered genially, "bad news for us, good news for you." What? the refugees inquired. "Paris fallen." It really surprised him to see that his information was not received with relief.

The state of mind of the refugees in this country differed immensely at that time from the British outlook. Their knowledge of what was going on, and capacity to imagine what could be expected, were beyond average British range. But their nerves were wrecked. Their main problem was how to get overseas. The conversations I overheard in foreign languages or in foreign accents were more often than not on such topics as "If you want a visa to Venezuela. . . ."

The British, as far as I could see, simply failed to notice this. Some of my refugee friends bombarded me with questions about "what the English said at the B.B.C." I answered that in our Department we were talking shop, busy establishing the Monitoring Service, discussing the prospect of having more hours on the air, and the like. "But what do the rest say? Please do me this favour, tell me the first spontaneous sentence you hear from an English person at Broadcasting House tomorrow." I promised and then truthfully reported. It was a morning of catastrophic news and bright sunshine. The first words I heard from a British lady at Broadcasting House were "What a lovely day!"

She is unlikely to have been a genius. But she knew the

---

* The story is related in detail in the Memoirs of Michael Károlyi, *Faith Without Illusion*, Jonathan Cape.

essential thing, which the more experienced and imaginative foreigners did not know—that there was *no alternative*.

It was this attitude which impressed me even more in the Blitz. People are willing to forget what an ordeal it was; I have hardly heard any reference to it since the end of 1956, when I again arrived as a refugee in Britain. We know today that the Blitz was Goering's hysterical gesture to avenge his defeat in the Battle of Britain and that it was ultimately, from a strategic point of view, a failure. But who could have known this at the time? For the people of London it meant damp shelters, improvised bunks in poorly ventilated tube stations, without sanitation at first. It means rushing home at dusk, and finding difficulty in reaching one's place of work as one quarter and another were closed to traffic.

Today the English are willing to belittle this. "We took it—But didn't others take it as well?" I think the answer is that nobody else took it in such circumstances. Many accepted the terror because they knew they would be shot if they opened their mouths to suggest they should do otherwise. Many took it after the great victories of their armies. This was not the case in the 1940 Blitz. The indiscriminate bombing of British cities came at a time when the population had no tangible proof of the ability of its own Forces to hit back. The Battle of Britain had been a victory, but expressed in abstract figures. The only realities had been the humming of enemy planes, the explosions and shakes and the destroyed homes visible after restless nights. I was worried that people less interested in political issues than I was, might say "We have had enough of it."

A woman friend of mine, employed by Mass Observation, sometimes spent a night in the shelters in slum districts. I asked anxiously what people had been saying. "It was awful," she sighed. "They are at the end of their tether." I was terrified to hear the rest. "But, what were their actual words?" I asked. "They said God couldn't tolerate that. It was *too* wicked." I asked whether no one wanted to make peace with the Germans. She was English enough to be quite astonished. "Peace, *now*? After all this? Of course not."

I used to visit Hyde Park. The open air speakers had always interested me; they struck me as an admirable British peculiarity, and it was a long time before I grew tired of watching them. Of course they are not representative of British opinion; any small sect can have its platform there, but probably not the Church of England; and all extreme political movements, but seldom Conservatives, Labour or Liberal. But it was a revealing experience to attend these meetings. I saw how every sort of willingness to give in to the Germans disappeared as the bombing harassed the population. But sense of humour remained, and a feeling of kindness. I remember a speaker—I think, exceptionally, a Government speaker—explaining to the crowd that if they happened to catch a German airman after crash-landing or parachuting, they must not offer him tea until the authorities took charge of him. An old working woman protested strongly: "That's inhuman. My son is in the R.A.F. and I know how *he* would suffer if he weren't given a cup of tea if ever the Jerries brought him down." On this she was adamant. Some in the crowd took her side, and even those contradicting her were kind and laughed a lot.

My happiest surprise was to discover how the feeling against refugees and a suspicion towards anyone whose mother tongue was not English, gradually diminished in those months. The blindness of putting together all "enemy aliens" in one crowd was being cured at the very time when people had to suffer most from enemy attack.

Four years later, when the V1's and the V2's were dropping over London, these British virtues struck me as less conspicuous. No doubt these were also taken courageously and soberly, and with an indispensable sense of humour. Jokes about the "doodlebugs" were circulating; and the Government order to ignore V2's in any expression which might reach the enemy (who was by then unable to carry out ordinary reconnaissance) was observed with perfect discipline. But it was no longer the elevating spirit of the Blitz. It followed D-day, and came as an anticlimax when victory had already been in sight. On the other hand, I found most of the refugees much calmer and braver than four years before. Partly because they no longer feared the greatest blow, Invasion; and partly because in the course of years they had to some extent become Anglicized. British and non-British had become like one another during the war and rejoiced together round the bonfires when V-day at last arrived.

In the middle of the war—after the Russians had become allies but before their successes made people worry about their glory—I was asked by the Ministry of Information to undertake a lecture tour in Cumberland and to talk about Hungary and the Balkans. I was glad to agree as both the subjects and the journey interested me. But I started the journey with terrible stage-fright. Was it not bound to be a flop? Even in Lodon, where people were used to foreigners of all kinds, my accent struck everybody as strange. How much more might I fear the response of farmers in the furthest North-West of England? But my friends at the Ministry were reassuring and I did not want to fail them.

In Cumberland, a young worker received me and showed me round; he was Information Secretary for the district. He was glad to learn I was a Labour supporter like himself, and advised me to be "cautious." He had difficulties in his factory through urging his fellows to join the Union. I was astonished: was this possible at the time of a National Government with a Labour Deputy Prime Minister? How could a management dare in such times to object to Trade Unionism? I asked my friend. "O no, the management does not mind," he replied, "it's the workers who object."

He warned me not to talk Labour too crudely when meeting the lady to whom he felt he should introduce me; she was, he added, apart from her views, a very nice person, the President of the local Conservative Women's Association. I entered a pleasant and stately country house, and we stayed there for dinner. We could not have shocked the hostess and her family with our party allegiance even if we had wanted to. Her younger daughter, a smart lady married in London but just then at home for a holiday, turned out to be almost Communist and not even that seemed to shock her Conservative family. My Red friend, however, was a little shocked by her. "Do people like this woman think," he murmured as we left, "that they'll carry on ruling the country under a red flag?"

I was less lucky with the regional Lady Patroness of the Liberals. I happened to express a flippant lack of sympathy with Prohibition, and got a quick rebuke. I did not know she was the great national figure of British temperance. Her son, a member of Parliament, could only drink beer in secret. But even he agreed with his mother on principle. In that district, my worker friend explained, it *was* a matter of principle; teetotallers had voted Liberal, and publicans and their friends Conservative, for generations. Labour was almost non-existent. The bulk of the population were farmers who did not feel strongly against Labour but did not care for Labour. They cared, however, for Russia. The enthusiasm for the Soviet Allies was even higher in Cumberland than in London. I remember talking to a miner's widow who ran a teashop and showed a very lively interest in public affairs. "The party I should like to join if there was one, is Christian Communists," she said. To some extent this was *vox populi*.

My friend thought it right to warn me also before some lectures. "Tomorrow you are going to talk to children in a Quaker School," he said. "Don't talk too much war to them, they don't like that." War propaganda for pacifists was a special problem. But I muddled through.

Altogether my contacts with the audience moved me. I do not claim that the response was a frenzy of enthusiasm but I found my listeners, whether farmers, artisans or school children, very attentive and full of good will. "What could we do after the war to help those peoples in the Balkans?" was the question most frequently asked from me. I blush to add that I was also greeted as a war hero for the simple reason that I had come from London and had a time-bomb near my flat on the eve of my departure for the lecture tour. That Cumberland district had never had an air raid.

My worries about language proved to be unfounded. I

understood the Cumberland (or, for that matter, the Yorkshire) accent much more easily than Cockney. To call a bus a "boos" was only too natural for my East European ears. Nor did my accent very much astonish them. On the contrary. They were used to hearing an English different from their own when addressed by people arriving from London. Whether it was King's English, or Popular English, or my Magyar English, did not make a tremendous difference. "Which part of Britain do you come from, sir?" a farmer asked me before he had been told about my nationality. No such question had ever been put to me in London. At last I felt quite at home in the British Isles.

Chapter 3

Hungary Liberated

FEBRUARY, 1946—at home again in liberated Budapest, my native city, after seven years away. Everything was dazzling: weird shadow creatures with haggard faces, still showing signs of starvation from the siege; dilapidated blocks of houses, with the terrifying marks of bombs, shells, and the looting and wilful destruction of the retreating Germans. Streets and cafés were crowded with people full of hope, ambition and the spirit of enterprise. Budapest had had seven bridges before the siege, some of them very fine; only the wrecks of them could be seen now. The Germans and Hungarian Nazis had blown them up before leaving. Instead, there was just one makeshift bridge in the centre of the city, named after Lajos Kossuth, the only bridge over the Danube at that time on the long stretch from the Black Forest to the Black Sea. Anyway this was the constant proud boast of the inhabitants. They were proud of the efficiency and speed with which it had been built. The Russians, who helped and robbed the Hungarians simultaneously, claimed credit for the bridge —or shared it with the Communist Minister of Transport, Gerö, who was often known as "Moscow's eye."

Hungarians were generally facetious and incredulous about Russian assistance. The Soviet soldiers for them were a horde of savages whose most characteristic deeds of heroism had been to rape seventy-year-old women, to get themselves intoxicated with wine and wristwatches, to defile sofas, to use books for fuel, and to mistake lavatories for washbasins. Hungarians were convinced that the best Russian tanks were of American or British make, and that without Western help the Soviet Army would not have had a chance to resist the Germans, let alone defeat them. This conviction was widespread even among Communist Party members. But even the anti-Communist bulk of the population was willing to join in rejoicing about the Bridge. Whatever lip-service had to be paid to the Glorious Liberators, all could welcome this chance to extol the energy and creative power of the Hungarian people.

The Bridge shook under the masses of cars, lorries and people—chiefly people, of course, old women in ragged skirts among them, carrying bundles of dry sticks on their bent backs. Among the smart cars, many wore the insignia of the Allied Control Commission, then technically still in power, British, American and mainly Russian. There were also the cars of cabinet ministers and other senior officials, black marketeers and other businessmen, various Party chiefs and other political busybodies, with an unconcealed preponderance of Communists. The slogan given by the leader of the Moscow-trained Communists, Vice-Premier Mátyás Rákosi, was Unite All Forces for Reconstruction! Freedom to reconstruct meant freedom to grab. Communists boasted of their liberality in allowing it. To be shocked by blatant differences between rich and poor was "unscientific petty-bourgeois equalitarianism" and thus a crime against the working classes, second only to Trotskyism. The creation of a bourgeois Republic was the rule of the day; Communists promised to protect private property, and in fact protected the racketeers.

Perhaps it was the only possible way at that time. Hidden resources had to be drawn to the surface, absent resources smuggled into the country. The masses of uprooted and impoverished people had to be allowed to pick what they could from the remains of forsaken buildings. Without corruption, this could hardly have been arranged. The champion of benevolent corruption was Second in Command among the Moscow-trained economists, Zoltán Vas. Unlike most of them, he was really a popular figure. A bespectacled fat Jew, he was liked even by anti-Semites. "Anyway, we have to thank *him* for having potatoes today . . . " Such talk could be heard all the time. He found ways into people's affections through their appetites and a sense of humour. Food and jokes defeat even political animosity. "You know what he said the other day," I heard from a civil servant who helped in his office. "In came a Communist colleague of ours, one morning, fifteen minutes late, shouting the Party greeting very noisily. Vas said, 'Next time just say Good Morning but come in punctually.' "

Corruption was alarming. To some extent it really was democratic; everybody could join in, and indeed few could afford to stay out. To deal in hard currencies was forbidden but no one took this seriously, least of all the National Bank. Occasionally such dealers were raided, and a shop-window trial staged, but everyone concerned took the risk without hesitation. When the National Bank needed more dollar notes or pound notes in a hurry, instructions went to the Economic Police that the black market in foreign currency should on no account be disturbed for the next hour. Thus in 1945 a Hungarian youth delegation arrived in London with forged five-pound notes. It was a nuisance but nobody cared. It was a happy-go-lucky arrangement.

But some were not satisfied with a fair share of the general anarchy. Stories went round about the rackets perpetrated by certain political leaders and their families. It was an inter-party racket. Communists frequently saved their non-Communist colleagues, and even their opponents, from the scandals of corruption; partly because such people could be blackmailed into subservience and partly because they themselves were also involved. Communist leaders had lordly households and indulged in extravagant luxuries—for the Party's sake, they said, since this was supposed to enhance the prestige of a proletarian leadership. "Only Trotskyites and sectarians would object to that."

"Personality cult" had been there from the start. The country was swamped with posters, paintings, photographs of Russian and Hungarian leaders. Next to Stalin, the commonest sight was the Deputy Prime Minister and First Secretary to the Hungarian Communist Party, Mátyás Rákosi. He could be seen on the walls, in leaflets and in cinemas stroking the hair of a proletarian child; or affectionately fingering an ear of wheat and greeting the leader of the Social Democrats ("Workers' Unity"); or parading with non-Socialist politicians ("National Independence Front"), kissing Russian emissaries ("Our Liberators"), addressing crowds with the gestures of a popular orator and, most remarkably, showing his aptitude for hunting like an aristocrat in a braided fur coat with a rifle on his shoulder.

Rákosi certainly enjoyed seeing images of his face everywhere, which must seem miraculous to anyone who knew the thing itself. Ugliness was of course the smallest of his sins; a plump, short figure, no neck, and greasy bald head —Arsehead, he was generally called. Caring only for power, he was skilful in hiding his feelings and timing his gestures of revenge. The one passion he could not control was vanity. During my first postwar visit to Hungary, he asked my opinion about a Labour member of the House of Commons, John Haire, who had visited Hungary some months before. I told Rákosi that Haire was doing his best to gain sympathy in England for the Hungarian Democratic Coalition Government which had been denounced as a Bolshevik dictatorship by British officials on the spot and also on one occasion by Ernest Bevin. Rákosi shook his head. "Perhaps Haire meant well but during his visit to Budapest he caused enormous damage." I was anxious to hear what it was; did he commit some indiscretion in talking with British diplomats? Nothing like that, was the reply; but when Hungarian right-wing people had complained to him about the campaign to popularize the Workers' Party leaders, pointing out that the faces of Rákosi and Szakasits (leader of the Social Democrats at that time) were to be seen on every corner, Haire had answered "I don't see why you should be worried about this. In my constituency, if a politician shows his face too much people draw a clown-cap over it and laugh." To give such ideas to the simple people of Hungary! Rákosi was horrified by the story. I was astonished at his childishness, and the oddity that such an astute man should so reveal his vanity.

It was not a Communist dictatorship, but liberal Capitalism in the eighteenth century Wild West style, *laissez-faire* and indeed *laissez voler,* personal freedom with no other limit than fear of the fists and guns of the more powerful; though in fact the wildest West hooligans had come from a Wild East Empire which ran on dialectical materialist lines. Rumour had it that some of the local Communists were zealots of the Leninist revolution—a young man called Rajk, for instance, then Rákosi's lieutenant in the Party; but this was not yet the Party line. At that time Communist storm troops had to restore damaged churches in their spare time.

General suffrage and the secret ballot were introduced, along with radical Land Reforms dividing the big estates among the landless and "dwarf-holding" peasantry; a system of workers' councils was started in the factories, and there was general re-establishment of civic rights. All these reforms were implemented chaotically and corruptly, and with a Party bias, but they were by no means a sham. They were the fulfilment of long overdue promises.

There was freedom of opinion, or anyway freedom to talk. People were not afraid to abuse Russian soldiers openly; they knew indeed that their opinion did not matter either way with the Russians. If the Soviet *patrouille* needed a new war prisoner to replace one who had escaped, they would catch and deport anyone, whatever his political affiliation; when in no need of a victim, their attitude towards any anti-Russian demonstration was "I couldn't care less."

Puns and stories about the Glorious Liberators were a mental opium to compensate for evils endured. Zoltán Vas, needless to say, gladly joined in the fashion. The greatest teller of stories among the politicians of those days was the Minister of Justice, a Socialist, István Ries. An engaging armchair talker, a friendly fat man, lover of football and books, and in a vague way of a proletarian world revolution, he was the most companionable person I had ever seen in high Government office. "Did you hear the story about the old Jew?" he asked me. "He was found stripped in the Városliget (City Park) at night. The police interrogated him: 'How did it happen?' 'Well,' he answered, 'I was assaulted by two fellows in American uniform . . .' 'Without saying a word?' they asked. 'Well, one of the Americans started by shouting *Davai tchassey* . . .'* 'Really? Must they not have been Russians?' The old Jew lifted his hands in horror: 'I didn't say that, *you* said it.'" Ries told the story with gusto, adding that his own *tchassey* had also been expropriated by a Russian warrior in the dusk. Another story I remember from him was in connexion with the foundation of the Joint Soviet-Hungarian Shipping Company. "You know the agreement came about on a basis of perfect equality," he said. "The Russians have the right to ship up and down the river, and we have the right to ship across it." In 1949, some days before my arrest, I had dinner with him. He was still in office as a Minister of Justice though practically a prisoner, with A.V.O. riflemen at his threshold "protecting his personal safety." In prison, I found printed notices still on the walls signed by him. In 1950, he was arrested and tortured to death.

In 1946, outspokenness almost amounted to honesty. Freedom of the Press was restricted, by Western standards; some subjects, mainly the wrongs done by the Soviet Liberators, were taboo. But under the Horthy régime Hungarians had been used to observing a stricter censorship, so this did not seem unbearable. In broad hints anything could be written.

Information could be obtained from anywhere, but too suddenly to be digested. I was staggered by people's failure

---

* Meaning in Russian "give me your wristwatch," a phrase widely current in Soviet-occupied countries.

to see either themselves or the world outside in the light of the tremendous changes which had come about. I remember a well-to-do middle-class lady—a new convert to Communist Party membership—who asked me intimately after a splendid lunch in her flat, "Tell me your candid opinion: is it possible to live in this country?" She thought of emigrating to the West. I told her that I had no idea how she would be able to carry on in her usual way, for instance, in Britain. She was used to having two maids which in Britain would be a luxury. She was disappointed. She started complaining about the difficulties of catering. I told her that in England hardly anyone could afford a meal such as the one she had given me: there was still severe rationing of food and clothes. She was amazed. "Is this possible? Rationing in England? Why then did they win the war?" But she knew more than I did about the Royal family and the hits of the London stage.

Communication between Britain and Hungary was still very scanty. I was one of the first London Hungarians to visit Budapest. I had come as a correspondent of the *Manchester Guardian* and the *New Statesman,* after getting leave for the journey from the B.B.C. So my arrival was a sensation. I was a prey to all sort of people, old companions and new lion-hunters.

Before leaving London I had been full of anxiety about seeing my mother, then over eighty. She had been in hiding under German occupation, and had lived in a cellar during the siege. For months after the retreat of the Germans I could not learn whether she was still alive. What would she be looking like—she and my two sisters, and my brother, and all the rest of my intimate circle who survived? I had been guessing how our meeting would take place. "Well, tell me how it *did* happen," a friend said after my return to England. I could not remember.

Most of my best friends had been murdered or starved to death. Others, who were said to have been killed, turned up like ghosts alive. Many had conspicuously aged but carried on with the very conversation which had been interrupted seven years before. "When shall I see you," an old friend's wife asked me amidst affectionate Hungarian embraces. I was trying to keep some order in my days. "Look here, tomorrow I shall have tea with your step-daughter," I answered; "couldn't you join us?" O no, that was impossible; her stepdaughter, she went on, had started an unpleasant rumour about her—and she began to tell me the recent developments of a family squabble which I had witnessed in its embryonic stage before leaving Budapest. Second World War, Nazi occupation, Bolshevik occupation, and a lot of family matters which they had to settle together—nothing could reconcile them.

Budapest life struck me as a tragic operetta, or sad ballet. I recalled, in particular, one ballet which I had seen in my childhood, *The Sleeping Beauty*. The *fiesta* was going on, the smart young man dancing with the smart young lady, the *gourmand* sucking the chicken's bone, the cook boxing the ears of the kitchen boy; and everything stopped for seven years. Then the Beauty woke up, and the smart young man went on dancing with the smart young lady, the *gourmand* went on sucking the chicken's bone, the cook went on boxing the ears of the kitchen boy. Was it not exactly like that in Hungary? More realistically of course, as the smart young people had become wrinkled, the *gourmand* had lost his teeth, the cook's hand had grown shaky, and the kitchen boy had been a storm-trooper for both Nazis and Communists for a while. But this did not keep them from carrying on.

We know today that it was a dance on a volcano. As a matter of fact, we knew it then; but what could have been done about it? To watch it angrily would not have helped. The thing for me to do in 1946 without doubt was go home and see everything with my own eyes, and point out the encouraging features among many depressing and alarming ones. Whether one can do this is a matter of temperament. I feel I could again in similar circumstances. My old friend, Arthur Koestler, was worried about my atti-tude; in his autobiography* published while I was in prison, he describes it as the gullibility of a naïve liberal. I believe it was chiefly a wish to make the best of things.

* *The Invisible Writing*, Collins with Hamish Hamilton.

I had known Koestler since 1935 when he visited his native city, Budapest. He was at that time a slightly shaken Communist, disturbed by what he had seen in Russia but unable to imagine that the Soviet doctrines would not go down in history as the leading ideas of our time, vindicated by general progress and happiness. After hearing a lecture I gave, he complained that I stuck to an outdated humanism. During the war when I met him in London he warned me about the Bolshevik danger, which he was unable to forget even in the joy we all felt at Russia's strength in resisting the Nazis.

Before my first post-war visit to Hungary, Koestler called on me in my flat. I was trying to cram as much as I could into a suitcase the weight of which was limited by the R.A.F., which still ran the continental services from Britain at that time. "Look here," I told Koestler, "I am going quite mad; people expect me to take parcels to their relatives in Budapest, and the only thing I can do is pick out vitamin pills from the trunks which arrive here. What can I do for you?"

A similar thing but dangerous, Koestler answered; a very great favour he wished me to do for him, and really did not know whether he could bother me with it. "Please tell me." Well, his old mother was living in Budapest, still in a dark room of the ghetto district into which she had been driven by the Nazis. He had not dared to get in touch with her lest the N.K.V.D. should find her. He saw how difficult my luggage problem was; but could I add to my burden a tin of sardines and a bar of chocolate, and take it to her?

"Certainly," I replied. "As soon as I arrive in Budapest I shall send her a postcard and tell her . . ." Koestler was horrified. For Heaven's sake, had I no idea of postal censorship? He was sure the N.K.V.D. would be after me. But I should do him this very great favour—one evening at dusk, if I was sure I was shadowed by no one, I should go and see her in that sordid ghetto block. Really did I not think it was too much to ask? I really did not, and consented.

In Budapest, in the editorial office of the Social Democrat daily, *Népszava,* of which I was correspondent, the assistance of a middle-aged secretary was granted to me. She was a kind and helpful and pathetic personality; I remember noticing a number, tatooed on her arm in Auschwitz where she had escaped extermination only by the skin of her teeth. She helped me in distributing my odd little parcels. I put labels of the addresses on each, and when I came to a tin of sardines and a bar of chocolate I said "kindly put this aside, I shall take these along myself to a friend."

Before having a chance to do so, I gave a lecture at the Anglo-Hungarian Friendship Society. People were even crowding the staircase. The strength of Atomic Britain would be explained, they thought, and the determination of H.M. Government to drive Russians out of Hungary. My lecture was a cold shower. I told them that the idea of Europe divided into spheres of interest was prevalent in Britain and that, within this, Hungary would belong to the Soviet sphere. Exclamations of pain were audible. People did not hide their disillusion. "Preponderance of influence does not mean exclusiveness of influence," I went on: "Hungary is expected to remain a democratic country, broadly speaking, on the present-day line." But these qualifications did not help very much. The horror of becoming a "member state" within the Soviet Empire was haunting their minds. As we know today, it was justified as a fear but inexact as a term.

After my lecture, people from the audience crowded round me. Especially women I had never seen before, asking with disarming straightforwardness "Please take me with you to England, it is surely no trouble for you." In that throng and whirl, while I was out of breath, I suddenly saw an old, slim lady in black in the back row as she lifted her arm and shouted at me "I must talk to you by all means, *Ich bin die Mutter von Arthur Koestler.*"

Heavens, this was the limit. What if the N.K.V.D. overheard it? What would my friend Arthur say? I ran to the old lady and implored her to be quiet, I would go and see her, I had talked to Arthur but I was so busy . . . She said she would come and see me, and could not be dissuaded.

The following afternoon, my provisional secretary at *Népszava* received me by announcing (in the way usual in Hungary, when referring to elderly women with whom one is on familiar terms) "Auntie Koestler was here to see you."

"Mrs. Koestler? Do you know her?"

"Certainly. Who wouldn't?"

"Why, is she such a well-known character?"

"Well, she is known to be the mother of a famous Hungarian writer and she complains everywhere that she cannot get news from her son."

"Everywhere? What do you mean by that?"

"At the Ministries, and the various Party headquarters, and at the Russian *Commandatura. . . ."*

"Indeed, the Commandatura? Not the N.K.V.D.? And what did they answer?"

"They were rather annoyed I think. Through our *liaison* with the Russian Military, the young man you know, they asked us to rid them of the old lady, saying it was our business and none of theirs to look after the mother of a Hungarian-born author."

We had a good laugh at that story in London afterwards. O years of National Independence Front! When Miss Kéthly, the well-known leader of Hungarian Social Democracy, visited London she made the Hungarian Minister invite Koestler to a reception in her honour. He came, rather reluctantly. Even at the party the story went round amidst cheers. One of the guests from Budapest was the editor of *Népszava,* who was reckoned a most active fellow-traveller. I told him privately how Koestler was worried about his mother and that he had asked me to inquire whether there might be a chance of granting her a passport to Britain. After all, an old lady who had never had anything to do with politics . . . "Of course," he smiled; "who would bother about her? Or even about him! He is an author. How hysterical fiction-writers can be."

Koestler had the sense of humour, though mitigated by noticeable nervousness, to join in the amusement my story caused. And here the story could end if there were not a double point to it. The grim epilogue followed years later, when Mrs. Koestler had already safely arrived and settled in London.

It was the doom of all those involved. Miss Kéthly and the fellow-travelling editor, who were anything but friends, and the young *liaison* with the Russian Military, and I as the *liaison* with the Labour Party, all irrespective of whether we had been regarded as pro- or anti-Communist in preceding years, were jailed and tortured. The middle-aged secretary at *Népszava,* with the Auschwitz tattooing on her arm, was interned. The Communist official, in charge of issuing passports in the Ministry of the Interior, was hanged . . . Of course, all this had nothing to do with Mrs. Koestler's case. It was a matter about which the Russians really did not care, and I can even imagine that she would have been left in peace in the worst years under Stalinist terrorism. But the nervousness with which Koestler had looked upon Western hopes for neighbourly relations with the East was sadly justified. His fears were premature. I should say he was right to warn us about the dangers lurking in Hungary—if he could have told us how to avert them. But neither he nor anybody else could do that.

I witnessed the Hungarian Peace Negotiations in Paris in the summer of 1946. It was a sad farce. Hungarians and Czechs were given the job of staging a cock-fight together. Both were dependent on Russia, but Russia wanted them to be "independent," which meant mutual squabbling. The Communists on both sides were chief spokesmen for old imperialist claims and grievances. Really it was the Czechs, belonging to the victorious group of nations, who were persecuting Hungarians. But the way Hungary's sufferings were used by Hungarian propagandists was also nauseating. "It is quite heart-rending," my old friend Count Michael Károlyi said. In a semi-official way he was also attached to the Hungarian Peace Delegation. He wondered whether a compromise with Czechoslovakia on the basis of a moderate territorial adjustment could be reached. During the war he had received encouragement in this direction from leading Czech refugees;

and now he asked me confidentially to explore with the Czech Foreign Minister, Jan Masaryk, the possibility of such an understanding. I did so in a Paris Hotel—and Masaryk agreed. But the Russians did not. They forced the Prague and Budapest Governments to carry on with their propaganda-fight. Some years later they ordered them both to forget about mutual grievances overnight and to be comrades in the defence of Communist World Peace.

On my first post-war visit to Hungary, Social Democrat leaders asked me to take over the job of Press Attaché in London. It was not a very high position but it attracted me: I thought that I could carry on successfully as a *liaison*, as I had been before, between Republican Hungary and Labour Britain. No formal objection was made by any of the Hungarian authorities, but there was a lot of hesitation and delay. However, in November 1947, I was offered and accepted this appointment.

My active service with the Hungarian Legation did not last longer than a year and a half. During that short period I witnessed the resignations of two successive Ministers to the Court of St. James's.

At first I enjoyed my job with the Legation. I had to grope my way towards knowing the people it was my duty to handle in this fairly precarious position, but I found it interesting to see diplomatic machinery from the inside, however false it was bound to be in those circumstances. Our Reports to the Government were not sincere, and could not be; we knew they were to reach Moscow. But we had to pretend in addressing the Government, and even one another, that we were the representatives of an independent country. We did our best to be so but it was hopeless. To meet British people and then boast of having met and won them over (whatever that meant) for the Hungarian cause was our main diplomatic activity. It was a difficult position for the whole staff and the only possible way for them was to take it easy. I congratulate them retrospectively for doing that most ably. The wives of our diplomats were charming, and our receptions as a rule successful. Too successful now and then. Some of the Great

Friends of Hungary, used to the entertainments of Horthy's Kingdom, and intoxicated now by memories of them at these parties, trod the toes of the ladies with enthusiasm in the heat of their scholarly dancing, and it was no easy job to manoeuvre them away late at night.

But the approaching liquidation of Social Democracy was bound to affect us all. Clashes within the Legation precipitated the resignation of the Hungarian Minister, Bede. Since the late summer of 1947 a young Secretary had been working on his staff, an over-zealous convert to Communism, Gábor Pulay. His appearance, manners, and political outlook made a caricature of what Hungary looked like at that time. A handsome youth with a twirled moustache, and with the characteristic manner of a heel-clicking provincial, he drank and swore and poured out dialectical materialism all the time. His devotion to the Cause knew no bounds, nor did his loyalty to leaders. I remember that once he arrived back from Budapest and unfolded with great satisfaction a poster which he had received personally from Rákosi. The poster contained no less a thing than portraits of Rákosi himself, at seven or eight different stages of his life. It started with baby-Rákosi, and ended with leader-Rákosi. Pulay tenderly pointed to eight-year-old Rákosi, a plump child with fleshy nose and centrifugal ears, quite nice, as all children are quite nice so long as one does not guess what they are going to become, but not such a portrait as hopeful mothers would dream about. "Look, what a *beautiful* child he was," Pulay said with tears which I saw then in his eyes for the first and last time. Power makes you beautiful, even retrospectively. I was opportunist enough to give a solemn nod.

Pulay did not waste his time; in fact, he worked twice as much as anyone else. He never stopped snooping. If I wanted him to know something without telling him about it, I had only to leave it on my desk. Though one-sided and hot-headed he was neither a fool nor uneducated. Between two glasses of whisky he would study Lenin's works, and then dash into the room of a colleague, tell him about this or that, and watch his reactions.

He quickly came to the conclusion that the evil spirit of our staff was another Secretary of Legation, Géza Luby, the most intimate colleague of the Minister. He reported to the Chief of the Political Department of the Hungarian Foreign Ministry, (now a refugee), György Heltai: "I suspect Luby is in touch with refugee Hungarian diplomats and has got letters from them." The answer was: "If so, get hold of those documents." Pulay decided for *action directe*. One night he stayed late in his office, and with an expert knowledge the origin of which I have never been able to trace, forced Luby's safe. Having calmed his Leninist-Stalinist conscience, he left and had a good sleep. The following morning, the housekeeper was horrified to find that the safe had been forced. Knowing nothing of diplomatic privilege, according to which the head of a Legation alone is authorized to apply for non-Hungarian assistance in the building, he asked the London police to enter. The scandal could hardly be hushed up.

Within the Legation it broke loose. There were unfriendly exchanges between the Minister and Pulay, of which a female member of the staff took minutes. Then the Minister rushed to Budapest to complain and, feeling he was complaining in vain, rushed back to London as fast as possible. Luby had meanwhile been sacked by the Ministry. Pulay rushed to Budapest after the Minister and by the time he was back in London the Minister had resigned and been followed by several members of his staff.

At his farewell I shook his hand amicably, but decided to stay. I did so for roughly the same reasons as in joining the Legation originally. My position had got more uncomfortable, but I still kept some of my *liaison* hopes, and my people were still in Budapest. . . .

The new Chargé d'Affaires of the London Legation was a former Counsellor of the Paris Legation (under Count Károlyi), János Erös. I had known him as a young journalist and scholar from pre-war Budapest. He arrived with the grace of a peace-maker. His first great deed of diplomacy was to reconcile me with Pulay as we had not hit it off very well before. Having agreed to stay, I played the game. Erös then asked me to put him in touch as much as possible with my Labour and Liberal friends. He himself did not conceal a scepticism about Communist Party doctrines and slogans. In 1948 such scepticism was still not sacrilege. It was already "People's Democracy performing the function of a Dictatorship of the Proletariate without Soviet form"—an authoritarian régime, but of a mild kind.

In the summer of that year I visited Budapest. The Three Year Plan for Reconstruction was declared at an end, and the Socialist Five Year Plan had started on its lamentable career. The first popular reaction to it was a story about the enthusiastic Communist who said:

"Do you know that we are ahead of schedule in fulfilling the Five Year Plan?"

"Are we?"

"O yes. Today we are already as badly off as we are supposed to be next year."

In the window of a leading bookshop I noticed *Darkness at Noon;* I presume the owner had no idea what it was about, but even an oversight like that could not happen at a time when it might have grave consequences. The masters of Hungary were still keen to keep friendly links with the West and to show that freedom of opinion existed in their country. "Decadent" or "bourgeois" art and letters, and jokes at the expense of the régime, were still tolerated. *Szabad Száj* (Free Tongue) the authorized Opposition satirical weekly, snapping alternately at the régime and its opponents, was still published.

When senior members of the Foreign Ministry asked me how Erös was getting on in London, I mentioned to his credit that he was behaving soberly and moderately. This was still acknowledged as a merit. Shortly afterwards, he was promoted to be Minister. I had a long talk with the ideological leader, and chief adviser on foreign policy, József Révai. He received me cordially as a fellow-writer —he had started as an *avant-garde* poet, a very bad one, and later published some historical and literary essays, which were rather better. I told him sincerely but cautiously what impressed me badly in Hungary. He took it with a smile, and asked me whether I did not consider staying at home: "After all, you are a writer . . ." I answered: "I would rather be a propagandist for our Government abroad, than its opponent at home." Again he smiled, and wished me good luck.

But this good-natured version of dictatorship had gone by 1949. It ended at the time of the Mindszenty trial and mass-arrests, first of Catholic, then of Lutheran, Calvinist and Jewish clergymen. A taste for the art or ideas of the West changed from a weakness to a crime. People began to disappear in the A.V.O. headquarters at 60 Andrássy Avenue, and no information about their whereabouts was given. Society was hypnotized by fear. In London, though appalled by much that happened, I was unable to realize the extent of the change.

The trend of events, of course, was clear; so was the growing British suspicion towards everything connected with the régime. The dwindling fortunes of the British Communist Party and its fellow-travellers were very noticeable; but how could this be reported to Budapest? My advice, naïve enough as I see it today, was to report sincerely. Erös disagreed with me: "Don't you see that they want to be fooled?" One day, he told me we were ordered to write a Report on British reactions to the "Peace Movement." I suggested we should answer there was no reaction. "Impossible, impossible," Erös insisted. So we invented some reactions.

Since the order was that we should maintain social contacts with as many important people as possible, irrespective of their reactionary leanings, he was keen to give frequent invitations to Mr. and Mrs. Kingsley Martin, for instance, and to meet Harold Laski. Our few encounters with Laski were particularly amusing. He was very enjoyable company, and though he must have struck every Continental as thoroughly British in his approach, he was really created more for Continental than British taste. Tiny, wiry, loud and over-clever, he was considered by many a British apostle of racial tolerance as too much of a Jew. His countrymen liked and respected him but not without reserve. When I first had a chance to talk at length with him, he was scathing about many of his left-wing comrades, and equally critical about Bevin and others from the right wing of the Labour party too. Despite his aggressive irony, he was generous in praising people with whom he disagreed especially, I should add, if they had happened to pay some attention to him. He praised Churchill, and Acheson, and Mountbatten, and of course many of his fellow-Socialists, and also Stalin who, he said, had shown some evidence of a sense of humour when they had met in Moscow.

I put my own problems to him frankly. "Do as I do," he answered, "administer your indiscretion."

"My dear Professor," I sighed, "it is not so easy to do that as a Socialist in a People's Republic, as it is in your hereditary Kingdom."

Laski thought he could help to bring about an East-West settlement. He broached the idea of a visit to Budapest to see things with his own eyes. Erös and I, after entertaining him to a long lunch in a Greek restaurant, reported his suggestion to the Foreign Ministry. The lunch was delightful but the answer from Budapest was less so. We got an indignant refusal and rebuke.

Amongst the many things which had changed in Budapest, was the Political Department of the Foreign Ministry. Its chief, György Heltai, was no longer regarded as a staunch Communist and Janos Beck succeeded him. Beck was a very staunch Communist, who had once been an officer in the Political Police. I myself got on quite well with Beck on his subsequent visits to London. His mind moved like a locomotive along certain tracks but he was not without ability. He had a gift for languages, a taste for engineering, and an observant eye for the differences between Woolworth articles in London and their opposite numbers in other countries. He could have been almost anything but a diplomat. His main task was to make the behaviour of Hungarian legations in the West as provocative as possible, and their reports as misleading as possible. At that moment, he was the right man in the right place. This had become the Line to follow. In Budapest he had been shocked by the un-Bolshevik tone and defeatist remarks in the Reports which came from the Minister in London. The most shocking were those I had succeeded in putting through, though in very mild form and against the Minister's judgement.

Beck had come to London personally to find out if we had been infected with Imperialism. A nervous swarming started at the Legation. One morning Erös asked me to come to a deserted store-room with him, and said: "I wish to tell you that some rumours about you are circulating in Budapest. For instance, Madame Károlyi and you are supposed to be the evil spirits of Michael Károlyi, I mean, the anti-Russian influences with him. I felt I should warn you in case you were planning to return. . . ."

"I can't help it," I answered; "I am in their hands, and I have got my people there." This was indeed how I felt. My eighty-year-old father was lying on his deathbed in Budapest. I was determined to go and see him as well as other near relatives and friends. Erös made a faint gesture of despair, and then bade me farewell for a while. His wife was pregnant, and he was due to go on leave. I just carried on talking to Beck about Spanish dialects and Woolworths. Some days later, Pulay rang me and in a dramatic voice read out the announcement from Budapest radio about Minister Erös's resignation. The reason, not made clear by the official announcement, was that Beck had insisted in his visiting Budapest at once, and he had refused to do so.

. . . These were the two ministerial resignations I witnessed in 1948–9. Their background stories I only learned much later—in the privacy of a prison-cell, talking amicably with the two embittered rival Communists, both former Directors of the Political Department of the Foreign Ministry, György Heltai and Janos Beck, who had both been jailed, as I had, in the summer of 1949.

Chapter 4

In Slavery at Large

IN BUDAPEST, June, 1949. The *communiqué* had just been issued about the arrest of three senior officials of the People's Republic; among them the Foreign Minister and Deputy to the First Secretary of the Communist Party, László Rajk. The *communiqué* described them as spies and made it clear that a considerable number of others had been arrested meanwhile. Everyone knew that. For some weeks, important Communists had been disappearing overnight. The Western Press and radio had reported the rumours; everybody in Budapest was nervous and uncertain.

What was it all about? The *communiqué* was too brief and hidden in Party jargon for us to judge. The one thing it made clear was that some of the living idols would henceforth be called traitors, Fascist beasts, enemies of the people, hirelings of the imperialists, and saboteurs. The posters with Rajk's portraits were speedily removed from hoardings. Newspapers published letters from readers who had always known that Rajk was a traitor and were relieved to find justice prevailing at last. All this was frightening and, in a grim way, amusing: *sic transit gloria mundi* . . . Among the reactionaries, malicious pleasure was more evident than panic. Jokes about Rajk spread like fire; in denigrating him, the anti-Government majority was at one with the pro-Government minority—all agreed that it served him right.

It seemed likely that a faction of the Party was being liquidated, but which faction? Some of the arrested, known to have belonged to competing groups, were now lumped together as the agents of a Truman-Bevin-Tito-Vatican-Francoist-Hitlerist-Zionist-Nationalist-Cosmopolitan-Trotskyite-Capitalist world conspiracy. That meant, in terms of Party jargon, "Right wing deviation" or "opportunism." But Rajk was a fanatic Communist. Was it not possible, some were wondering, that Rákosi had simply chosen a pretext, formulated in the Kremlin way, for getting rid of his extremists?

Ever since his return to Hungary in the wake of the Russian Army, Rákosi had posed as Wise Moderator among the Communists. He ordered secretly that the adjective Wise should only be applied to him. "We can't split up wisdom," he explained. With his appearance, the manner and voice of a bright horse-dealer, he could easily persuade people that he disliked violence and rigidity. He exploited this faculty to blacken the reputation of his likely rivals. He complained to many that Gerö was too rigid, and Rajk too violent; and he succeeded in building a reputation for himself on this foundation, among anti-Communists at home and abroad. Behind the dutiful posture of a Jacobin orator, some paternal and patriotic sentiment was supposed to linger.

People were fooled by him, and so was I though I had never liked him personally. He was quick-witted, an amusing talker, and his grasp of practical matters was impressive. But this was the mental quality one knew well from many lively East European businessmen. Mixed with ambition to shape the future of a country it became rather repulsive. When I read in the anti-Communist Western press, about his "intellect," I was flabbergasted. It was only vulgar cleverness.

I disliked him for being a snob, which is not rare among Communists or other revolutionaries. The son of a well-to-do country grocer, he must have suffered from his social background which was not high or low enough to be impressive. He must have suffered even more from being a Jew, and from his coarse appearance. This is why he was jealous of Rajk, a good-looking young man and the most important gentile among the Communist leaders at that time. For the same reason, he made a point of establishing himself on friendly terms with people who were known to be anti-Semitic. When Stalin turned against the Jews, in the frame of a campaign against Zionism, Rákosi eagerly joined it. This on the whole did not surprise me; but I did not think he was fond of carnage for its own sake. In the light of later events we learned that he was, along with glory and power. In his character, the quick-witted commercial agent was joined with a Himmler.

Today it is not difficult to realize how, in 1949, the torture and massacre of masses of Hungarians started. Indeed it started with the victimization of Communists. To gauge the proportion of victims who simply had bad luck, as against those who had really shown some spark of patriotism or humane feeling, would be difficult. In general, those who survived the purge unharmed were probably more sycophantic and barbarous than others who were murdered, imprisoned or at least pushed aside until Stalin's death. But some of the executed were chiefly sorry for not being among the executioners. The selection of criminals was based quite openly on assumptions about potential deviation, rather than upon anything they had actually said or done.

Rajk himself was a telling example. I knew him personally. He was not a particularly bright man—quite intelligent, fairly well read, leaving an impression of youthful sincerity. Away from the field of battle he had calm and charming manners. When he was trying to analyse a problem I found him rather vague and inarticulate. I knew from friends that he had often had doubts about one or another Party directive, but the refrain with which he had concluded was always "One must have a compass, and my compass is the Soviet Union." After the war he carried out orders from Moscow in his important position as Minister of the Interior and in other senior offices. There were certainly some clashes between him and the head of the Political Police, Lieutenant General Gábor Péter. But as Péter was a ferocious megalomaniac, Rajk's disapproval did not necessarily mean disagreement about policy. He would not have enjoyed cruelties and encouraged corruption as Rákosi or Péter did, but the "compass" was too holy to be disregarded for the sake of such trivialities.

After the rupture between the Cominform and Jugoslavia, Rákosi pushed Hungary to the front of the anti-Jugoslav campaign. His reason for this was simple: he knew that Russia wanted it, and felt convinced that for years to come Russia would remain the master of Hungary. "I don't want to become a refugee again," he answered half-humorously when something was suggested which might have displeased Stalin. It seems likely that Rajk once warned him against running too fast in the anti-Jugoslav campaign; but he was told to shut up and did shut up.

In 1949, the order came from Moscow that "Hungarian Titoists must be liquidated." To liquidate them, one had to produce them. The A.V.O. had provided the N.K.V.D. with a long list of suspected Hungarian Titoists. The most dangerous of them, according to the A.V.O. chief, was the head of the rival Security organization, the Communist Military Political Police, Major-General Pálffy-Oesterreicher, a former officer of the Horthy Army. There was no evidence against him but the treachery of a man in his position and with his background could be "assumed." Similarly assumed was the culpability of the Chief of the "Cadre Centre," for the simple reason that he had spent the war years in Switzerland and on Communist instructions had got in touch wtih Allen Dulles, the emissary of American Intelligence. Masses of people were liquidated together with them; but who would be the chief figure, or symbolic head of the group?

Rákosi hesitated between two possibilities—László Rajk and Imre Nagy. Nagy was the only man in the Party who really had contradicted him. He too had spent years in Moscow in the inter-war period and had been helped to return to his own country by the Liberators. As a farmer's son, mainly interested in agricultural matters and knowing the ways of the peasants, he was appointed Minister of Agriculture in the first post-war Government and was thus instrumental in carrying out the Land Reform. Later, when "liquidation of the *Kulaks* as a class" and the campaign for compulsory collectivization started, he condemned these Government measures. Rákosi, in the Central Committee of the Party (the body to which the Politbureau was technically responsible), indignantly rebuked him for doing so. He accused Nagy of "Buckarinism" (a crime second only to Trotskyism-Titoism) and demanded that Nagy should make "self-criticism." Nagy temporized: he asked again and again for an extension of the time granted to him for examining the question and drafting his statement; and did not, ultimately, make any self-criticizing statement at all.*

By that time he had already left the Ministry of Agriculture and been elected President of the National Assembly. It was a decorative position but no one took it seriously, as everyone knew that the Party Politbureau decided about policy and not the Government or, for that matter, the nominal legislative body. There was but one man who took Nagy's position seriously, and that was Nagy himself. A senior economist of the Party and Government once rang and told him as a matter of routine to undertake some measure which Comrade Gerö had ordered. Nagy answered with the calm of political innocence that if so, Gerö should first get permission from the Council of Ministers—the proper and constitutional procedure. The economist thought Nagy had gone mad. When he reported Nagy's reply to his leaders they simply shrugged their shoulders. In the subsequent years of integral Stalinism, Nagy was pushed aside and kept in an unimportant position but no harm was done to him. The choice for martyrdom fell on Rajk, not on him.

The reason lay in the Communist mind. Assumable and potential deeds were more important than those which had been committed. Personal jealousy was weightier than political disagreement. Nagy had friends in Moscow; his imprisonment or execution might have caused bad feeling there. Besides, Rákosi did not fear Nagy as a rival at that time. Nagy was little known among the general public and his popularity on account of the Land Reform was set off by the fact that he too had come from Moscow. Rajk, apart from fighting in the Spanish Civil War, had no political past outside his own country. As a potential rallying point of resistance in the Party he was doomed.

* I got this story from a former Communist high official in prison, and it rings quite true. But on other occasions, Nagy, too, had to "confess to error of judgment," both before and after his return from the U.S.S.R.

Most of the former members of the International Brigade were imprisoned together with him. My friend Michael, from the Southwark days, would certainly not have escaped this if he had lived in the world which he thought Paradise. Janos Beck, the staunchest of all Communists, did not escape it either. He was so constant as to insist even in prison that Rajk, who had been his chief and comrade-in-arms, must have been guilty. "I suspected him because of his negligence in office."

Most Communists imprisoned under Stalin have been released since that time; some of them are in high positions today. In the present-day Communist Party jargon, they had been victims of "dogmatism." This explanation is completely false. Rákosi was not only undogmatic but completely unprincipled; lust for power, vanity, and personal revenge was his sole detectable impulse. Led by it, he wished to reassure the Kremlin and eliminate whomever he disliked. These tasks could easily be co-ordinated.

Hungary had to be Russified. Her soldiers received uniforms modelled on the Russian (indeed, on the old Tzarist) pattern. Russian became the second compulsory language to be taught in schools. The streets of the city were renamed after Russian heroes—and bus conductors had much trouble pronouncing them. Leaflets explained that Russian science, art and military strategy had always been the best in the world; that some of the Russian Tzars and generals, known hitherto as tyrants or mass-murderers, had really been fighters for progress. The West had simply stolen and expropriated the inventions of the Russian people.

The response from the Budapest storymongers was quick. "Do you know who invented the wireless?" they would ask.

"Popov, of course," the reply was.

"Who discovered the permanence of matter?"

"Lomonosov."

"Who was the first man?"

"Adamov."

"Who created him?"

"Jehov."

Hungary had to be restratified. She must have a clear hierarchy of ruling and subject classes. This would be led by the members of the Politbureau and their families, and followed by others of steadily diminishing importance. The broadest level of society, praised in words but cruelly exploited in other ways and deprived of any civic rights, would be crowded with workers and working peasants. Last of all came the outcasts—those who had once been landlords, aristocrats, capitalists, senior officials, army officers and clergymen—and the kulaks; unless subservience to the régime or some other special reason induced the Party to forgive their past lives. Otherwise they and also their children were to be expelled from offices and schools, and dumped in concentration camps. The Communists felt they must distrust them regardless of Party allegiance. Relying upon mass sadism, they comforted common people for their sufferings by publicizing the predicament of their former overlords. In the event, this campaign only produced sympathy for its victims.

The economic and political privileges of our Soviet guests and the Party oligarchy were not concealed; in fact, they were stressed in order to increase the authority of the rulers. Special shops, special schools, rows of luxurious villas, special bathing resorts fenced with barbed wire were reserved for them and their children. "The New Class," or the new caste system, was a tangible reality.

So were the new "Führerprinzip" and Gestapo rule. Today, they are retrospectively condemned by the Communist parties as personality cult and lawlessness. Such descriptions are correct, but give no idea of what was going on. It was a Party order that at meetings whenever there was mention of the Soviet Union or Stalin or Rákosi, the audience must spring to its feet and clap rhythmically. If somebody clapped out of time he got into trouble. I am sure that from St. Stephen, the founder of the Hungarian Kingdom, to Szálasi, the local Hitler, nobody in the history of my country had expected or received half so many expressions of humility and obedience as the Communist dictator imposed upon us by Russia. Next in organizing self-glory was the Minister of Defense, General Mihály

Farkas, most wretched thug of all. His troops had to sing a march starting "I am the soldier of Mihály Farkas. . . ."

The new secret police, which had swallowed all its rival bodies, was called A.V.H.; which stood for the Hungarian words meaning State Security Authority (though most people continued by habit to call it A.V.O. which had stood for State Security Department). Terror grew into a national nightmare. A.V.H. officers and men, in ordinary clothes or their ill-famed uniforms with blue lapels, supervised cabinet ministers along with ordinary citizens, made concierges report on the private lives of tenants, and carried out surprise raids all over the country. Their arrogance and cruelty were indescribable. Their venality was well known—indeed the only comfort for many a possible victim. They issued passports in exchange for flats and furniture and jewellery, though more often than not they took their loot and gave nothing in return. Just one group could not manage to bribe them—those who had been picked by Rákosi and his followers as "spies" and "traitors." In Budapest, people were guessing and fearing and making grim jokes day and night: who would come next?

This was the atmosphere in the Foreign Ministry to the staff of which I belonged. No one knew who had been denouncing somebody, nobody dared repeat more than the slogans of the day, just spiced a little with the facetious accent of the Budapest vernacular lest it might sound too solemn to be genuine. It took some days for me to find out that the chief of the Political Department who had summoned me to Budapest had since been arrested. I saw the Minister of Foreign Affairs, Gyula Kállai; he was so embarrassed that I had to address him as a tutor to his pupil. I saw the Chief of the Press Department, Boldizsár; he praised Rákosi nervously, and told stories even more nervously. I learned from him that my old friend, Francois Fejtö, had resigned his Hungarian Government post in Paris. He learned from me that Zoltán Horváth, an architect of the Party merger, and then editor of the Trade Union journal, had been arrested. "Impossible," Boldizsár said and looked at the last copy of the paper; Horváth's name had disappeared from it. Boldizsár went pale and smiled. "You know," I told him, "Oscar Wilde said: 'Awful this uncertainty; I hope it will last.' "

I saw the real head of the Foreign Ministry, acting as Under-Secretary of State, Andor Berei. He was quite polite in his own repellent way. He explained to me that the resignation of the Minister in London, Erös, must have been the result of a manoeuvre by the British Secret Intelligence. They had got hold of him through the psycho-analysts who were in fact political agents of the imperialists. "Do you know a psychoanalyst called Michael Bálint?" he asked me. "I met him once or twice," I answered; I had in fact known him well, and had introduced him to Erös.

Berei asked me about developments in England. I told him what I new—though not everything I knew—and pointed out that Labour was losing some ground. "Of course, polarization," Berei said; "both the great capitalists and the Communists are getting stronger." I told him he was wrong; it was a general slide towards the Right, not a Fascist right but rather neo-Conservative, and that the Communists were likely to lose even their two seats in Parliament, as the Foreign Editor of the *Daily Worker* had admitted to me. "All this is very interesting," Berei said; "would you make a summary in writing of all you have told me?" He said he would like me to return to my post in London, but that I should first spend some time in Budapest to get familiar with current ideas. I had established myself for the time being in a fairly expensive hotel on Margaret Island, and told him I wished to look for a cheaper place. "By no means," he answered; "it is important that you should live in comfort and at a place where you can meet foreigners and entertain them. The Ministry will cover your expenses."

At the request of Berei and Boldizsár I gave a talk to the youths who had been trained to act as tourist guides. I did my best to be People's-Democratic. I did not succeed at all. I gave the audience such advice as "Do not obtrusively impose your own opinions on our British visitors; do not talk to them about starvation in England, for they know that is nonsense; do not praise too eagerly such welfare arrangements as we have got, for they might think you have never heard of the welfare institutions which started in England earlier than anywhere on the Continent. Just let them discover with their own eyes the marvellous achievement of our People's Democracy." The response was perfectly frigid. Many of the audience clapped because they did not discover that that was an exceptional occasion when they ought not to have done so. The Foreign Ministry officials on the spot said nothing. Nor did Berei a few days later—except that a World Youth Congress was shortly to be held in Budapest, and that he would like me to stay a little longer and assist the gatherings.

My father was near his death. His cruel illness, Parkinson's disease, kills gradually. It atrophies the nerve system, starting with the limbs, ending at the brain. My father's brain was already affected; his wit still shimmering from time to time, but memory failing. "I think it was a very clever thing for you to come home because . . . what did I say?" Physical pains tormented him in spite of morphia. Why should I disturb him in his optimism about me, the one comforting thought he had at that time? Once, when he mentioned political developments and noticed that I shut the door before replying, he asked, "Well, has fear come to that?" I was glad that the next moment he forgot what he had been saying.

I lived as happily as anyone can who knows he may be hanged at any moment. I visited the beach on Margaret Island, and Lake Balaton with friends who took me in their car; I strolled over the city with my friend Bernard, who had arrived from England for the International Youth Congress. Bernard was an extremely intelligent man but as adolescent in his zeal as many a middle-aged Westerner who gets fascinated by the revolutionary spirit of young people further east. Why disappoint him? We had had long theoretical arguments in England; but as I had chosen to return to Hungary I simply said, "I see that to save peace and the Socialist achievements of the present régime, we must co-operate with the Communists, whether we agree with them or not"; and this satisfied him, the more so as he was fascinated by the cream and wine of Budapest, and by some girls who were with me, no less than by the current ideology. "Did you tell Bernard that . . ." one of the girls started to ask; "I did not tell him anything," I interrupted her.

Try and escape from Hungary? I was haunted by the idea but could not even decide to take it seriously. What would happen to my relatives? And how could I risk shattering anyone's feeling of security by approaching him about this? One Hungarian visitor from the West, in a rather similar position to mine, had got another member of the Congress to give him his passport, and had left the country with it. The other man could easily say he had lost his passport, as so many people really do. Should I ask Bernard? Whether he consented or not he would for ever be tormented by his conscience, either as a bad friend or a traitor to the Cause.

At the beginning of September I heard of more arrests. Almost all Communists who had held leading positions in the London Hungarian Club had been arrested. "Stalin's eyes," as Károlyi used to call them, all under lock and key now. "God, what about you?" a friend could not help asking; "didn't you work with them in London?" "Why should I bother?" I said feebly; "I have never been a Communist. You know, in Hungary it was always very dangerous to be a Communist, and apparently we are just keeping the tradition."

My father meanwhile had died. At his funeral an Under-Secretary of State of the Ministry of Education made a speech, stressing the fact that he was speaking as a writers' representative. The State already kept apart. The obituaries were restrained in tone. The time when "bourgeois progressive authors" could be appreciated had passed. Not only Communists were in danger.

Before coming to Budapest, in May, I had left a letter for my sister in London in case I might be unable to return. I had asked her to look after my belongings and not come to Hungary, whatever happened to me. The only point on which I could congratulate myself now was that I had taken this precaution.

I remember my last talk with Count Károlyi on the 2nd or 3rd of September. He had come home to wind up his affairs before going on long sick-leave with his wife; and he also hoped to intervene in favour of Rajk and his associates. On the way into his room I bumped into one of his relatives, a princess who was just leaving. Distaste for their aristocratic connexions had forsaken the Károlyi couple when they found themselves in plebeian Hungary; now they wished to preserve the cousins and sisters-in-law from Bolshevik persecution. The princess who was visiting him had been received into the Communist party with enthusiasm in 1945; then it was "National Independence Front." But in 1949 her comrades discovered she was "class-alien," pushed her aside, and expelled her son from the Party.

"She complained to me but what can I do about it?" Károlyi said. He was very depressed. "There are more important things than that, and I am helpless." He had seen Rákosi about Rajk, and told him he could not believe in the "spy" charges, and they had had a very disagreeable discussion. He had seen others about complaints against the A.V.H.; on behalf of people beaten half dead merely for being caught trying to cross the frontier . . . "But what can we do? We are a 'member-state.' What do you think of the new crest?" The new draft Constitution had overnight introduced a variation of the Soviet star and hammer as the symbol of the Hungarian People's Republic, declaring that the old one had stood for class oppression. Károlyi made a gesture of despair.

On September 4th, late at night, after a cheerful dinner with intimate friends, I was walking home to my hotel room on Margaret Island. Though rain was spitting I strolled in shirt-sleeves, my jacket on my arm. It was a stuffy late-summer night, in which life and nature seemed to join in frightening harmony. I had not written poetry for twenty-five years, but now a poem was shaping itself in my mind. It was about futility and time passing, the passage of years, clouds and lives through a universe in which one still remained afraid. "Like hare hypnotized by snake . . ." I was muttering a verse under the long shadows of the chestnut trees, on the island, when a friend came up to me: "Paul, are you still here? They haven't sent you back? Terrible." I found it depressing that he said what I knew anyway. "Don't worry," I answered and said good-bye. When I entered the hotel, wet from rain and sweat, and asked the porter as I usually did whether there was some message for me, he avoided looking into my face but with a stern expression pointed with his head at two men standing next to him. One of them turned up his lapel to show the symbol of the A.V.H.

Chapter 5

Why Did I Confess?

"How strange that I don't feel any fear," I thought as, crammed between the two A.V.H. agents who pressed their thighs to mine and never stopped watching me, I was driven towards 60 Andrássy ut. I presume exhaustion was responsible for my calm. I simply did not care about anything, and if at the next moment I had been led before a firing-squad I should have thought it quite a good solution. At number 60, I was led to a small room where an officer searched me. He took my wallet and wrist-watch and all other unnecessary objects from me. He put them into an envelope and carefully sealed it up. All this has of course disappeared for good as have all my belongings at the hotel room. Indeed more valuable objects than these have been Communized by the A.V.H.; I am only sorry for some books, inscribed by the authors who are dead, which I shall never be able to replace.

They buffeted me into a neighbouring room, with men and women sitting round, all facing the wall and forbidden to turn their heads. I got the same order. My socks, braces and tie were taken, and the clasps torn off my sandals.

Then I entered my first prison cell. Its length was some three metres, its breadth some one and a half metres, its height two metres. A wooden bunk was fastened to its stone floor. Being situated in the cellar, there was no window; only a tiny vent-hole letting in more dust than fresh air from a courtyard. The soft and mouldy walls were full of scribbles, left as souvenirs by my predecessors. From above the iron door, an electric bulb was throwing light at the bunk all the time. "My crypt," I felt; "that's the end of the journey." The gaoler gave me a dirty rag and told me I might lie down but that I must turn my face towards the light and hold my hands outside the rag. Precautions against suicide. I asked him how I could let my relatives know. "Your interrogator will tell you," he answered; which was the reply from him and all his colleagues, whatever question I asked. After seeing me to the lavatory, in which a couple of rats were expecting me, he escorted me back and looked through the spy-hole to see whether I followed his orders. I did. I was sure I would not get a moment's sleep that night. In five minutes' time I was fast asleep.

I was woken up by a broom pressed into my hands: I must sweep the cell. Half an hour later I was ordered to have my wash. As prisoners in police custody were not allowed to see one another, this had to be done in great haste, over a sink in running cold water. And this was all right. But to wipe myself I was given a big towel, used apparently by dozens before me, wet, muddy, blood-stained, and of an awful stench. An hour or so later my breakfast came: at that moment I could hardly touch it but, on the basis of later experiences when I grew less fussy, I should say it was quite good: caraway-seed soup with bread. Altogether, I hasten to point out, food at the A.V.H. headquarters at that particular period was quite decent and sufficient. At midday, we had soup and vegetable or the sort of sweet noodles which Hungarians are very fond of; in the evening, vegetable again; and also, two or three times a week, meat and a handful of plums or grapes. Before that period, food had consisted of thin soup and a piece of bread; and afterwards it deteriorated again, as I have learned from other prisoners. Allegedly, the reason for this generous treatment concerning food, along with the greatest cruelty in every other field, was that the crushing and brain-washing of the "Rajkists" was on the agenda; the A.V.H. liked to apply carrots and whips simultaneously.

On the first day of my imprisonment, my fingerprints were taken and nothing else happened to me.

At night, already half asleep, I was woken by a harsh voice: "Come out at once." Two gaolers grasped my hands and led me at last to see my Interrogator. He was sitting at a desk, in a dark room, and received me with great solemnity. I was certainly in no laughing mood myself, yet I could hardly suppress a laugh when he suddenly turned on to my face the spotlight that I had read about in *Darkness at Noon.* He began to question me, and after the personal details asked dramatically: "Why are you here?" "That is the very thing I should have liked to ask you, sir," I answered. He said I knew the reason very well myself. Everyone, he added, started by denying and finished by confessing; I had better confess at once. They would help me as much as they could if I were co-operative; if not, I might endanger not only myself but also my relatives—my half-brother, for instance, a doctor then in his sixties, who had been a Social Democrat party member and a Budapest town councillor. "We know," he told me, "that you received certain information from him when you were on the staff of the B.B.C. We don't care about the old fool for a moment, but if you obstruct our efforts you may well meet him here one of these days." He ordered me to sit down and write a true "autobiography." Some hours later he perused it and tore it to pieces. "You know very well this contains nothing of interest," he added.

The following night, another interrogator dealt with me. He said I must confess plainly that I had been "organized in." To be organized in is a solecism in Hungarian no less than in English but the Stalinists loved it. It means that one was recruited for the Secret Service. "Who do you think should have organized me in?" I asked. The answer was *Ee-ash.* I must admit that I really had no idea what he meant. "Ee-ash you say, sir? Who is he?" The Interrogator winced as though showing his impatience. "Don't try to fool me by pretending you don't know what *Ee-ash* is. It was they who sent you to Hungary." After a while I guessed it. "Ee-ash" is the Magyar pronunciation of the letters "I.S.," standing for Intelligence Service, which according to what I should have known, is the authority in control of the British spy agencies. The A.V.H. officers used this abbreviation with the pride of the initiated. I overheard them later whispering to each other, "Is this I.S. or Deuxième Bureau? Or maybe C.I.C.?"—the latter pronounced by them *Tseets,* and standing for the American Counter-Intelligence Corps. They seemed really sure of knowing the secrets about world political developments by getting familiar with such magic words.

I was naïve. My arrest had not surprised me; my fairly outspoken talks both with Englishmen in London and Hungarians at home could well have provided sufficient reason to inculpate me. But one thing I had never done was work for any branch of the "I.S." In the war years I was allowed to deal with secret material at the B.B.C. but so were many people known as Stalinists. Since the beginning of the cold war between East and West, and mainly since my employment with the Hungarian Legation, I had been careful never to disclose any internal detail of Government or diplomatic machinery, however frankly I gave my opinion of political developments or personalities to many a friend. In fact, I had no idea of how either Secret Intelligence or Counter-Intelligence was working in Britain; my main information of them came from cartoons making fun of M.I.5. In spite of the widespread enthusiasm for creating spies, this accusation at the first moment staggered me.

"Don't try to fool me!" the second Interrogator shouted at me. "Do you deny having served on the staff of the B.B.C.?" I admitted having done so. "Well, everybody knows that the B.B.C. is but a covering organization of I.S." Again, I was naïve enough to argue with him. I told the Interrogator it was none of my business to defend the B.B.C. with which I had parted in a fairly strained atmosphere, but that it was an organization with more than ten thousand people on its staff, broadcasting round the clock in some forty languages; was it possible to imagine that all this should only happen to cover spies and counter-spies? The Interrogator shook his head. He was shocked to think I was "trying to defend the B.B.C., even now." His fondness for the phrase *covering organization* equalled the obsession about *organizing in.* I was told to disclose all secrets of that covering organization, or else they would teach me a lesson.

From then onwards, for about eight days, the two alternately interrogated me. I had again and again to rewrite autobiographies; to make notes about everybody known to me in Britain and Hungary; to describe the links between "I.S." and Hungarian Social Democracy; and so on. The interrogations became increasingly violent. I was often ordered to stand for half an hour without moving, my face turned to the wall; or to do physical jerks, squatting and standing up rhythmically. I began quite ambitiously, so that a friend of one of the Interrogators, attending the performance, exclaimed: "Cheers, he does it quite well." But at the end I collapsed.

Then I was deprived of sleep for three days. The method was to question me all night and then tell me that "in daytime sleeping is not allowed except by special permission of the interrogator." Such a privilege had to be "earned."

I do not know what would have happened to me if these orders had been carried out strictly. In the cell, every third minute when I was caught shutting my eyes, someone banged on the door to wake me up. There was one guard who, when nobody was watching, let me alone to sleep surreptitiously for about half an hour. And I fell asleep even when standing on my feet, turned to the wall. Whether it can truly be called sleep or not, is hard to judge: my eyes were shut, and nightmare pictures chased one another in my mind until I fell and the kick of a guard helped me to stand up again. I had an overwhelming sense of panic and apathy: panic of nerves rather than thoughts. A constant shudder ran through my veins but I did not fear anything, because I could not care any more.

Holding out against these tortures was less a mattter of strength than of absence of interest in my own fate. The one problem which I consciously kept in mind was how to save my relatives from A.V.H. acts of revenge. But, by then, I could not help feeling fatalistic even about that.

My first Interrogator sometimes fell short of his duty of torturing me. He had once been a turner, and kept a suppressed admiration—mingled with hatred and suspicion—for men of letters. His very brutality gave him away: "Now you crouch and stand up," he shouted at me, "once anyway in your life you'll do some proper work instead of scribbling nonsense as you have always done!" Sitting by as I performed my jerks, now and then he pretended to drop off. Once he pretended so well that he dozed, and snored as rhythmically as I should have squatted. *If* I knew ju-jitsu, or *if* I trusted my strength enough to knock him out, I wondered, and *if* I were clever enough quickly to slip into his uniform, and *if* I knew the password to leave the building . . . But it was hopeless with so many ifs. The only thing I ventured to do was open a drawer to see whether there might be a knife or anything like that with which I could slit my veins.

In the intervals between tortures, I had some curious conversations with that Interrogator. He was interested in me and in my stories, even encouraging me to tell him how I felt. "I could give you an instance," I said; "well known but you may not have heard of it. In 1919, after the collapse of the Hungarian Soviet Republic, when the White Detachments overran the country, they arrived at a big estate owned by an industrialist, a nobleman but of Jewish origin. He was relieved, like all titled people, industrialists and landlords, to see the uniforms of the Whites. But as the White terrorists learned that he was a Jew, they arrested him and without inquiry hanged him. He was so astonished that under the gallows he could only say 'But that it should be the Whites. . . .' These were his last words. If you hang me, my last words may be 'But that it should be the Reds. . . .'"

"Petty bourgeois way of looking at it," he answered scathingly. "If ever I was ordered to leave this post and go back to the bench, I would do so with no word of complaint."

"So would I if I were ordered to go back to my desk instead of dwelling here."

"Now you have chatted enough, start squatting." Sounds were faintly audible from the neighbouring room: another Interrogator in the vicinity. On such occasions mine would start to shout savagely "Wildboar, wildboar!" I could hardly suppress a smile: it is an abuse fairly unusual in Hungarian, as well as in English, and was certainly meant to impress his colleagues. This Interrogator would also constantly kick at the heel of my sandals but, again, mainly to calm his own conscience. At dawn, when I was already prostrate on the floor I said to him: "Anyway, sir, you could give me a cigarette." "What, you would take my last cigarette, you dirty swine!" He showed me his case in which there was indeed only one. Then he put it in my mouth and lit it.

Several times in the course of these hearings I expressed my willingness to "confess" if they wanted to try me; but this did not satisfy them. They wanted to get "facts," especially about the Socialist I.S. spy-ring and the rest. Who had been Miss Kéthly's contacts in Britain? I told them what was well known, that she had come as a guest of the Labour Party, but I could not of course supply any spy-stories about her. My pigheadedness on this and similar matters, they told me, made my case hopeless. They would like to have helped me but now they would simply allow me to rot alive in the cellar.

They allowed this for about three weeks. By day I walked up and down the cell, day-dreaming or making up poetry. I began a prison diary in verse. A volume of it has since been published. I also started a history, in the manner of sixteenth century Hungarian bards, of the last twenty-five years of my own country, including my own misfortunes. It was quite a fruitful short period. "Shall I try and commit suicide?" It was partly these verses which made me decide against it. I never did and do not today think much of myself as a poet. It seemed then to be worthwhile writing verses—in strict traditional metres and full assonances—just in order to remember the facts they testified. Out of prison, I thought, my memory will give its biased version of what happened, however much I try to be honest. But the verse would preserve something authentic. To give some account of what was happening to me, however small the chance of being released—that was indeed the force which kept me alive for approximately seven years which I was to spend in prison.

One night I was taken before a colonel. He said he would give me now a last great chance to save myself. "We know much about you," he went on, "far more than you think we know. But we shall give you an opportunity to show goodwill by telling us frankly about your dealings and about those of your accomplices. We know, for instance, that you acted as a messenger between the British Labour Party, which you very well know is just a covering organization for I.S., and their agent, Arpád Szakasits."

Szakasits was at that time nominal head of the Hungarian State, "President of the Presidential Council." He formally appointed high officials, received diplomatic representatives, granted audiences and paraded as a leading symbol of national sovereignty. Once a leading figure —though not the Leader—in the Hungarian Social Democratic Party, he had after 1945 come to loggerheads with most of his former comrades just because of his moderation towards the Communists. In 1948, this turned into subservience combined with the posture of a proletarian king. After the compulsory union of Socialists and Communists, he became nominally second-in-command of the United Workers' Party, the first being Rákosi himself. My contacts with him had been very scanty since then. When visiting Budapest, in 1948 and 1949, I had made courtesy calls on him lest he should be offended with me for ignoring his position. Both times he just repeated the current slogans which sounded particularly painful in 1949 when he added excuses for the imprisonment of some of his near associates. The Hungarian Social Democrats despised him. The British Labour Party held him in contempt. Even if he had had the courage to act as a

British spy, no agency of that mythical I.S. would have bothered to ask for his services. The colonel's allegation was a self-parody of the People's Democracy.

But then, I wondered, was it my task to prevent our Communists from making fools of themselves and martyrs of their puppets? If they wished to do so, and to reward me for letting them do so, why should I object? I could well imagine Szakasits in his fools' paradise telling a courtesy-caller, as he had told me some months before about others, "O he committed very serious crimes but they cannot yet be disclosed." I assured the colonel of my willingness to co-operate. He wanted to hear "facts."

Now, where should I take these from? I had heard a lot of gossip about Szakasits, particularly from his former comrades; but one thing which he had never been accused of was intrigue against the People's Democracy, either as a British agent or in any other capacity. The colonel, however, insisted on such "facts." When in the heat of argument, I asked him, "Do you really think Szakasits so brave as that?," he lost his temper. "I am not interested in your witticism. Apparently you don't know where you are . . ." Threats and expletives followed, and then he calmed down: "Now look here, let us talk business. We two belong to similar worlds; mine is the A.V.H., yours the I.S. You know you are in our hands, so why this fuss? Would you like Wienerschnitzel for dinner?" He ordered me one and gave me English cigarettes.

In spite of the honour of being addressed as a colleague by an A.V.H. colonel and of the Epicurean delights granted to me, I felt rather miserable. The colonel apparently wanted me to invent "facts" about the "I.S." activities of Szakasits without allowing me to make a distinction between truth and fiction. I visualized the short and inflated figure of poor Szakasits. He was not really a bad man; vain and weak, no doubt, to an extent which is criminal in a politician, but quite an amiable fellow and good-hearted whenever he could easily afford to be so. I knew he had no power. In some weeks' time, on the basis of the facts invented by me, he might be taken to the A.V.H. cellar and tortured for not confessing to my fabrications which he could never guess. I felt it was something I could not take on my conscience. After many an hour, many a night of fruitless arguments and torments, I frankly told the colonel "It would be foolish of me to get myself beaten to death, or let my relatives be imprisoned or tortured, for the sake of Arpád Szakasits. I know I am in your hands, sir, and accept the view that for higher reasons which I cannot judge I must make a confession against Szakasits. But there is one thing I cannot do, and that is to invent matters which he does not even know about and which he may later be tortured for not confessing. I am willing to draft a confession against him, but must make it clear to you that the facts contained in it are not true, lest you should later try and torture him into confirming them."

The colonel indignantly rejected my offer as "an impudent provocation"; he said he wanted "the truth." He took me to the chief of the A.V.H., Lieutenant-General Gábor Péter, whose study, if so it may be called, was a huge wood-panelled chamber. He sat by a vast writing-desk. Everything connected with him was on a big scale, except himself. He was a short man with rodent eyes and a Hitler moustache. I was interested to see him face to face; he had acquired the reputation of an evil demon by then. Evil demons in human skin usually turn out to be dull creatures when they open their mouths. He was surely a fairly unimaginative Sadist. He could be rude and cruel and liked, as I know from others, personally to attend scenes of physical torture. He did not do this in my case, but received me with patronizing and sardonic courtesy. I was shivering from cold in the linen suit in which I had been arrested and which had got ragged since. "Comrade Colonel," he started, "let us give that man a decent suit." "He does not deserve it, Comrade Lieutenant-General," was the stern reply. "We shall see," Comrade Lieutenant-General nodded. "Would you please kindly take a seat? Care for a cigarette? Please."

He had been a tailor's assistant, and his taste for good tailoring had never gone. He was in an impeccable grey suit, with a silk tie which went with it perfectly. He fingered the tie all the time. "Look here, it is up to you to decide about your fate. Do understand us. We are not interested in"—an ironical bow—"Paul Ignotus. We are interested in Arpád Szakasits. You tell us all you know about him. If you do, I shall not worry about what you want to do." Now a smile: "You may go back to England if you like. I shall see to that. It is up to you. . . ."

I repeated apologetically that I had already declared everything I knew. But before I had finished either my sentence or his cigarette he lifted his hand and, with the gesture of a sovereign putting an end to an audience, said, "Well, I was prepared to spare these few minutes . . ." The colonel led me away and asked his assistant, called Fonyó, to take me to the place where "they will talk differently to you."

This meant the office of expert torturers. What I had received till then had been merely preparatory work, more or less of an amateur character. The chief of the beating-up squad—who was also supervisor of the gaolers in the cellar—was a Major, later Lieutenant-Colonel, Gyula Princz, a former coal-man. Before the decline of Nazism he had belonged to the Arrow-Cross Fascists—allegedly carrying out underground Communist orders, and allegedly suffering from the hands of the gendarmes who had caught him. Who could check all these allegations? Underground heroes of Communism grew like mushrooms after 1945, particularly amongst the rabble taken over by the A.V.H. from the Nazi side. My impression of Princz was that if he had a political opinion at all it must have been Communazi all the time. "Do you know what it means to be beaten up?" he asked me. "When were you last beaten up?" "Some fifteen years ago, by the Fascists," I answered—hinting at a scrap in which I had got involved. He had a good laugh. "Served you right. You will get the same from us. Not the same but worse. You will be electrified as I was by the gendarmes. If repeated for a week regularly, I can assure you it will drive you mad."

He was a stout man with an inflated face, apparently a drunkard. When sober, he got drunk with the delights of his job. He loved it. He seasoned it with humorous performances. He was sitting on a writing-desk and talking to a girl typist, playing with his rubber truncheon, when I was led to him. He winked at the girl as he ushered me to his own study. Inside, surrounded by four or five junior experts, including the colonel's assistant, Fonyó, he started gabbling a speech which he had obviously made a hundred times. "Now you see, this is the place for people unwilling to tell the truth. . . You will get your portion three times a day, at eleven a.m., at six p.m., and at three a.m. as I suffer from insomnia." He looked round to see the effect of the joke. "Now show me your palms." He hit my left palm with the truncheon; the right one had to be saved in case I changed my mind and was willing to write "the truth." Then he took a pencil: "Now look here, you stand on your toes and clasp your hands behind you and press the pencil with your forehead to the wall. But don't dare to drop it for I am very patricular about my pencil!" As the pencil was of course dropped eventually, he exclaimed with facetious amazement: "You dare to break my pencil!" The fists and rubber turncheons showered on my head, my shoulders, I was thrown to the floor and kicked about. After a while, the colonel's assistant, Fonyó, said: "Now, you piece of dirt, I hope you've had enough of it. Let's go back to the colonel." The colonel asked me: "Well, has your memory at last been refreshed?" I repeated again and again that I had told him everything I knew.

I cannot tell just how often similar scenes were repeated through the following days. All my body was swollen with purple bruises, a couple of teeth kicked out, my ragged shirt sticking to my wounds. It was extremely painful and, indeed, I think if I had had a chance to kill myself on the way to Major Princz's study I would have done so. But being trapped as I was I just let myself be dragged about. My behaviour was not virile. On the first occasion I did not wail—simply because it is not my instinctive reaction to do so when I feel pain. But I found out that until I did so they would not stop. After that I screamed as much as I could.

One night the colonel suddenly asked me: "Why don't

you use some writer's imagination for your confessions?"
"That's just what I offered to do, sir, but you rejected it as
a provocation." A lengthy explanation followed on his
side: the essence of it was that I must not write absurd
things but credible lies only. I agreed. He ordered me a
good supper, with plenty of black coffee and cigarettes,
and I sat down to write for him "the truth that need not
correspond with facts."

I had been ordered to reveal the names of our "spy-
contacts"; and to comfort myself I named one of the I.S.
directors who organized me in, General B.L.O. Odylie,
and the other Sir Fai Rytale. Similar names could be discovered, as I later found out, in other depositions made to
the A.V.H. The journalist and broadcaster, Géza Rublec-
zky, confessed to having been organized in by the Directors of the Deuxième Bureaux, Gay-Lussac and Boyle-
Marriotte and was sentenced on these grounds as a
French spy. He died in prison.

Otherwise, I was indeed careful to avoid, so far as possible, "provocative" absurdities. The colonel said my account was "something, though not enough." For the time
being, however, he assured me they would leave me in
peace. I was ordered to get six cigarettes a day in my cell
—which the gaolers either gave me or not. I resumed my
day-dreams and poems to fill in the time.

One day, I heard knocking on the wall of my cell: the
messages of life from a fellow sufferer. This is a time-
honoured way of communicating between prisoners.
Clever and well-versed prisoners do it in morse; others use
simply the prisoners' alphabet, under which one knock
means "a," two knocks "b," three knocks "c," and so
forth. There are various ways of abbreviating it but this is
its essence. The father of Hungarian letters, Kazinczy, described in his memoirs how he used it in the dungeons of
Kufstein after being imprisoned for his share in a Jacobin
conspiracy at the end of the eighteenth century; and the
English reader may be familiar with the method from
Darkness at Noon. I was glad to find a talking partner,
however dangerous and tiresome it was to talk to him. I
reciprocated the knocks, and asked him who he was. But

he turned out to have no idea of the system: he merely vented his longing for company. I was disappointed and stopped knocking. Some days later, I got knocks from an apparently new prisoner. "Surely another fool," I thought, and hesitated to reply, but I could not resist the temptation. He turned out to know the prisoners' alphabet. And he turned out to be a friend. Peeping through the keyhole he had recognized me when I was led to the lavatory. It was no easy job to get used to such talk, always fearing the sounds of gaolers' boots—the more so as I have always been very absent-minded by nature. But as we had plenty of time, we managed somehow.

He had been arrested some time after me. I learned from him of the sentences passed in the Rajk trial—five men hanged after the first round. We exchanged mutual A.V.H. experiences and worked out a system of abbreviations. He was on the point of telling me about his interrogations when the gaoler suddenly opened the door and ordered me to take my rag and move into another cell. For two days, I lived in terror: did the gaoler discover us and interrogate my friend while keeping me waiting deliberately? Later I was amused by these anxieties. An A.V.H. gaoler would never take such care in catching someone; he would either strike at once or if in a good mood just make a row and forget about it. I always made the mistake of thinking people more subtle than they were.

About another year passed before my trial. I spent it shuttling about between the cellar of No. 60 and the comparatively civilized, pre-war prison of Markó-utca. Food in the latter for those awaiting trial was even better than at No. 60. I had a toothbrush and some books to read: mainly Soviet novels and Leninist pamphlets but also what had been left behind, after some perfunctory expurgation, of the old prison library, including many of the classics. It was delicious to reread them; when could I spare time for such pleasures while at large?

My final deposition before trial was taken at the end of summer, 1950. An A.V.H. lieutenant took me at night to his office at No. 60; he was to dictate my confession. I did not know at first whether I ought to contradict him as it was so strikingly absurd; but I quickly decided that the more absurd the better. Now I discovered why my lies had not after all been "enough." Again I had over-estimated them in thinking I should take care lest my allegations might "provocatively" sound absurd. I could certainly not have invented anything more provocative than what my torturers invented for me.

I confessed to having spent my life in a sinister campaign against the working class. I had been organized in as early as the beginning of 1939 by British and Hungarian I.S. agents in order to prevent Communism from spreading in Hungary after the collapse of Nazism. The list of I.S. agents who had commissioned me to do various tasks included the names of Denis Healey, Richard Crossman, Kingsley Martin and Zilliacus, besides, of course, Odylie and Rytale. My most important chief, however, was Mr. Morgan Philips, who in 1949, before my last return to Budapest, had ordered me to order Szakasits to send him more detailed espionage reports.

When our trial was approaching, my new Interrogator, A.V.H. Lieutenant Ervin Faludi, made it clear to me that it would be a mere formality. In case I hoped to achieve anything by retracting my confession before the jury, he told me in advance what my sentence, as well as those of my fellow-defendants, would be. These sentences, however, were also "mere formalities," necessitated by the interests of the party; if we gave proof of a "co-operative" spirit now, we would be sent to a special place with all facilities for intellectual work, would be boarded as in a first-class hotel, and would be released in one or two years' time—that is soon after public interest in the vanished Social Democrats had died down. I did not, of course, believe those promises, but I felt that unless the trial were held in public it would be simply ludicrous to contradict the A.V.H. and the judges under their control.

The Trial was held, as foreseen, *in camera,* at the end of October, 1950. The room where it took place was packed with A.V.H. officers and in charge of maintaining order was the very Major Princz whom I had known as

team-leader of the beaters-up. When the trial had already
started my Interrogator took me along to my "lawyer": I
was to tell the latter, in the presence of the police officer,
that I regretted my past crimes and thought the only thing
to be said in my favour was that I had made my confession freely and that I had an old mother to support. My
"lawyer" in the course of the trial added as a third miti-
gating circumstance that his client had "lived for a long
time in London, the capital of imperialism, and so been
very much exposed to evil temptations."

Some of my fellow-defendants were people whom I had
never heard of before. The first defendant was Arpád
Szakasits—sentenced, as predicted by my Interrogator, to
hard labour for life: the second, George Marosán—today
a Minister in the Russian appointed Hungarian Government—received, as also predicted, a death sentence
"which will not be carried out." All of us recited our
lessons according to the texts put down in our last depositions. Our Interrogators had carefully coached us in them,
with the typewritten pages in their hands.

I was sentenced to fifteen years' hard labour. When the
president of the Court asked us whether we wished to
appeal, I whispered to my Interrogator, the A.V.H. lieutenant who sat behind me, that I did not see any point in
doing so. "Oh, yes, you must appeal," he answered,
"otherwise it wouldn't sound natural."

Chapter 6

Why Did We All Confess?

WHY DID WE all "confess," almost without exception, at
the Stalinist political police and afterwards in their Courts?
For myself, I wanted to live in spite of despair and exhaustion from beatings, compulsory sleeplessness and
other tortures, and despite my anxiety about the fate of
my relatives. Moreover, it seemed that the more absurd
the confession I had to make, the more obviously false it

would appear to everyone. And apart from this, my trial was held *in camera*. I felt it would be pointless to perform heroically when nobody was about except those who would beat me to death afterwards. Whether I would have "confessed" in an open trial I simply cannot tell; I do not know myself enough to judge.

Some months after my trial I was taken back to the Budapest A.V.H. headquarters from my prison cell in the country town of Vác. A.V.H. Lieutenant Colonel Márton Károlyi* received me very cordially. "How are you getting on in Vác?" I told him frankly that life was hell there; I had not expected that it would be such a "sanatorium" as had been promised by my Interrogator before trial "but I should not have expected it to be so abominable as it is, sir. If an American reporter could ever take pictures of us there, they would make more powerful imperialist propaganda than anything your enemies could invent." The lieutenant-colonel did not seem to be hurt. He was one of the few A.V.H. officers who enjoyed my stories. "What I like about you," he said, "is that we need not trouble to ask anyone to report on your opinions. You save us the bother. I know you dislike us. But you would like to live in tolerable conditions, wouldn't you?"

"That's right, sir," I answered and did not contradict his allegations about my political hostility. Was this sincerity on my part? It may have been. But I had come to the conclusion that A.V.H. officers were most irritated by the prisoners who were, or pretended to be, their comrades. For spying on other prisoners or the like, they would accept their services and reward them. But if someone hesitated about going to any lengths, he only angered them by insisting on his faithfulness to the Idea. Faithful Communists in Communist prisons—that was a thing which should be ignored, even if it happened. I felt I should play the opposite rôle, of the honest opponent. I stood before the lieutenant-colonel simply as a man seeking his own interests. It should be a clear give and take.

"Now listen," the lieutenant-colonel went on. "We want to make a series of open trials, to inculpate Social Democ-

* No relative of Michael Károlyi.

racy. Some of you who I think are sensible enough to know what it is about—Zoltán Horváth, Sándor Szalai, George Pálóczi-Horváth and yourself—you would be the defendants in the first Social Democratic trial, and from your confessions the rest would follow. The verdicts of your secret trials would of course have to be quashed on some formal grounds, you needn't bother about that . . . If you help us to do this, we shall consider it a great service. However disappointed you are with the conditions you found in Vác, I hope you see that I wish you well. I promise you will have better treatment, and plenty of food and cigarettes, and congenial work—translations for instance, if you like—and that you get wages to support your mother, and even permission to write to her, though you know political prisoners are not really allowed to do so. Would you like to write her a letter at once? . . . Well go back to your cell and think it over, and give your answer tomorrow."

In my cell, I got decent food and cigarettes and books—none of which I had known in Vác—and the following day at an interview with Lieutenant Colonel Károlyi I said I consented. I felt that to refuse his offer would be suicide or worse. But I made up my mind to break my promise to him and to reveal everything I knew of the A.V.H. tortures and the fake trials when I got a chance to talk in public.

Every day either Lieutenant-Colonel Károlyi or his assistant, Lieutenant Szántó, spoke to me about the deposition which I was to make for the open trial. I pretended incessantly. I talked over with them carefully whether this or that statement about Anna Kéthly or Szakasits might be believed or not. I soon found that although they had decided now to concentrate on "credibility," they were as keen as before to include obvious absurdities. "So much the better," I thought and made cheerful use of the good books and decent food.

By then any pretence on their part that our statements must be true had gone. They would never have said that we should tell lies. But the ways of compiling the truth became quite farcical. I remember Lieutenant Szántó acting as messenger between Pálóczi-Horváth and myself, only concerned with fitting together the tales we were both concocting but never inquiring about their foundation in fact. "Pálóczi tells me we can't say he gave his spy reports to Macdonald at the B.B.C., since everyone knows they were hardly on speaking terms." "Well let us say that he handed them to Macdonald through Tarján," I suggested. That settled it. By the way, Pálóczi-Horváth had never been a Social Democrat but a Communist who had worked for a while on the staff of the B.B.C. The reason for including him in a so-called Social Democrat trial was that before the war, in the service of a British agency in Budapest, he had been in touch with Arpád Szakasits, as he had with a great number of people of most different political denominations, united in resistance against the Nazis.

Simultaneously, I was working out my own plan. If the president of the Court asked about my proceedings in Britain, I would start to quote one or another of my spy-contacts in English, and say: "Everything we say here is a foolish lie. This is a framed trial as were all those staged by this régime. We were beaten to shreds and threatened that our relatives would be arrested and tortured if we were not to consent . . ." And so on and so forth. I hoped that by the time someone had checked and silenced me it would already be too late: the scandal could no longer be hushed up. I knew Hell would be Heaven compared with what would happen to me, and perhaps also to my mother and sister and brother in Budapest. But there must be one man, I felt, to tell the truth to the world.

Would I have done this had the trial been held? I cannot vouch for it. But I knew that when Lieutenant Szántó came to tell me that "we have decided for the time being no open trial will be held" a great stone rolled off my chest. My impression was that our depositions had been shown to Rákosi who had not found them "credible" enough to be aired. But whatever the reason, I was very glad to be released from this rôle of hero and martyr which I had meted out to myself.

What was the reason for the confession of others? No answer can be given which applies to us all. The accusations made by the A.V.H. were fairly uniform—spying in the service of imperialists, conspiracy to oppress the working class, and so forth—and very few if any had committed what they were sentenced for. But their cases were very different both politically and psychologically.

The position of those who had committed approximately what they were accused of was easiest. In the Vác prison hospital I spent some weeks in the company of a former Member of Parliament, the Very Reverend Father Bozsik. After the imprisonment of Cardinal Mindszenty, he had really acted as the President of a Shadow Cabinet "in case the régime changes," and had negotiated with American diplomatic representatives. In a democratic country, of course, there is nothing wrong in heading a shadow cabinet and talking to the diplomats of any foreign power with which one's own country is not at war. But to confess as much as that was enough for the A.V.H. to draw up the rest. Bozsik told me he had known about a "military line leading to Americans" but he himself had not been concerned with it. The A.V.H. simply accepted his admission, linking it with the "military line" and with the murder of two or three Soviet soldiers which had happened years before and had nothing to do with Bozsik's activities. Bozsik was harshly treated, like everybody else, under police arrest and afterwards in prison; in addition, he could expect kicks from young armed ruffians whenever his occupation was asked and he answered "priest." But he did not suffer any special torture. Having agreed to confess to the truth and not to contradict the "completion" of his admissions, he was sentenced to ten years' imprisonment—substantially less than myself.

This does not mean that all Right-wing people got away so easily. The most notable case is that of Cardinal Mindszenty of which I learned some details in prison and afterwards—from my first Interrogator, and some Communist officials who were later imprisoned, and from other sources.

How much of the charges against the Cardinal was true? He was doubtless a frantic opponent of Communism and of the Republican régime established after the war, and of many a social reform it had introduced. To be against the régime was by no means illegal. Did he then conspire with the representatives of foreign powers? This depends on how one defines conspiracy. He certainly advised the Americans not to return the Crown of St. Stephen to Budapest but to deposit it at the Vatican. He was also accused of illicit dealings in foreign currency through his co-defendant, Prince Esterházy. Whether this was true is of no interest; currency regulations, as I pointed out above, were not meant to be kept in Hungary, and everybody broke them with the blessing of the Government except when a scapegoat was required.

Surely it was not single acts like these which turned the fury of the Government machinery against him. It was his general attitude from 1945 onwards. It is an open secret that many of his senior priests objected to his rigidity; so did some leading Jesuits. These same Jesuits were imprisoned a year or two later. The Rákosi régime persecuted religion. According to some, the Cardinal's attitude was thus vindicated. Others take an opposite view and think that it was much cleverer to be flexible and so demonstrate the impossibility of coming to terms with the Rákosi Government, than to allow them to persecute religion on the pretext of "fighting Reaction."

It is also true that the Cardinal buried in his grounds a tube which contained his secret notes. It was a great triumph for the A.V.H. to discover it. But the secrecy of those notes was their single interesting characteristic. When they were made public one merely wondered why they had ever to be secret.

The Cardinal had an unflinching faith in his own status, dignity and vocation. On the question of education, but also in other matters, he was unwilling to yield to government pressure; though he was often approached by Catholics of high standing who wanted him to be more conciliatory. At the end of 1948 he made small gestures in the direction of compromise—presumably when he realized that the help he had hoped from the West was not forthcoming. But the campaign against him was already at its height, and Rákosi made up his mind to have him arrested. The Cardinal made a statement that if ever he were arrested and made any "confession" in prison, people should know it had been made under duress. He felt what was approaching. Nevertheless the fact that a Cardinal could be gaoled must have come as a terrible shock to him.

To be isolated from every soul with whom one might exchange a human word, and to feel oneself at the mercy of cruel enemies, is bound to disturb anyone's mind; but chiefly the mind of a man who had filled the position and had the outlook of Cardinal Mindszenty. There is no saint who cannot be in some way broken by humiliation—especially in solitude. The Cardinal, as far as I know, was not beaten up. But his treatment was hardly less cruel than the shower of truncheons. He was deprived of sleep, and ordered to do physical jerks like other prisoners; in addition, the thugs made him a special butt for their coarse amusements. The fact that a Cardinal had the same biological needs as everybody was a special pleasure for them. They made fun of him in the most revolting way. The leader of the torture squad, Princz, pressed his buttocks to the Cardinal's mouth.

At that time—(1949) a Yellow Book was published in several languages by the Hungarian Government on the Mindszenty case. It contained the well-known charges levelled against him at his trial. It showed the secret manuscript documents found in the Primate's park. It also showed photographs of documents signed by the Cardinal in A.V.H. custody. Since then, as we know, the handwriting expert employed by the A.V.H. has escaped from Hungary and made clear that some of these documents were forged. I was in London at the time of the trial and did not know that; but two of the documents gave away their origin beyond doubt. One was a letter addressed to the Minister of Justice, István Ries, the typical manifestation of a disturbed and tormented mind, alternately blaming and defending himself in almost incoherent sentences. This was obviously genuine—if I am wrong about it I should have to alter all my opinions of the A.V.H. and congratulate them for having once, exceptionally, produced such a masterpiece of a fake. In this, truly, nothing was "confessed," except that the Cardinal was feeling miserable and wondered whether his ideas had all been right. He had every reason to feel and express himself thus. The other was a deposition starting with the phrase "I am a nobleman," then confessing he had hated the common people and been a spy. Anybody could tell at once, whether this document was forged or not, that its text must must have been dictated by the A.V.H. Talking about the case with friends in London—for instance, with a Left-wing Catholic priest, the Basque Dean Onaindia—I gave my honest opinion about these papers. When interrogated by A.V.H. officers I confessed this crime, but it was not important enough to prove that I had acted as an "I.S. agent" so they did not bother about it.

The Cardinal's trial, it will be remembered, was a shock to those who expected him to appear in the posture of heroic martyrdom. He did admit the truth of some of the allegations against him. His manner was embarrassed and apologetic, though not servile. The first reaction in the Vatican press was that "he admitted what was true and denied what was untrue." I think this was the case indeed. Later on, those who felt disappointed that he was not more pugnacious in the dock spread the belief that he must have been doped with a mysterious drug. I think this is nonsense. I spoke to a great number of prisoners who confessed under torture, and never heard of anything like that, except for morphia injections after tortures.

But I learned much later that the reports and broadcast commentaries of the trial were edited to the extent of falsification. The Cardinal may not know this, even today, but his hosts at the America Legation in Budapest might tell him. By the time he was tried, the Iron Curtain had become almost impregnable. Only very few non-Communist Western correspondents were admitted to political trials in Hungary, and these were surrounded by interpreters who had been carefully trained in the Party office. They had been told what to translate and what to forget about in unpredictable events. The version of the Cardinal's confession which reached Western readers was thus to some extent distorted; the tape made of his confessions, and transmitted by the Budapest radio, had been carefully cut. His voice, however, was genuine. In his trial the most substantial cuts and deletions had to be made from the confessions of his co-defendant, the former editor of a Catholic daily paper, László Tóth. When imprisoned he was almost deaf, and his evidence in the dock was a most pathetic sight. But he had the courage to describe the tortures which he had undergone at No. 60, naming and describing exactly the rooms where they had taken place. Later, he died in prison.

Catholic priests and non-Socialist politicians were as a rule ordered to confess that they had acted as American spies. Spying for Britain was the rôle meted out to the Socialists. In the Socialist Party, bitter factional fights had been going on before their merger with the Communists; not only between those who were for and against the merger, but also among smaller groups. Now, however, they were all united in the I.S. ring. Most fortunate among them was the man to whom the A.V.H. interrogator showed a great map or diagram, representing the British Socialist World Conspiracy which had to be "revealed." The interrogator was a comparatively good-natured man who wanted his victim to save trouble. "Look here, we shall have to prove this and you are a fool if you do not help us." There was a criss-cross of lines on the map, with such captions as Political line leading to the Foreign Office; Military line leading to the British Military Attaché; and so forth. There were the names of well-known Socialist leaders such as Kéthly, Bán, Peyer, Szakasits. . . .

The Socialist questioned in this way got a hiding now and then but was far more fortunate than most of his comrades who could not get access to such helpful maps of their crimes. Usually the A.V.H. started the sessions with maltreatment, partly as a way to break the morale of their victims and partly because they really hoped that the victims might thus spill something worth knowing. In any case they had nothing to lose by it. Miss Kéthly herself has told me she was not beaten up, but all other methods of maltreatment were applied to her. Since, owing to her international reputation and her sex, the crime-in-

ventors apparently hesitated about what her rôle in the
World Conspiracy should be, she was kept in prison for
years without sentence. In a way the most fantastic case
was that of Madam Ries, the wife of the former Minister
of Justice. She was arrested at the same time as her husband; she was put in solitary confinement without a word
of explanation and kept there for years and when the
Thaw came she was suddenly released. She had never been
asked to confess—but I wonder whether her position was
better for that.

I remember also the case of Z, a Socialist intellectual
of the fellow-travelling wing, who started by confessing to
as many imaginary crimes as anyone could invent. He was
panic-stricken, worried about his wife and children, and
knew enough of A.V.H. methods to judge that nothing
short of ludicrous self-denigration would satisfy them. He
put down such things as "The C.I.C. agent posing as an
American editor, X, gave me so many dollars for disclos-
ing the production figures of the Y armaments factory.
The I.S. agent, posing as a British editor, P gave me so
many pounds . . ." This should really have satisfied the
most sanguine expectations. But his interrogators were
insatiable and reproached him for "not coming down to
the heart of the matter." He was, as so many of us were,
taken to Major Princz, and received the treatment known
as "wolf's bandage." This meant tying his wrists to his
knees and hanging him on a pole, head downwards. In
this position they spat at him and beat him, mainly on his
testicles. After such treatment, he was ordered to drink
salt water so that his swollen tongue nearly strangled him.
This went on for days or, more exactly, for nights. After
dusk he had to crawl—for he could no longer walk—up
the stairs and was "interrogated" overnight while he lay on
his back on a couch. He implored his torturers to tell him
what else they would like to hear from him; but the answer
again and again was torture and the same shouts: "You
know very well yourself, you won't get away with it until
you have confessed the real thing."

He was hardly alive when Major Princz, after one of
his performances, bellowed: "Now we have had enough

of the nonsense you talk; you must describe how the Jugoslavs organized you in." This was indeed something which could not have occurred to Z. As a political writer, he had been in touch with a number of Western intellectuals and diplomats but hardly ever with Jugoslavs. His response, of course, was prompt. "O yes, forgive me, I quite forgot about them . . . I shall write about that by all means . . . But so many things have happened since, and so many names have escaped me. Could I perhaps get the list of the Diplomatic Corps of the Jugoslav Embassy in Budapest? There is a copy at the Ministry of Foreign Affairs. If I saw that I should be able to describe the thing." "All right, now at last you are talking sense. But beware if you try to deceive us again." After a day or two Z got the list and sat down to work at once: Counsellor of Legation X . . . itch had offered him so many dinars for this information, and Secretary of Embassy Y . . . itch so many for the other. Dates were given in the deposition, with diplomatic receptions where these talks had taken place. "Well you old bastard this seems all right; you could have begun like that," the Interrogator patted him on the back. After a few days there was a question: "Look here, Z, you say you met Y . . . itch on the . . . But he had not yet come to Budapest, had he?" "O yes, I forgot to point out that had really taken place by correspondence through some other agent I had seen. . . ."

This was reassuring. Z was given medical assistance: an operation on his testicles was carried out while he lay on the wooden bunk. He was allowed some months to recuperate before being tried. On the eve of his trial, the officer in charge summed up his depositions. He redictated Z's confessions about C.I.C. and I.S., dollars and pound notes, spying and Socialism. He was already at the end when Z told him, "Now, sir, I think I should add that the Titoist agents . . ." The officer interrupted him with a gesture which gave him to understand that all that was of no importance. The A.V.H. had changed their minds; they had first thought of including Z in a "Titoist" trial but had later decided that he could be better used in the context of Anglo-American spying.

The Tito agents were *ex officio* arrested Communists. In addition to Jugoslav spy-links they had to confess British, German, French, American, South-American, Swiss and other spy-contacts if they had spent any time before or during the war in such countries. Theirs was the most complex situation: they could not sensibly say they had opposed Communism, as to some extent everybody else could. Their confessions, known now to be nonsense, were particularly puzzling to some people. Did they simply yield to threats and torture? Did they believe the promises that even if they were sentenced to death the sentence would not be carried out, and that they would be allowed to live in comfort away from the public eye? Or were they persuaded, like the hero of *Darkness at Noon*, that they owed this moral sacrifice to the Party?

It was a mixture of all this. But in general, torture was surely more decisive than one would think from the otherwise often startlingly accurate descriptions in *Darkness at Noon*. I knew some Communists in prison who had not specifically been tortured under arrest before trial but the threat had been permanent and minor samples had been given of its fulfilment. At the other extreme, for example, one was "electrified" while he sat in cold water for hours, day after day, and wrapped in a rag and beaten until his ribs were broken—all for not confessing to crimes which he could not have guessed, as they had been invented by another imprisoned Communist under duress. The average was a cross between the two.

As to Rajk, my information is that he was so shocked by the call of the three A.V.H. agents who came to fetch him that at first he resisted them. They had to struggle to take him to No. 60. Then, the various methods of breaking a man were applied simultaneously. He was beaten up and tortured. He was informed that his wife and was also under arrest and might also be tortured. They threatened that his baby son would as though by accident be run over by a car. He was promised "sanatorium" treatment after his "purely formal" death sentence. Meanwhile, appeals were made to his belief in Communism. It was explained to him that the Party needed this great sacrifice on his part: Tito's Jugoslavia had to be revealed as the agency of a capitalist world conspiracy "which it really is," and he, Rajk, alone could convincingly perform the rôle of its leading figure in Hungary. Among others the Minister of the Interior at that time, János Kádár, is said to have personally called on him in his cell, bringing Rákosi's most comradely messages and assuring him of the Party's profound appreciation and gratitude in case he consented. The coaching of "accomplices" and "witnesses" was managed on similar lines. Rehearsals for an open trial were staged in the presence of the A.V.H. chief, Péter. Rajk then was a nervous wreck. Now and then he forgot his lesson and was reprimanded by Péter.

At his trial, he acted perfectly as prescribed. When asked by the president of the Court "And who finally foiled your attempts?" he answered like a model schoolboy, "Great Stalin and wise Rákosi." Among all the promises they had made, there must have been one he found it hard to believe—the "purely formal" nature of his death sentence. Under the gallows he did not seem to be surprised. His last words allegedly were "Long live the Soviet Union." Was it for the sake of his wife and son? Was it meant to demonstrate that he was a better Communist than those who were murdering him? Or was he ultimately convinced, whatever his own tragedy, that his "Compass" must be right? We shall never know.

Others who shared his fate did turn out to be surprised. Major-General Pálffy-Osterreicher shouted "we were deceived," and a young Communist, András Szalai, cried with the rope round his neck "I perish innocently, how can Rákosi tolerate this?" He could, quite lightheartedly. But surprises can always crop up in a "planned" society, including the surprise of a promise honoured. In prison we met in comparatively good health a Communist whose hanging had been reported in the Budapest press, and there may have been other similar cases.

Many of those who had endured grave tortures to bargain off at least some of their alleged crimes felt it had been worthwhile if they had thus escaped hanging. This may have been so in certain cases—but in others, unwillingness to confess yielded a different crop. A memorable example was that of the two Szücs brothers. Both started their Communist careers in the underground movement before the war. One of them, Miklós, was my friend. He was a leading member of the London Hungarian Club during the war,* and afterwards correspondent of the Hungarian Communist Party paper and chief of the Hungarian Government-sponsored information bureau in Britain. At first he struck me as tiresome and parrot-Communist, but I became fond of him. He was sincere and honest to the limit of party loyalty and occasionally beyond. In the course of years he acquired a real sympathy for the British Labour Movement and, so long as that was possible, really hoped for a mutual arrangement "between the two workers' parties." He could hardly hide his disgust at the outrageous attacks on old Hungarian Socialist leaders at the time of the merger and showed an open concern for their fate. But, needless to say, he fulfilled Party orders obediently and served the Communist Government loyally. His authority among Hungarians in London was much increased after Rákosi, arriving on a Government mission at London Airport on one occasion, looked about for him and cordially shook his hands: "I am so glad to see you; you know your brother and I are old friends."

They were. Ernö Szücs was Rákosi's cell-mate in Horthy's prison. After the war he became a senior official of the Ministry of the Interior and later, as a colonel, one of Gábor Péter's deputies at the head of the A.V.H. When Miklós from time to time visited Budapest, he used to stay with his brother. "Do you always see eye to eye with him?" I once asked him. "Let's not discuss family matters," he answered with a faint smile. I did not of course press the question. Among prisoners of the A.V.H. it was common knowledge that Ernö Szücs was one of the great confession-forgers, together with Lieutenant-General Péter, Colonel Décsy and Colonel Janikovsky (who was to the best of my belief responsible for my own suffering, the man who had taken me in to see Gábor Péter.)

* His was a Magyarized surname; in London, he was known by his original surname, Szüsz. He had been an engineer.

Miklós Szücs, visiting Hungary on an official trip in the spring of 1949, was suddenly ordered to appoint someone else to his post in London and to stay in Budapest as "an important post" had been found for him there. He was made director of the Technological Institute. When I last saw him, in the summer of that year, he spoke with some nostalgia of England but felt quite happy—especially, I think, as he had parted from his London girl-friend, an ardent but unattractive comrade. He was arrested two or three days before me. The order was given by his brother Ernö.

Six months after my trial I was taken once again to the Budapest police headquarters where Lieutenant-Colonel Károlyi and Lieutenant Szántó started by overfeeding me, as they always did on such occasions, and went on to torment me with threats and questions—this time about the "spy-links between the Szücs brothers." As an agent of the I.S., I must know that the British authorities, once having learned of the family ties between Miklós and Ernö, made use of them. In spite of my worries and jitters, I was unwilling to give conclusive evidence and was ultimately left in peace about them without getting the promised "hiding." I learned the background and sequel later.

Lieutenant-General Péter fell out with his Colonel Ernö Szücs, according to some informers, because even Ernö Szücs thought that his chief overdid the fabrication of evidence. Péter announced to Rákosi his suspicions of a "spy-contact" between the two brothers. Rákosi authorized him to arrest Ernö Szücs. From then onwards the Szücs brothers were alternately tortured and brought together to confess. Their belief was that if they yielded they would be executed. They were taken to a spot in A.V.H. headquarters known as the *lefolyó*—the drains. At that spot the bodies of victims were made liquid with an acid and then let down the drains into the sewage of the city. A former assistant of Colonel Ernö Szücs, having witnessed a bit of the scene, was horror-stricken and ran to Rákosi: "Comrade Rákosi, I don't know what to say, Comrade Ernö Szücs is being beaten up over the *lefolyó*. . . ." "What?" Rákosi exclaimed, "those people are simply mad,

what did you say? Awful. I'll ring them at once to stop
that. You go back now to assist the Comrade Colonel."
The man hurried back and at the entrance to the A.V.H.
was caught by the guards who were waiting for him: "You
swine, you dared to squeal against us to Comrade
Rákosi?" He was terribly beaten up and later interned.
The bodies of the Szücs brothers meanwhile vanished
down the *lefolyó*.

I cannot vouch for the truth of all details in this story.*
But the essence of it—that the Szücs brothers were beaten
to death by the A.V.H. for their unwillingess to "confess"
to imaginary crimes—was admitted to me personally, at
the time of the Thaw in 1956, by György Nonn, then At-
torney General of the People's Republic, formerly private
secretary to Rákosi.

There may have been some who refused to confess anything at all. Certainly some were unwilling to confess
everything demanded from them. It was comparatively
easy to confess lies and conceal the truth. This was to some
extent what I did. During my years in the prison of the
A.V.H. I was in constant terror of what might next be
asked from me. The interrogations were a nightmare. I
leave it to the imagination of the reader to realize what it
was like to be pestered on one occasion—in 1951 I think
—by questioners who wanted me to confess that my
brother and sister had acted as my informers when I had
been a spy in London.

Confessions were not uniform. The behaviour of prisoners was not uniform. Differences of moral strength and of
mental awareness, even at the moment of prostration and
fainting, manifested themselves in the various depositions.
But in one thing there could be no difference between us:
none of us could be dignified. In prison I often recalled
the various romantic descriptions of saints and heroes who
would not falter under whips and hot iron: there was, for
instance, the excellent and in many ways realistic Italian
film, *The Open City*, in which the Resistance hero spat in
the face of his cruel interrogator, the Gestapo officer. This

* I have heard that in despair Miklós Szücz shouted; "I am
ready to sign any confession you want."

is just the scene which in such circumstances cannot happen. The Resistance hero, or his opposite number in A.V.H. custody, by the time he faces the demands of his interrogator, is physically unable to show pride. The Gestapo or A.V.H. see to that. To be proud and dignified while cigarette ends are stamped out on one's skin is surely more difficult than cinema-goers would think. But it can be tried. To be proud and dignified after being forbidden to go to the lavatory for twenty-four hours cannot even be tried. It is this sort of torture which all A.V.H. prisoners had to undergo from the beginning. They were dirty, miserable and exhausted by the time their conclusive interrogations started. Sense of honour may not have gone but their self-respect must have been crushed. Coming from damp cellars, they were shivering— in itself a bad start to dignified composure. Many of the Frenchmen guillotined under the Terror behaved magnificently. But even they trembled. "Tu trembles Bailly," a guard sneered at the great scientist, and former Mayor of Paris, seeing him on the way to the guillotine. "Oui, parcequ'il fait froid," Bailly answered, so that the crowd should hear. But no crowd attended the interrogations at No. 60. Proud gestures in the circumstances would have been grotesque and silly as well as suicidal.

Few people are able to bear witness to that. Most rewrite in their memories the stages of their ordeals. Self-deception started even in prison. I remember the hospital room in Vác where I spent some weeks with, among others, Father Bozsik and my old friend, the former Secretary General of the Social Democrat Party, Ferenc Szeder. About fifteen of us were in that room for suspected heart trouble. We were a motley little crowd which ranged from the former Arrow-Cross Fascist Lord Mayor of Budapest to a "Trotskyite-Titoist" who insisted even there that "history will vindicate our People's Republic": the representatives of all political shades and of practically all social strata. We were treated abominably, buffeted about, threatened all the time, spied on, and fed on fodder. I asked a very soldierly former Fascist whether he had been beaten up and he answered "O no, if that had happened, I shouldn't be here; because whatever the result, if anyone dared to strike me I couldn't stop myself from hitting back."

One night our room was raided. Seventeen-year-old thugs with rifles chased us out of our beds, kicked us, abused us, and searched our beds and drawers; and one of them slapped the face of my soldierly cell-mate. We all took it humbly. The day after, we started whispering about what had happened. What a shame, how disgraceful!— we all sighed. After a pause, one of us began: "But at least I had my own back," and told us a witty answer he believed he had made. We all nodded, confirming that he had been very brave. In the course of the following days some three or four of us remembered equally brave remarks we had made. If our whispers had been tape-recorded, that night of humiliations would have gone down as a heroic act of Resistance. If the night itself had been tape-recorded, we should all have emerged as cowards. We were but human in a sub-human world.

Chapter 7

Gaol and Gaolers

I BEGAN to write a long poem on the morrow of my arrest, at 60 Andrássy ut, and finished it on New Year's Eve, 1950–1, in my prison cell at Vác. I put in it "Worn-out and threadbare after the nights of interrogation and torture, I felt it would be seventh heaven for me to be committed to penal servitude. There at last my personal identity would be dissolved in the collective sweat of all convicts. Longing for that, I confessed to everything except the truth, and felt an exhilarating relief when I learned that I had been sentenced to fifteen years of Vác." But it was far forse than I had expected. I often wondered whether it would have been better not to be sentenced at all.

Our trial closed, we were huddled into a lorry and

driven to Vác, some 15 miles from Budapest. Our belongings, if any, had to be left behind. Mine by then consisted of a toothbrush, a packet of cigarettes, a Russian school book granted at my own request for learning the language of the new Master Race, and some sheets of paper on which I had put down, by my interrogator's special permission, some of my verse translations, the results of more than a year of almost uninterrupted solitude.

In Vác, we were stripped and given frieze uniforms and ragged prison underwear. Before slipping into them we were disinfected, which meant a hot shower-bath—the sole good part of the procedure—and haircutting over our heads and bodies. The latter was performed by a robust, muscular prison barber. He received us with a broad grin and did the job with gusto; he would suddenly tear away his haircutting gadget so as to cause pain to the novices, especially when approaching the genitals. Subsequently he shaved us so as to make our faces sore and bloodstained. We found later that he had served in the French Foreign Legion and then escaped; had become leader of a Nazi firing squad, and been imprisoned as a war criminal. He shouted dirty jokes about, showered the humour of the underworld, and was the gaolers' favourite. In some weeks' time we became friends and then he shaved us perfectly. "It's because of you that I am here," he told one of my co-defendants, "but damn it all, now we are in the same boat." He suggested he would smuggle out letters from the prison as "I have the means to do so." Amongst those known well to me no one was reckless enough to make use of these services, and I am not sure whether he would not have done it honestly for some. Such characters are too erratic to be consistently wicked. I knew however of some cases when he hurried along with the private letters thus obtained to the prison Commander, and the result was innumerable blows on the head of the hoaxed prisoner. In these proceedings he seemed politically unbiased: he gave away some of his former Arrow-Cross comrades as lightheartedly as those whom he knew to be responsible for his being here.

This Vác prison consisted of old buildings inherited

from previous régimes. We novices were huddled into the block MZ—which stood for "Magánzárka," that is, solitary confinement. Its cells had been planned for one person each, but four or six were crammed into most of them. While my co-defendants were at once crammed together I was first given solitary confinement—I think simply by oversight. A sturdy sergeant, with a swollen face, bloodshot eyes, and bulging belly, showed me to my cell and in a rattling N.C.O. diction recited a text which he knew well by heart: "Every morning and every evening when we open the door you put the water jug and the bucket out to the passage and say in a soldierly way 'I respectfully report, the number of cell inmates is one.' If pieces of paper, or books, or tobacco, or matches, or anything other than what is specifically allowed, is found in the cell, or if you are caught knocking or scribbling on the wall, or peeping through the keyhole or the window, the punishment is in the first instance: *short-iron*." This was indeed the most frequent corporal punishment in the A.V.H. prisons: the prisoner's hands were fettered to his feet and strained as much as possible from four to sixteen hours, according to the gravity of the offence. I was strictly ordered to go to bed at the time of Retreat and to get up in time: I must "make my bed" in a soldierly manner and not lie down in daytime. My bed was a strawsack or rather a rag full of dust on the floor—it should have been restuffed about a year before. The window was so placed that one had to stand on the chair to open or close it; I was allowed to do so for ventilation. Sick of the stench coming from the bucket, I took advantage of this permission several times a day, despite the cold which made me shiver all the time. For this I was reprimanded and ordered not to do it more often than after getting up and after supper for a few minutes.

The first night we were left without supper and went to bed exhausted by strain and hunger. The following day, I began to get acquainted with the political prisoners' food. I found it meagre and hardly eatable, and could not have imagined that in years to come it would steadily further deteriorate. But this was the case, at any rate, until

the summer of 1953 when, as in politics, recurring tides
of improvement and again deteriorations were manifest in
our diet. On the average food was sufficient in quantity
for some but too little for most. Many a prisoner lost
several stone in a few months. As to the kind of food one
got, it is difficult to give an idea of it by describing the
menu. Nominally, it was quite satisfactory: black coffee
in the morning, one dixie of soup and one of vegetable or
pasta at mid-day, and again vegetable or some kind of
farinaceous food in the evening, for weekdays; sausages
or the like on Sundays; and a piece of bread every day.
Besides this, one was supposed two or three times a week
to get some meat. In reality, however, all the food one got,
with the exception of bread, bore hardly any likeness to
what it was supposed to be. Potatoes were black stuff,
dehydrated or processed in alcohol factories and then used
for animal and prisoner consumption; the carrots were a
kind of cattle fodder; the lentils were full of worms; of
the meat there was often only some gravy left by the time
it reached the ordinary prisoner because most of it had
been eaten already by the few prisoners who acted as
gaolers' assistants. Most of the food was simply refuse,
and what was not refuse was stolen by the guards and their
assistants.

In the first weeks after my sentence, no books, no walk,
no "favour" whatever was granted to me; even my application for some work was refused with an answer that
"this must first be earned." Most prisoners in M.Z. had to
"bobbin" in their cells, that is, to reel up yarns from old
socks and pullovers on an old-fashioned gadget which I,
by the way, never saw.

I had been there for about two days when the sergeant
with bloodshot eyes suddenly entered my cell. As I stood
up and said nothing he shouted at me: "You will be short-
ironed at once if you behave like that, you . . . didn't I tell
you what to do when anyone in Authority enters?" "I
don't remember, sir." "Don't you, you . . . didn't I tell
you that you should say 'I respectfully report, the number of cell-inmates is one.' " "I thought only twice a day."
"And also if someone of us enters, you . . . Well, this time

I forgive you. Now hurry along. Clasp hands behind you while you go along the passage." This way of walking was no surprise to me; it had been the same when in custody before trial. Nor was it surprising that I had to turn against the wall and stand stiffly when waiting in the passage. But what awaited me in the office of the prison was the worst of surprises. I got some comfort from the warmth in the office room as my limbs had already been numbed with cold. But I had to pay dearly for this solace. One of my former Interrogators, Ervin Faludy—well known for his cruelty and cynical lies—received me. After hearing my complaints and assuring me they would be remedied ("there are of course always misunderstandings and difficulties at the beginning") he started questioning me about the alleged spy-connexions of my friend Mrs. . . .—exactly in the A.V.H. fashion which I had known only too well. So not even that ordeal could be dismissed from my seventh heaven of penal servitude. It was to go on and on, for years.

Whenever I was summoned to the office rooms, this same mixture of feelings overwhelmed me. I got some minutes or hours of warmth and some cigarettes to soothe the pains in my limbs and nerves; at the same time, I had to be prepared for the most trying arguments about the persons whose spy-activities, according to my Interrogator, I was concealing. Not only the threats disturbed me, but also the questions themselves. What should I say if asked whether I knew Mr. So-and-So? I could simply answer No. But he may be interrogated at the same time, and differences between our depositions would be a reason for torturing both of us. Should I say I knew him as a reliable Communist? My vouching for his reliability would be the worst of recommendations. The best I could do was to blur the subject with vague and incoherent narratives such as: "I knew him only through his fiancée who had died. I really do not think he was very much interested in politics . . . certainly he was anti-Nazi. . . ." It took some time for me to find out that to refer to the anti-Nazi records of the suspected was far from being a service to them. If one was against Hitler he must have been in touch either with

Royalists or with Socialists or with "Titoist-Trotskyites";
the fact that someone had been in the Resistance against
the Nazis before the Russian occupation was a reason for
suspecting that he was in the resistance against Bolsheviks
now. The reliable and patriotic Hungarian, in the ruling
view, was the one who had blindly obeyed the orders of
pro-German generals (apart from the handful of Moscow-
trained Communists and A.V.H. leaders). Those in particular who had worked for Britain were traitors.

A piece of good luck in my distress was that comparatively little was asked of me concerning people with whom
I had really been in close touch before my arrest. The
A.V.H., as an instrument of investigation, was astonish-
ingly incompetent and muddled. They piled up towers of
compromising information about as many people as possible, but apparently the officer in one room did not know
what his colleague in the neighbouring room had already
found out, and was not even very much interested in it.
My staying in the Grand Hotel Platinus on Margaret Island had been decreed by Under-Secretary of State Berei,
in agreement with the A.V.H. where his son-in-law, Lieutenant-Colonel Vladimir Farkas, held a key post. They
wanted to keep their eyes on me, and this was facilitated
by my staying in that great hotel. Nevertheless, on the
night of my arrest they looked for me at my mother's flat
and blocked that until I was safe in their hands. They were
similarly misinformed about my "contacts" in Budapest—
to use one of their favourite expressions. They did not
bother even to read my diary which they had taken from
my pocket: not even the letter to London which I had
planned to post the following day. They were simply too
lazy to do so. I should add that they did not lose very
much by their laziness. The utmost they could have found
out about my friends was that they had made disparaging
comments on the régime and perhaps one or two of them
had smuggled some money out of the country. These were
no spy-contacts, and nothing short of spy-contacts satisfied the A.V.H. As to the people about whom I had to be
interrogated, the catchwords in the sentence passed on me
—I.S. and Social Democracy—were supposed to be more

revealing than the dates found in my diary. To most questions, therefore, I could easily answer that, having lived in Britain during the ten years before my arrest, I had hardly known the person concerned.

As I mentioned in previous chapters, I was taken for such hearings not only to the office-rooms of the prison but also, occasionally, to police headquarters in Budapest. After the planning and shelving of the open trial which was "to inculpate Social Democracy," my solitary confinement ended for several years and I was crammed together in one M.Z. cell with three of those who would have been my co-defendants: Zoltán Horváth, Sándor Szalai and George Pálóczi-Horváth.

It is difficult to decide which is worse, compulsory solitude or co-existence without breathing space. I myself, in the long run would always decide for solitude. Nevertheless at that moment it was a great relief, after many a month, to meet old friends who spoke my language and had undergone experiences like mine. Not only my limbs had been numbed in prison, but also my universe. Cut off from people other than interrogators and gaolers, I was simply unable to imagine that the world was carrying on outside as though nothing had happened. When, shuttled about between various prisons, I got a chance now and then to look at people freely strolling about in the streets I could hardly believe my eyes. They struck me as shadows from another world. The universe had stopped being real for me. Even the wall-knocking—which I still exchanged with some neighbours in Vác and Markó utca as well as at No. 60—gave only a shadow-picture of other people who were suffering like me. When sitting at last together in a dingy cell with three other fellow-shadows, life had become somewhat less unreal. And there are moments when nothing is a greater gift than that.

We had to pay for it by getting on one another's nerves. This cannot be helped. There was only room for three straw-sacks in the cell for four of us. We had to share straw-sacks and a wash-basin and bucket and air. To cram people together in a close community is the best way of making them hostile to one another. It is ludicrous to ask, after many a year, whose fault this or that quarrel was—either in that particular cell with those cell-mates, or later in others with others. We were breathing the same air, and that accounted for everything.

One of our disputes, however, seems worth recalling. A dispute and not a quarrel, though necessarily couched now and then in the irritated terms of compulsory day-and-night companionship. Two of my cell-mates, Horváth and Szalai, had belonged to the "crypto-Communist" wing of the Social-Democratic Party and, though disapproving of much that had happened, still stuck to their opinion that the régime was a dictatorship of the proletariat and popular with the poor. I contradicted them: "I never met in Hungary, outside the special circle of Party favourites and careerists, one single person who liked this régime. Certainly no worker and no peasant, not even the poorest peasant. . . ."

"When did you ever meet a genuine worker? Those you met were concierges and waiters, tied to the bourgeoisie."

"But their brothers-in-law and their cousins to whom I also talked were, one a turner, the other a bricklayer, and so forth. They hated all that was going on more than did the intelligentsia. And I moved about in suburbs, too. I did the same in Genoa and Paris. There, you see at once that Communism is popular. It is brought home to you by clumsy scribbles 'VV Stalin' and the like. Ever seen such a scribble on a Budapest wall or hoarding? Carefully painted party slogans—but scribbles? Occasionally a reference to the Old Man's Arsehead." Rákosi was the "Old Man," and Stalin the "Very Old," in case we were overheard by the guard.

In our capacity of sentenced convicts all of us were still novices—which means the deepest pit of hell. Habit can alleviate any ordeal. One gaoler takes a liking for one prisoner, and another for another. The ways to persuade and oblige gaolers are found out by experience. But at the start there are only kicks and threats from them and suspicious glances from unknown fellow-prisoners if he meets any. We had not yet heard anything from our gaolers but "you bloody . . ." It was in a way touching but even more irritating that the fourth of us, Pálóczi-Horváth, still stubbornly stood up for the régime. He knew, he said, that a great injustice had been done to him and to many others. But scientific truth . . . he still believed in it in a "Marxist-Leninist" way. He had come from the landed gentry, a near-aristocratic family, well known in Hungarian history. It was a family of Whig traditions but incidentally the richest of his uncles, dead by then, had been a frantic die-hard, a Jew-hater, the sort of man who would have supported the Nazis except that Hitler was a corporal. But if he hated Hitler for daring to be a general he hated his nephew, George, no less for besmearing the historical name Pálóczi-Horváth by joining the staff of a "Jewish," liberal paper and being friends with disreputable Left-Wing people, though perhaps not yet with Communists at that time. They had hardly been on speaking terms. George had broken away from him and also from far less radical non-Communists later on because, as he liked to say, he accepted the cause of the working classes as his own. Now we were receiving together the kicks and threats and shouts of "the working classes."

As we were talking, the peep-hole opened and a representative of those working classes, in the person of an A.V.H. corporal, called in, rather hesitatingly: "Is there a Pálóczi-Horváth in this cell?" After learning that there was one, he disappeared and later reappeared: "Are you this Pálóczi-Horváth . . . Come here for a moment." We, the other three of us, went on whispering—trying to guess what the interview could be about. When Pálóczi-Horváth returned, he seemed quite flabbergasted. "Well," he told me, and it was the first time I heard anything like that from him, "really . . . I wonder whether you are not right to some extent. I don't think so of course; but that gaoler. . . ."

That gaoler had asked him whether he was a relative of the die-hard uncle, the semi-Fascist landlord. "Yes," Pálóczi-Horváth answered, in alarm; he was prepared to apologize for having had such a despotic and reactionary relative. "O," the gaoler sighed, almost with tears in his eyes, "You know, my father used to be his farmhand.

What a fine, what a splendid gentleman he was! Never again shall we have such a good master." Then, after some musing: "Well you will understand me . . . what *can* we do? We must serve *these* here." It did not occur to him for a moment that a thorough-bred Pálóczi-Horváth, gaoled by the Communists, should be scientific enough not to see eye to eye with him in such matters. Pálóczi-Horváth did not give himself away but simply thanked him for his kindness. "I shall do everything I can for you," the gaoler concluded. He could not do much because in about one week's time he was transferred to another post. But we have never stopped recalling that dialogue since. The first human word granted to us in Vác prison under the Reds was a tribute to the memory of a fiercely White landlord.

What were other gaolers like? In describing them, I should not confine myself to Vác only but to all types I came across in other prison-blocks as well—60 Andrássy ut and Markó utca, and the great prison camp in the suburbs of Pest, "Gyüjtö," and the prison-block used later as political police headquarters in Buda, known as "P.V.," to which I was transferred afterwards.

Most of them were either soldierly Sadists or simply gangsters: and on the average, it was more agreeable to communicate with the gangsters. An incarnation of the "soldierly" type was the sergeant with bloodshot eyes, Mocsáry* by name. In 1945, he was cashiered for having maltreated Communist prisoners as a gaoler under the Horthy régime, but was later admitted to the Party and got his pips back again. During the drive against "Titoite-Trotskyites," he got some Communist prisoners back and told them jocularly: "See, sooner or later we always meet again." He once heard we had complained about food and uttered some critical words about the authorities. He gave a furious grunt and we feared he would denounce us. We

* Previously "vitéz" Mocsáry. The Order of the Vitéz (of the "Brave") was a new nobility of a military character, with the Regent at its head, established after the 1919 counter-revolution. Like some other nonsense typical of the Horthy régime, it was abolished in 1945.

learned later that this should never be feared from him: he hated writing so much that everyone to whom he had not done harm on the spot could feel safe from his anger. But he was an intolerable maniac. In those winter months, when all of us suffered from the cold—many with chilblains turned into septic wounds all over their limbs—we comforted ourselves by using either stuff pinched from the "bobbin" industry, or our sheets, as supplementary underwear. Mocsáry would search the cells to discover such "illicit" acts and make terrible trouble. Once, he called me and my cell-mates to the shower bath at an unexpected moment when I had no chance to rid myself of the sheet under my jacket. I had never so panicky a shower bath as was that one. When I undressed he happened to watch others. But when I had to dress he was glaring just at me. I was temporizing as much as I could, looking for my boots. "You bloody . . . What are you mucking about for, dress at once!" "God will help me or not," I thought and, my heart ferociously beating, the sergeant no less ferociously staring at me, I touched my shirt under which the sheet was hidden. At that moment, there was a short circuit. I never knew I could dress in the dark so quickly.

While the true gangsters had been recruited by the A.V.H., most of the soldierly gaolers had previously belonged to the personnel of the Ministry of Justice. They had been taken over from the Ministry by the A.V.H., together with the political prisons themselves, in 1950.

In the previous period, from 1945–50, the treatment of sentenced political prisoners had been humane in every way. The political police and their military sister institution, the Kat. Pol., started committing brutal and illegal acts as early as 1947, if not earlier; but the convict after trial—even though on partially false charges—was committed to a place where he could move about freely during the day, order food and books from outside, listen to the wireless and read the newspapers, even attend football matches and film performances held inside the prison. The Minister of Justice at that time, the Socialist Dr. Ries, though guilty of extreme weakness and ultimate subservience to the Communists, was undoubtedly a man of high humanitarian standards, and the golden age for political prisoners ended at the time of his own arrest.

When the A.V.H. staff took over from the Ministry of Justice, they made a "disciplinary" tour of all prison establishments and beat up about 50 per cent of the prisoners. Their procedure usually followed this pattern: the warders would ask the prisoners: "Why don't you stack all your dixies?" The prisoners would reply that they had never been told to do so. "You swine, how dare you argue with me," was the rejoinder, and the beating up started. Many of the Ministry of Justice gaolers who acted as guides outdid their A.V.H. colleagues in brutality in order to get taken on as reliable Communists. Nobody doubted that they would be pleased to indulge in "soldierly" Sadism under a White régime at least as willingly as under a Red one; but for this very reason, they showed off their eagerness to brutalize their "Fascist" victims.

Amongst the gangsters, my favourite was a young corporal with glittering black eyes and thick eyebrows. As we found out, he had served as a volunteer in an S.S. brigade but been forgiven for his past in 1945 when he joined the Communist Party. He was proud of his skill in eavesdropping. One morning he burst into our cell: "Ignawtoosh, what did you say last night about Rákosi?" Indeed I had forgotten I should refer to him as "The Old" only. I was stammering something about the necessity of venting my feelings at least in jokes. "You had better shut your mouth, you old bastard!" he told me, and thus friendship begins. Some days after, he showed me the photograph of his girl-friend, a tramway conductress. "Pretty thing," I said; "your fiancée?" "My whore," he answered. "At your age one shouldn't look for tarts who only cost money but for elderly ladies who pay." "I get money even from the young," he replied, and thus friendships develop. He was very kind to us. He several times overheard our talks not destined for gaolers' ears, but he never made use of them. Later he was imprisoned for undisciplined behaviour.

Political faith was the thing no gaoler had—with one exception, who ranked as my favourite No. 2. He was a pleasant-looking, short young man, an A.V.H. recruit but, exceptionally, a muddled semi-intellectual rather than a gangster. He liked middle-brow novels, especially when they described rapes and incestuous scenes in order to denounce the *ancien régime*. One day he decided he must learn book-keeping and started picking the brains of one prisoner, but gave it up quickly. Another day he started something else and gave it up even more quickly. There was one thing which he could not give up, and that was studying Marxism-Leninism. So he was busy all the time picking the brains of my cell-mates who prepared compendia for him, to be used at the Party seminar. He could not suppress his liking for Social Democrats and "Titoist-Trotskyites," in spite of his Party loyalty. My name and my father's he had vaguely remembered from literary text-books, and he would chat with me for an hour if no other gaoler was in the neighbourhood. Altogether the only occasion when a gaoler could be comparatively kind was when he was not overheard by his colleagues. When in company, they outdid one another in rudeness and cruelty—partly to show their "guts" and partly to help their careers.

Our transportation from Vác to the Budapest Gyüjtö was a splendid opportunity for such competition. Before being pushed into the lorries, we were ordered to stand stiff turned against the wall. We were abused as dirt and murderers and told we would be hanged before long. Now and then we felt a gaoler's fist on our necks, bumping our noses into the wall, or a kick in our pants. When leaving the building I saw my intellectual friend and tried to catch his eyes as it were for a farewell. He was gloomily turning his eyes away. I later learned from fellow-prisoners that it had been he who gave me the kicks. Was it because of the presence of the gaolers who perhaps suspected him of liking me? Or did he himself feel guilty because of doing so and did he want thus to relieve his conscience?

In Budapest Gyüjtö, torture reached its peak in 1951–2. Sometimes I could hardly sleep at night for being awakened again and again by the howls and cries of "short-ironed" prisoners. At dawn, I used to welcome the concert of the birds not so much for its beauty as because it superseded those deadly human sounds. The guards had the right to beat or torture prisoners as they liked, and also to have it done by those prisoners whom they picked out for their assistants, mainly from among the former Fascist Arrow-Cross storm-troopers, S.S. men, agents of the Nazi White political police and so forth, and Communist A.V.H. and "Katpol" officers who even after their imprisonment carried on their former work. Tortures differed according to the different temperaments of the gaolers. "Short-iron" had to be ordered by the prison Commander on the evidence of reports from the guards; but some guards did not bother with reports, and beat up or otherwise tortured prisoners on the spur of the moment. Sergeant Berkes—a former gaoler in the Horthy régime—was known for never beating prisoners but having them "short-ironed" *en masse* for no offence whatsoever, whereas Sergeant Pintér—a former butcher's assistant—disliked writing, even a report of misbehaviour, and specialized in beating up. Some people were literally beaten to death—for instance, because of an alleged attempt to escape—in the presence of other prisoners, one man picked out of each prisoners' "work-brigade," "so that everybody should learn his lesson." One of these memorable scenes was attended by a woman Sanitary N.C.O., a well-known figure all over the prison camp, Irénke by her first name. It was she who dutifully reported that the criminal had "farted out"—which in the A.V.H. Glossary stood for "he died." The prisoners who were on the spot to learn their lesson said she had faintly winced. In general she was not very tender and had some people short-ironed herself. She owed her fame however to her language rather than her deeds. When a privileged prisoner, who had been allowed cigarettes but not given matches, respectfully asked her for light she replied indignantly: "Why not ask for my ——?"

Corruption in the prisons knew no limit. There were some factories operated in the prison camps to make them profitable: a branch of the Gamma precision instrument factory in Vác, a button factory and later a children's toy factory in the Gyüjtö. According to expert calculations, these were bound to be unprofitable because in spite of sweating the prisoners—they were made to work fourteen to sixteen hours a day—the waste of material and man-power, the outdated mechanical arrangements, and not least the theft of goods by the guards, severely limited output. One guard, for instance, used to arrive every morning with an empty bag and go home with one filled with expensive buttons which he sent straight off to the black market; another took away sham "gold" rings which the prisoners made illicitly of tin, and sold them on the black market as genuine wedding rings: a third was known to put on about five brand new prisoners' shirts every day, also for black marketeering. Up to 1953, such proceedings were not, on the whole, discouraged by the authorities; the idea was that whatever the A.V.H. men committed did not matter so long as they were loyal to the régime. But when one A.V.H. clique succeeded in overthrowing the other, they used against the vanquished their knowledge of these illicit acts. The gaolers were much amused by the misfortune of their colleagues, espe-cially of those formerly of higher ranks; Sergeant Pintér is reported to have given a pail full of water with great pleasure into the hands of his former prison Commander when the latter had been arrested: "Now carry on at once and scrub the floor."

There were many wicked, many actively cruel and many callously dull A.V.H. gaolers. In one thing, there was no apparent difference between them: they were all oversexed. "Tough guys," well-fed and confined to a day-long idleness except the hours of crashing boredom spent on their ideological education, often tired of the delight to bully and humiliate the former overlords now at their mercy, the only thing in which they could indulge was the vision of crude erotic scenes. Most of the conversation one overheard was of such matters as "She wanted to get money from me for she became pregnant but I kicked her . . .," and the one thing with which a prisoner could be sure of pleasing them was to tell dirty stories or, even more, to provide them with obscene drawings. There was

a strange young fellow-prisoner of ours, deaf and of proletarian origin, who had been snatched and made use of as
a genius of the Hungarian people in his 'teens by the
Arrow-Cross Fascists. Heaven only knows why that crime,
easily forgiven to others, was not forgiven him; he spent
at least ten years in prison. But whatever favour could be
granted to a prisoner was granted to him—for the simple
reason that he provided all gaolers, including majors and
captains (and also, I should add, some lady N.C.O.s)
with ribald sketches. What I liked most in them, and in
the taste of the recipients, was their conservatism; the men
were all tail-coated in their unbuttoned trousers, and the
women as if taken out, before half stripping them, from a
Vogue of 1939. Irrespective of changes in ideologies and
fashions, belief in the pre-war symbols of social superior-
ity had prevailed in that most sincere mirror of popular
fantasies—pornography.

As to *good* A.V.H. gaolers—were there any at all?
Most people in Hungary would answer No; and surely so
would most of my former fellow-prisoners. But they
would not be fair and could not really be expected to be
fair. The blue-lapelled uniform grew into the symbol of
human abjection in their eyes; I could well understand
them when they said "If our time comes, the best of the
A.V.H. gaolers must be fried in the fat of the worst." Indeed, even comparative kindness on the part of A.V.H.
men was as a rule due to negligence or cynicism and, in
the years of the Thaw, to a wish to re-insure themselves,
rather than to honesty. But there were exceptions. I remember one who as early as the autumn of 1949, round
the torturing cells of 60 Andrássy ut, always did his best
to help me; he was a very simple man who had accepted
this job, unknown to him, for the high pay and, once
caught in it, could do no better than be helpful to prisoners when not watched by his colleagues. To apply for release from A.V.H. service was itself a risky step. This was
particularly sad for those who had never applied to be en-
rolled and had got this unwished-for present as a surprise.
I remember particularly one, a slim young man, an ama-
teurish but enthusiastic singer, specializing in folksongs

and rather sloppy pseudo-folk songs. He had asked for a
musical training, hoping he would finally be admitted to
the stage. The answer from the authorities concerned was
that his request would be considered but for the time being he must do his military service; and he woke up in a
blue-lapelled uniform before he knew where he was. This
happened in the Thaw period when some at least of the
worst A.V.H. torturers were already transferred into less
conspicuous posts, and recruits with a record of innocence
required. On the whole, the A.V.H. had still remained a
riff-raff of legalized Sadism and gangsterdom, and the
folksong gaoler, despite the risks involved, ran from pillar
to post to be transferred to another armed unit, but in
vain. He took even greater risks in siding with the prisoners. When we were walking under his supervision, he told
me "Now you talk to whom you like; I shall warn you
when necessary." He hated, as he told me, the very sight
of a uniform and would ask me, his bright brown eyes
flashing, "Do you know the song 'It is not I who grew un-
faithful to you, but you who deserted me.' "

In the days of the Revolution, in October–November,
1956, a general hunt after the A.V.H. men was raging in
the streets of Budapest. I and some fellow-writers—including two or three imprisoned today—protested against
it and urged that everybody suspected of crimes should be
handed over, without harm to his person, to the authorized Courts. Many thought (even amongst my most
charitably-minded friends in Britain, for instance) that
our attitude was an excess of humanitarianism and legal-
mindedness: after all, a gang such as the A.V.H. should
learn their lesson and remember in future. There is much
to be said for this trend of thought. One must not be
sentimental about mass-murderers. Had I heard that some
of our expert torturers were tortured to death in their own
style, I might have deplored it as poor propaganda but
would not have felt the slightest pity for them. But who
could know about the people simply caught in blue-
lapelled uniform or denounced for personal reasons in
those days? I bore in my mind the face of my singing
friend with his flashing brown eyes—he might, I felt, be

caught and massacred together with the rest. He was an
exception. There were very, very few such exceptions, one
tenth of one per cent perhaps. But the main lesson to be
learned of Gestapo, N.K.V.D. and A.V.H. stories is that
no one should be punished for what others have done.

Chapter 8

Murderers Murdering Murderers

IT WAS MY GOOD FORTUNE for years to be in the "Translating bureau" which was set up to provide Party and
A.V.H. headquarters with the material they wanted. The
material included literature on spying, technical reports
on the developments of methods that might interest the
political police (such as microscopic photography) and
such "reactionary" literature as no one else in Hungary
was allowed at that time to read. I had great pleasure in
translating a volume of Sir Winston Churchill's memoirs
and books by Hungarian political émigrés published in
France. Others received even more confidential material,
such as the contents of the wastepaper baskets of one or
another legation in Budapest, and secret documents stolen
from Italian atomic research bodies and Austrian Government offices. We had U.N.O. material on conditions in
countries all over the world, so in some ways we knew
more about them than our own countrymen at large. And
all this time we were not allowed to see even the official
Hungarian Communist Gazette or to listen to broadcasts.

This degree of trust in the branded enemies of the
régime had a simple explanation. Those who had imprisoned us meant to keep us in gaol for good, to let us
rot alive. This is not a figure of speech, but literally true.
At the retrial of my case, in June 1956, the A.V.H. officer
witnesses spoke with equanimity of their discussions about
who should be sent to prison to rot alive and who might
get away with internment which, though no less painful,
would end when the authorities so decided. For this very

reason, no political convict was allowed to have contact with his acquaintances outside, by letter or any other channel; if very exceptionally one got permission to exchange letters with near relatives these were carried each way by A.V.H. officers, and no information of the whereabouts of the prisoner was given to anyone.

At Vác, translators worked in isolated cells unaware of one another. Our single cell not only housed four of us, but served also as an office, equipped with a typewriter and dictionaries. As a reward, we were granted a ration of cigarettes and some extra food: one day some lard with extra bread, another some lumps of sugar, and so forth. The cigarettes reached us more often than not, the food was withheld more often than not. We had books from the prison library to read and, as a special privilege, permission to play chess. We would mould the chessmen out of bread, and if they turned out too attractively, a warder would step in and confiscate them on the grounds that he had never been told about this privilege of ours. Another time he would tell us he had heard of our privileges but we should make another set—three in fact, for he would be willing to accept two of them. It was a gracious present for his nephews.

In the Budapest Gyüjtö, the Translating officers were merged into one single unit and after some months of hesitation, were allocated to the most comfortable prison-building, the "Little Hotel," together with the most privileged working unit, the Engineers. There were beds to sleep in at the Little Hotel and W.Cs. with something near privacy—a rarity in prisons. The Engineering unit, including its clerical and auxiliary staff, amounted to 80–120 men; ours came to thirty or forty men, about one third of them concerned with translating from Serb, Croat and Slovene. We had amongst us Jugoslav diplomats who, at the time of the break between the Cominform and Tito, turned against their own Government and sought refuge in Hungary. They had been extolled as true Communists and used for a while in propaganda against Tito, and then suddenly they were arrested as Tito's agents. Most of them had little idea of politics and even less of what an expert translator is supposed to know. But assisted by the Hungarians who had spent some time in Jugoslavia—and who were also called Tito's agents—they managed somehow. They excelled in various labours: singing folksongs and operetta, and moulding most decorative chessmen after hours of collective chewing.

Our Jugoslav section had to translate literally whole volumes of the Jugoslav *Official Gazette* into Hungarian. All advertisements and announcements had to be included. There was apparently a race between all Stalin's agencies, to prove the truth of Stalin's charges against Jugoslavia. They spared no time and money to seek evidence. Our Jugoslavs from time to time disappeared from the Little Hotel; they enjoyed the hospitality of N.K.V.D. headquarters, and obliged the Russian interrogators with stories of Titoist conspiracies with the Anglo-American emissaries which they had noticed as early as in 1942.

The engineers were entrusted with even more confidential work than ours: they made plans for constructions of a military character, and some were taken to the spot under special supervision to attend the works. Our two units were allowed now and then to consult each other, the Engineers needing our help in translating scientific literature, and our unit needing technical advice to make these translations properly. We managed to arrange very pleasant social gatherings under these pretexts—and it would be hard to decide when they were pretexts only and when genuine reasons. I am grateful for what I learned on such occasions of the theory of relativity and of nuclear physics; and I did my best to answer questions the engineers asked about English grammar, British living conditions and Hungarian literature including, I am ashamed to say, my own prison poems. Much of our talk was not meant to be heard by the guards; if one came in, we could always point to the texts which we were supposed to be discussing.

In other ways life and arrangements in the Translating bureau changed all the time as in all prison departments. One day we were told that a special norm system was to be worked out for paying us; so much of it could be used for extra food and cigarettes, so much transferred to our relatives, so much put aside in our accounts. We did receive extra food now and then—tomatoes and sausages and raw onions and garlic and the like. Their arrival was a great event, and for days we were quite drunk with the treat we gave ourselves. The engineers were good at the illicit technique of using the electricity for frying, and though often caught and reprimanded they carried on and made us share in it. My main discovery was a fondness for garlic. I had always detested it but the smell in prison filled me with nostalgia for the taverns and cheap restaurants of the outside world. Since then I have remained a passionate garlic eater, with all the grave consequences involved for those near me.

But no sooner had the norm system been worked out than we learned it had been dropped. The officers responsible for catering made it their rule to withhold from our accounts the money for goods which had been offered to us but which turned out to be "unobtainable." It was a great improvement, in the time of the Thaw, when an exceptionally honest catering officer had the idea of buying, say, paprika in place of the out-of-stock tomatoes for the prisoner concerned, instead of pocketing the money.

Equally sudden were the changes concerning the prisoners' behaviour and routine. One day we were ordered, whenever we met "someone in Authority," to say loudly "Good morning, Sergeant, Sir," or "Corporal, Sir"; the next day we were told not to say a word but just to take our caps off; the third day, we were ordered never to take our caps off when not in the cell but to salute with our fingers at the peak of our caps. One day we were solemnly allowed to walk with whomever we chose from among the Engineers and the Translators; the following day we were no less seriously told that each should walk only with his cell-mate at the time of communal walking in the courtyard. One day we were ordered to turn, without saying a word, with our faces to the wall when someone in Authority entered our cells and, on the next, respectfully to report the number of cell inmates and to wait for further instructions. It was no secret that those in charge of the prison-block themselves were unable to make up their minds about these questions of high importance. As a rule some prisoners were punished for forgetting or not obeying one or another recently issued order but the orders themselves went into oblivion automatically after a few months until they were either renewed or modified.

My work, when not translating, consisted in revealing the secrets of "I.S." I was most pleased to share with others my expert knowledge of that devilish machinery which haunted the minds of the A.V.H. chiefs. In their view, the world outside the Soviet sphere was pulled by I.S., C.I.C. and U.D.B.A. wires, and I who had spent years with the B.B.C. and in friendship with British Labour M.P.s must have had deep insight into such machinations. The reader may ask whether they knew that my I.S. affiliations were their own inventions. In fact, they knew this while inventing them but were able to believe in their own lies the next moment. They had excellent formulas enabling them to forget what they liked. When interrogating us and finding that the facts did not tally with their preconceived ideas, they would say "There is not only factual but also political truth, and political truth is the more important." When taking my depositions they knew very well that my talks with Richard Crossman or Kingsley Martin had not been spy-contacts; they had only been so in a "political" sense. But some weeks later they would ask me quite seriously about those spy-contacts which, they would add, "you yourself admitted." They would again and again consult me on spying and counter-intelligence techniques in the British Empire—and I saw no reason to avoid describing and inventing as much as I could manage.

All the same I could not help now and then challenging their beliefs, simply because they interested me. Once when interrogated by a conspicuously cynical (and therefore comparatively intelligent) A.V.H. major, Vajda by name, about the activities of the London Hungarian Club which was "in a political sense a British spy-organization" I said to him:

"Sir, it is not for me to argue with you about the prevailing political ideas. But could I ask your personal opinion on a matter for my information?"

"Please."

"You say that the London Hungarian Club must be regarded objectively as a British spy-organization because it was in close touch with all sorts of British anti-Communist groups during the war. You say their leaders must therefore be regarded as Trotskyites. But during the war, the cry from Moscow was that everybody willing to fight Hitlerism should unite, and just those reluctant to do so were denounced as Trotskyites. Now what do you really think the Hungarian Club people should have done?"

"Nonsense. Of course we wanted a united front with every political party—but not with the Secret Service."

"Now what do you mean by Secret Service? Not to argue with you but just to clear my mind. After all, during the war, practically everybody fighting the Nazis had to share and keep secrets. The leaders of the British Communist Party were all engaged in secret political warfare."

The reply was a gesture of contempt: "O, that Party . . . That's typical of them. All police spies. We know very well that when we get power over Britain, ninetenths of the Communist leaders will be hanged."

My friend Basil Davidson, at that time still doing his best to exonerate the Bolsheviks when comparing their practices with what went on under Anglo-American rule, was flabbergasted in 1956 when I told him he had been on the A.V.H. list of "Imperialist spies." But I can assure him that he was in quite good company and surely not in a fanatically anti-Communist setting. Harry Pollitt, Arthur Horner, Klugmann, Picasso, Joliot-Curie were all registered as I.S. and Deuxième Bureau directors in the archives of the A.V.H.—as well as such "petty bourgeois reactionaries" as Thomas Mann and Julian Huxley, or "Trotskyites" such as Stephen Spender.

Whether that cynical major who was so keen to hang his British comrades ever fooled himself into believing that they were really spies I could not tell. But his subordinates and the later vintage of A.V.H. officers were certainly never told that the spy-stories found by them in the depositions must not be believed. They had to find out for themselves that if their bosses had declared something, theirs was the duty to prove and not to check it. He who acted differently dug his own grave. Does it sound too ridiculous for words that I was now and then worried about some of them? A young interrogator, a comparatively kind one, that is, one who did not threaten the arrest of my relatives, or to have me beaten up again, once asked me about that very boring subject on which I had been interrogated so often, the London Hungarian Club. Some unimportant people who had been members were suspected of "I.S. activities." I told him quite sincerely that it had been a Club run in conformity with Soviet wishes. I was frank about all details. He cast an alarmed glance at me. "But what then was their crime?" Should I tell him that it was nothing? If he reported the remark without further comment he would be imprisoned like me and I might be maltreated once again. "Leave it to me, sir, I'll make the report for you," I told him. "After all, I have had longer A.V.H. experience than you." He was most grateful. I phrased the minutes of my interrogation in usual A.V.H. jargon about the Trotskyite-Titoite-British-Monarchist covering organization called London Hungarian Club, and minimized the importance of the people involved by pointing out that they could not have had a great number of spy-contacts since they hardly knew English. This was the best one could say in their favour. Indeed they were not arrested. Their unfamiliarity with the English language had saved them. One of them became, after the Thaw, Hungarian Minister in Sudan.

I like to remember the few kind interrogators amongst the many unkind; in fact I found their behaviour more characteristic of the lies permeating them than that of those who were cruel for cruelty's sake. The most polite of all, the one who addressed me as "Mr. Ignotus" in the Stalinist period, used to offer not only cigarettes but also great slices of ham for my help in revealing the secrets of I.S. He brought me the latest edition of *Who's Who*. His request—for in the polite form of a request it was made—

was that I should carefully look through it and translate everything it contained on people of Hungarian origin. "Certainly," I answered, and tried to find out what his motives were. "Well, I suppose, all those included must belong to the Secret Service." That the Secret Service should thus put into the shop-window its own agents was a surprise to me even after my prison-years. The interrogator saw the expression of astonishment on my face: "Well, don't you agree? Or do you think all of them paid to be included?" A third possibility was hardly imaginable. Anyway, I was glad both to see a recent *Who's Who* and to eat the ham.

One of my memorable interrogations at A.V.H. headquarters conducted by Lieutenant-Colonel Márton Károlyi started with the question: "What was the opinion of I.S. about the dissolution of the illegal Communist Party in Hungary during the war?" I was stupid enough at first to reply "Sir, you know that I was a spy only in a political sense . . . Indeed how should I know?" He encouraged me to rack my brains: I must still remember something about it. He gave me the sanatorium treatment usual on such occations; its only disadvantage was that one had diarrhoea as a result of getting human food after many a month of fodder and refuse. He was really very patient with me, just hinting at the great damage done to the workers' movement by dissolving the illegal party. In fact, I had not even known of that tragic dissolution, let alone what I.S. had thought of it. But why not oblige the lieutenant-colonel? Twice I had about a week's sanatorium treatment, first for writing essays on the matter, and then for appearing as a witness at a secret trial where I had to tell my invention to the Court. The gist of it was that I.S. had wanted the illegal Communist Party to disappear from the Hungarian political scene; I.S. was confident that the underground leaders - of Hungarian Communism were prone to Western influences and that the masses behind them could be lured into an anti-Soviet attitude once their Party had been dissolved and renamed—as it was—a "Peace Party," not properly a Communist one.

Who was to be discredited by such depositions? I had

no idea. I only knew that Communists were most keen on persecuting Communists. As early as 1950, before my sentence, Lieutenant Szántó—Károlyi's assistant—asked me to write a report on those Hungarian Communists whom the British had reckoned to be likely deviators from the Soviet line. "For a while they thought Rákosi might," I candidly replied. He answered I should leave out the names of "serious personalities." How could I know which of the personalities were serious? I asked him, and he told me: "Rákosi, Gerö, Farkas, Kádár, Péter." Three of them were Moscow-trained Communists; the fourth was Minister of the Interior; and the fifth was chief of the A.V.H. "May I refer to any of the Communist leaders except these five?" I asked. "By all means," he assured me, and I wrote rubbish, mixing in as many Communist leaders as I could, only careful to leave out Zoltán Vas and George Lukács whose unorthodox behaviour in some respects was really known to me.

Now again, Lieutentant-Colonel Károlyi asked which Communists were regarded in a friendly way by the British; but the names I mentioned at random did not seem to impress him. I certainly never thought of a "serious personality" such as Kádár. "Well, you need not mention names," he told me. With Pálóczi-Horváth, who was summoned to Budapest on the same occasion and for the same reason, I was trying to guess who the victims might be. Pálóczi-Horváth had by then stopped being a Communist; what he had heard by chance from recently arrested workers had completely shaken his faith. "Whoever the victims are," I told him, "we must not be worried about them. I don't see why we should not help murderers to murder other murderers."

Before the trial I was given a smart mufti suit and an assistant asked me to walk into Court with arms hanging naturally, not clasped behind my back as I usually had to. Why they took such trouble to make our appearance "natural" was their own secret: it was a regular A.V.H. trial *in camera*, the same group which had tried me, the same President of Court, the same faces in the seats for the Counsel for the Defence . . . Amongst the defendants, I knew only one, my meek and embarrassed erstwhile chief, the former Minister of Foreign Affairs, Gyula Kállai. But Pálóczi-Horváth, when we met in our special cell again, told me who the rest were: the Defendant No. 1 was no less a personality than the former Minister of the Interior, János Kádár.

After his betrayal of the Hungarian Revolution, in 1956, I cannot feel that I owe much to Mr. Kádár. But I owe him an apology, for my remark that they were but "murderers to be murdered by other murderers." I should apologize even more to some of his co-defendants and other comrades who were to be "politically liquidated" along with him for their criminal share in the Hungarian Communist Underground. Among them were, to mention only two, the distinguished journalist, Sándor Haraszti, once a fanatic Communist but a man of the purest moral character, and his son-in-law, Géza Losonczy, later a cabinet minister in the Imre Nagy coalition government. Haraszti was sentenced to death and then kept for three years in solitary confinement, so that whenever the door opened he might imagine that he was to be hanged the next moment. Losonczy, a man of a very well-ordered mind, became insane for a while and was kept in the prison hospital. I met them, and met others who had shared their fate, after my release in the heyday of the Thaw. No one bothered to recall testimonies made against one another: their backgrounds were clear. No doubt I did the best I could, for there was nothing else to do. But I should not even to the extent of a crack have forgotten that one Communist is not like another, though what we call Communism was—and is—responsible for making them appear so.

This and much else could not be foreseen just after the secret trial of Kádár and Haraszti, when I was led once again to Lieutenant-Colonel Márton Károlyi, in his office. He bade me farewell:

"Well, you did it quite well. Now, what do you feel like?"

"I feel rotten, sir."

"Why? Sorry for those dirty traitors? They are scum."

"Let me tell you sir, that frankly I am less worried about them than about myself. To go back again to that cell full of bugs, in Vác, again to be fed on pig-fodder and dishwater, to suffer day and night from cold."

"O, don't worry, we shall invite you here again before long. There are always new problems. . . ."

"May I expect another Minister of the Interior?"

The lieutenant-colonel was gracious enough to reply with a painful grin only. He did not know, nor did I indeed, how well justified was the pain in his grin. The turn of another Minister of the Interior came shortly afterwards: he killed himself and exterminated his family before being arrested by the A.V.H. chief, Gábor Péter. Stalin had not yet died and Socialist Legality had not yet been proclaimed when the campaign of mutual extermination between the chief thugs, Mátyás Rákosi, Mihály Farkas, and Gábor Péter, reached its peak. Now it was unequivocally a case of murderers murdering the murderers; they alone had been left in power, each dreading the presence of the other and trying to get rid of him. They denounced one another to their respective protectors in Moscow as imperialist agents. As a result, Gábor Péter was arrested as the leader of a "Zionist-Cosmopolitan" conspiracy, and so was his former deputy, later Minister of Justice, Gyula Décsy, a man of purest "Germano-Aryan" blood, who had started his Zionist career as a candidate for Roman Catholic priesthood. Among the arrested was Lieutenant-Colonel Márton Károlyi. He too turned out to be a "dirty traitor," one of the "scum." Allegedly he committed suicide in prison.

Many of the A.V.H. officers and their puppet judges and attorneys committed suicide in the years to come. Most of the Moscow-trained leaders were from time to time tempted, I gather, to commit suicide. On the whole, they have survived. Some are enjoying the hospitality of the Soviet Union, like Rákosi has been confined to living in the Soviet Union: an exile in Paradise. Others who also took refuge in the U.S.S.R. have since returned to Hungary, Gerö and Berei amongst them. Again, others such as Mihály Farkas and his son, Vladimir, and Gábor Péter and Décsy and Princz, were imprisoned for a while, but were later released by the Kádár Government. Before cutting one another's throats, they were removed from absolute power. Their lives were only saved by what showed them all up as the gang of murderers which they were—that is, by the Thaw.

Chapter 9

Thaw Starting

"WHAT WOULD YOU like to eat now?" we would ask one another. Indeed it was the thing which most stubbornly haunted our minds. The destiny of the world and our country, our relatives and ourselves, could be left in the lap of the gods. The dixies handed in to us three times a day were the present, and we started guessing each morning what they might contain. Perhaps that heavy farinaceous stuff which was some small improvement upon the fodder offered as vegetable. So our day-dreams started but grew quickly beyond control. Why not imagine something better? For instance, paprika-chicken, the favourite dish in Hungary? We arranged competitions as to who could plan the most perfect menu if we had a chance to eat it. The winner was, I remember, a fellow-prisoner called Stolte, once an underground Communist, one-time Trotskyite, one-time Smallholder Party propagandist, one-time adviser to the American occupation forces in Germany, a man who had been about fifteen times in prison. He started the ideal dinner with mushrooms most carefully prepared, and ended it with brandy. The very idea was delicious. Then, we brushed all these fantasies aside and concentrated on scrambled eggs. After many a vote taken on the matter, we always concluded that what we really would most like to have were scrambled eggs, fresh and pure, perhaps as a reflection of modest and respectable home-life. It was a dish unobtainable even in our periods of "sanatorium" treatment, for it was unsuitable for mass production. We dreamt of it day and night. Then, a familiar sound would strike our ears: doors of the cells opening one after another. Lunch was served. We got a can of stinking lentils, and our dreams were interrupted for some time. When that was forgotten, or replaced by another smell, we started dreaming again.

Our other serious hunger was for news. To learn something of the world outside we would have accepted much pain and sacrifice. When chased round the courtyard in front of the M.Z. building, in Vác, before day-break, on the pretext of "communal walking," prisoners would peep out of the ground-floor cells and ask us when we were approaching their windows, "Any news?" "No news," I answered. There was a particularly daring young fellow who could not be warned away. "Get away from the window, the gaoler is just coming," I told him as I was passing by. "Tell me some news or I'll kill you," he said at the next turn. "News, news, it needn't be true but it should be news," he repeated.

In fact we did get some news, wishful more often than truthful. The items varied according to the sources. In the Vác prison hospital, I learned of the Conservative election victory over Labour. As this information came from a Fascist, there was the addition that forty members of the Mosley Party had been elected to Parliament. Some few "Titoists" who had always been Stalinists said they knew the Communists had made great headway in France. They interpreted this optimistically: the U.S.S.R. would then feel safe, and an amnesty would quickly follow. Average information moved between these two extremes but was no more reliable. One of our "domestic prisoners" —who brought round the dixies, and were responsible for neatness—said he had seen with his own eyes the *Party Gazette* left behind mistakenly by a gaoler: Albania had been invaded by the Western Powers; in Norway, N.A.T.O. bases for atomic attacks had been established; Mao-Tse-tung had changed sides and was attacked now in the Russian press as a "dog on the leash of the Imperialists" like Tito. How disappointing to find out, months later, that all this was nonsense! But by then we had other comforting news—either true or false.

Where did true news come from? One of our main sources was the gaolers' affection for dance music. Very cheap receiving sets were distributed at that time in Hungary, but sealed so that only transmissions from a short distance were audible. The gaolers wanted jazz which was only broadcast from the West. The prisoners wanted news which was also broadcast only from the West. The gaolers asked the engineers to unseal and rearrange their sets; and the engineers used this opportunity to listen in to some Western news bulletins. What they subsequently disseminated turned out to be rather coloured with their own wishes; but the hang of what was going on could still be understood from them.

Another source was the actual machinery of A.V.H. investigations. We had found in the course of years that the interrogators never questioned to gain information but to seek confirmation. If they started to ask about the life of some public figure, we could be sure he had already been black-listed. One day, an interrogator began by threatening that if I went on concealing the truth as I had hitherto I would be hanged at once. "We are not tender-hearted," he repeated again and again; and I could well believe that his heart would not suffer from my execution. He wanted to get "facts" about someone who, he said, had been in touch with leading A.V.H. officers and acted as a *liaison* between these and the British Empire. He called me every name and then, suddenly turning pompous, told me that there was still hope. "Look here, you see my cigarette-case and my despatch-case. A great conspiracy will now be revealed, a conspiracy which compares to the Rajk case as the despatch-case does to the cigarette-case." I told him the usual mumbo-jumbo, and though not satisfied, he allowed me for the time being to return to the Little Hotel. I hastened to warn my fellow prisoners who might have to face similar questions. Others, just returned from the Police Headquarters where they had been interrogated, told us about similar experiences. A.V.H. chiefs suspected of "cosmopolitan" conspiracy! Then a fellow prisoner recently transferred from Vác to the Gyüjtö supplied the explanation. He had worked at the prison-store and noticed among the prisoners' belongings an A.V.H. lieutenant-general's uniform. Gábor Péter alone could have worn that. His arrest was known to the prisoners sooner than to anybody else in Hungary.

The third source of information was the muddle in the A.V.H. They had very strict regulations about which prisoner to keep in solitary confinement and so forth. The regulations struck us as mysterious; they would suddenly isolate someone who had before mixed with anybody. But even these mysterious regulations were broken, simply by oversight. Convicts summoned to the Police Headquarters for special interrogation under great secrecy would be crammed into a common cell with people who had only been detained some days before. It was due to such a muddle that we learned, at the beginning of 1953, of Stalin's death. It spread like fire. Then, another item started circulating: Beria shot. He had been declared the sworn enemy of the people. After our many disappointments with wishful news, we were doubtful about this one. But one of us decided to try it on a gaoler. "In any case," he told him, "I presume you are happier in your sergeant's uniform than you would be in that of Gábor Péter or Beria." The gaoler nodded. He as well as his fellow gaolers started being more courteous with us.

In the summer of 1953, we learned that Rákosi had resigned as Premier though not as First Secretary to the Party. His successor at the head of the Government was Imre Nagy. "Personality Cult" was to stop. "Collective leadership" was to take over. Power was divided, and our hopes were flying high for its being divided even more. Whatever the outcome, it was a justified hope. We heard of the new Premier's speech, often rightly referred to as a turning point; peasant farmers must be allowed to leave the Kolchozi if they wished; more consumer goods must be produced, and unrealistic plans for capital investment abandoned; in the factories, better working conditions must be established; no more deportations into labour camps must take place; internment camps must be disbanded. What interested us most was Imre Nagy's criticism of the A.V.H. which had "lost touch" with the people. A very euphemistic description of its proceedings this was; but what a great thing that so much should be said! A new era was dawning, that of "Socialist Legality." In December, the prison Commander walked round the cells and told each prisoner, looking up his name on a list: "You are allowed to send a postcard of so many lines to your closest relatives. You are entitled to get a food parcel, weighing three kilos, for Christmas. You may give the prison as your address, and mention your sentence; but nothing else concerning prison conditions or politics is allowed to be written. About further communication with your relatives, including perhaps visits in prison, you will get information in due course."

I still had to spend more than two years under lock and key after that news had been broken to us and, as far as my person is concerned, a long stretch of time in quite extraordinarily bad conditions. But this must not obscure the fact that after 1953 prison life was incomparably less bad than in the Stalinist peak years. The prisoner felt that he was not completely at the mercy of anyone who happened to wear a blue-lapelled uniform. Though maltreatment occasionally recurred, corporal punishment on the whole was abolished. Communication at least had become possible with human beings who enjoyed the right to open and lock their rooms when they liked and to have a stroll in the streets. To get a whiff of it was more than we had dared to dream of. The period of rotting alive had come to an end.

This seems to contradict what I said about our dreams of liberation. But it is not the sole contradiction one experiences in observing oneself. We were sanguine and daring in our day-dreams but intimidated in our real dreams. While in prison, I had dreams about the years before my arrest as though nothing had happened. I had dreams of prison-life. I had a strange series of dreams in which I was to be sent on leave from prison or, for instance, allowed to walk by myself from Gyüjtö to Markó utca. Such absurd situations so often returned in my dreams that even while sleeping I argued about them with myself. "What nonsense," I thought in my dream, "how often I have caught myself indulging in such fantasies. But how strange, this time it is true." And so I thought until I woke. Never did I see myself in dreams as properly released from prison, and only on one occasion as escaped from prison. I threw aside my frieze jacket which could give me away, and in my ragged shirt I was running across a bridge. In panic, and panting with exhaustion, I reached a park where some sort of fair was going on. I did not dare to join the crowd but sat down on a bench in a dark corner and wondered where I might get hold of a little money. How could I try to slip out of this country or at least find an abode for cold nights to come, without approaching others who would either denounce me or endanger themselves? It was a nightmare. Waking and finding myself safe on the smelly straw-sack, I was quite relieved though ashamed of my cowardice which had given itself away.

The replies to our post-cards and the first parcels were a greater gift than any dream with which we had hitherto comforted ourselves. "My wife alive." "My children alive." "My family apparently getting on quite well . . . In a country town, as they have probably been deported, but they have apparently taken it quite well." The first peeps out of a crypt. The first bits of food recalling a white table-cloth over which it could be eaten, and a wife or mother who could have cooked it. However hungry we were for choice bits, the messages conveyed by the parcels moved us more than the pleasure of eating them. "I don't want to ask anything from them, I am sure they are almost starving themselves," one prisoner would say. "You can't do this to *them*," we would reply, "how miserable they would be if they heard of others sending in parcels, and not being able to do this for you." We were right. All friends of all our relatives were only too glad to contribute to these despatches, however bad living conditions in Hungary were. Amongst my friends, something like a competition was going on to that effect. The post officials, seeing that a parcel was addressed to the prison, were never reluctant to write on it "3 kg.," however much it weighed.

The ordinary convict's food remained very bad till the end of my captivity. But some slight improvements even in that were a godsend. The reappearance of ordinary potatoes on our diet, instead of the dehydrated black stuff, was received with cries of triumph. Every week would present us with such marvels. A medical inspection was arranged at the Little Hotel. A friend returning from it dashed at me: "Go at once and report some illness. A nice-looking woman, smelling of *eau-de-Cologne* and saying 'please' to us. Never seen such a medical N.C.O. before. You mustn't miss it." I did not. Indeed, though a little plump, she was quite pretty. She said "won't you sit down? What's wrong?" It was a miracle. The first human word for years. And not only human but feminine. I confess I wrote a poem to her.

Imre Nagy made a fashion of being human. Rákosi had to join in. He did so in his own style. He denounced the "mistakes made in the last few years" as the machinations of bandits with whom he had nothing to do. They had simply deceived him. He was undeceivable but all the same it had happened. Moscow ordered *rapprochement* with Jugoslavia. Rákosi made a speech courting Jugoslavia. There had only been misunderstandings between our two Socialist countries, and he, Rákosi, had been misled by the "Gábor Péter gang." The interrogations about the practices of that gang were going on. But Zionist-Cosmopolitan conspiracy, and links with I.S. and U.D.B.A., had suddenly dropped out of the agenda. Interrogators started asking us about the tortures we had undergone at No. 60. It was the Gang that had violated Socialist Legality. A gang of left-wing deviators, sectarians, dogmatists and, by the by, gangsters. How could Rákosi and the whole Party leadership have been aware of all that?

Gábor Péter behaved quite bravely under arrest. It was his good fortune to be treated better than he had treated others. Now it was Socialist Legality; maltreatment of detainees had to be reduced, at any rate, to the extent of being unnoticeable. He made great rows on his way along the passage and shouted "Rákosi knew about everything! Now he wants to smear all the dirt on me!" No less plucky though somewhat more rhetorical was his comrade-wife, née Jolán Simon, arrested simultaneously with him. She would shout: "Justice to Jolán Simon!"

However great a blessing the Thaw was, it did not spare us new A.V.H. mysteries and new personal tragedies. A number of prisoners including every alien and several Hungarians were suddenly divided from the rest, put into a separate wing of a building, and denied the right to communicate with anyone outside. The prisoners called this special wing "the ghetto." Whatever the reason for this increased vigilance about aliens, we could never find out why Hungarian subjects were included. In the next years, most of them were taken out of the ghetto, again without apparent reasons. I had myself been shifted into an odd kind of semi-ghetto. All rights now due to the average prisoner were granted to me, except that of receiving a visitor. This curtailing of my rights was the more astonishing as I had been amongst the few who could from time to time exchange letters with their relatives in the Stalin period. But to see them seemed very dangerous. Only about a year and a half later did a prison Commander by an oversight allow my sister to come and see me, and once the rule had been broken, the visits continued as a routine.

Tragedies were in store for those who had permission to notify their closest relatives, but received no answer. The wife of Péter Mód (at the time of writing this the representative of the Budapest Government at U.N.O.) turned out to have killed herself after her husband's arrest. The wife of Imre Vajda (also a high official of the present régime in Hungary) had died in her place of deportation. Parents and wives of many prisoners had met the same fate. Some prisoners knew their relatives to be alive but were unable to see them because for financial reasons they were unable to leave the country place to which they had been confined in the years of Rákosi's dictatorship. Some learned that their families were living in stables, huddled together with other deportees. Some learned that their children had been ill and refused admittance to a hospital on account of their father's "crime." Wives turned out to have divorced their husbands and remarried. One of the wives bravely resisted the Party pressure to divorce until she saw her husband again. Then, after two or three prison visits, she told him she no longer felt able to live with him: they must divorce. A young colonel of the traffic police was released after four of five years' imprisonment. He only spent one week at large. Finding that his wife had deserted him, he shot himself.

Most astounding was the news of babies who had disappeared. This only happened, as far as I know, in "Titoist-Trotskyite" families, particularly when both husband and wife had been sentenced. Their babies had for a while been left with grandparents or uncles, but later suddenly a representative of the authority concerned would take and despatch them to unknown destinations. Some of these babies had been born in prison and went to their "safe homes" straight from there. After the release of Titoist-Trotskyites it took a long time to trace these children and to identify them. They had been renamed by the authorities and placed in orphanages without an indication as to their origin.

It was an era of hope and relief but also of embarrassment and indecision. Most embarrassed among the prisoners were those few who had been and remained all the time diehard Stalinists. They had thought it their duty to take the blame on themselves for the crimes never committed. They would argue that they had been traitors and would be hurt by anyone doubting it. Now the news was leaking through that all these farcical allegations were to be done away with. The friends of Tito's Jugoslavia were to be vindicated. Did that mean relief for all those involved? The thing was not so simple as that. Those who had excelled in self-denigration "in the service of the Party" were now blamed for having given a helping hand to the violators of Socialist Legality. If they held to the ideas disseminated from Moscow, as they always would, they had to plead guilty again now though for opposite reasons.

Most amusing was the chaos noticeable in the A.V.H. *vamzer* camp. In the time-honoured slang of Hungarian prison life, the German sounding word of obscure origin, *vamzer,* means the prisoner used by the gaolers for spying on other prisoners. In a state where practically all citizens are encouraged, if not compelled, to *vamz* on one another, it was no surprise to see that the same technique was applied under the direct supervision of the A.V.H. The prison authorities cajoled and forced in this way practically everybody they could get hold of. They would first, for instance, invite one "just to write a little essay on the state of mind of prisoners" so as "to show good will"; and then, if he consented, press him further and blackmail him with what he had already revealed. Later, they would get tired of him and suddenly drop his services. Prisoners supposed to have been favoured for a while for such services were later found in most lamentable positions.

Suspicions that one or another prisoner was acting as *vamzer* were going round all the time both in the Stalinist years and afterwards. I should add that I could never get these suspicions confirmed—except when the case was so obvious that there could be no question of mere suspicion. As a matter of fact, the dividing line could not always be clearly drawn between the man who told something in terror or embarrassment, and another who really denounced his fellow prisoners methodically. Many, no doubt, used this as an opportunity to harm their political or racial enemies. In the Stalinist years, everybody was offered such opportunities. Nazis claimed they had heard Trotskyite and pro-British talk from Jews and Reds. Communists reported on reactionary remarks made by non-Communists; they concentrated their hatred on branches of the old aristocracy, former capitalists, clergymen, Horthyite military officers and Social Democrat Leaders. There was one good thing in these denunciations: they cancelled each other out. I cannot judge how often harm was caused to a prisoner by such reports but on the whole they were useless because, fortunately, all *vamzers* lied and the authorities were thus unable to get a truthful picture from them. In some prison-blocks, raids were organized on "Zionists," that is, Jews, by Nazi war criminals who assisted the gaolers; and the "Marxist-Leninist gaolers"—usually subconscious or quite conscious Jew-haters—watched these performances with broad grins. In Vác a most privileged convict, a former S.S. man, beat up a former colonel of the International Brigade shouting at him "Now, sir, you will get what you deserve" and the gaolers found this very amusing. On the other hand, I knew of people who were "short-ironed" for anti-Jewish and anti-Communist remarks after being denounced by a Jewish Communist cell-mate. When the authorities had to decide whether to torture someone or not, they decided for torture, and so far as that went neither occasional nor professional *vamzing* was fruitless. But as a detector of the prisoners' state of mind it completely failed; the sole fact which emerged was that the prisoners on the whole hated their gaolers—which could be guessed without special investigations anyway.

Further complications in the A.V.H. *vamzing* machinery arose after the Thaw had started. These were aggravated by struggles which had been going on within the A.V.H. Apart from controversies touching higher regions of politics, as for instance between Gábor Péter's followers and his enemies, there were departmental antagonisms due to the organizational structure of the A.V.H. within each prison. Broadly speaking, there were three A.V.H. hierarchies working side by side or rather against one another. There was the ordinary gaolers' organization, with a Prison Commander at the top and lance-corporals at the bottom. There were the officers of the "Economic bureau," in charge of the various industrial plants and other enterprises run within the prisons. And there was the "Operative Unit," an A.V.H. within the A.V.H. The "Operatives" were appointed to watch the A.V.H. gaolers from a political point of view and also to interrogate prisoners about them. Confidential political tasks were given by the Operatives behind the back of the Prison Commander. They were therefore hated by the A.V.H. men, just as the A.V.H. were hated by the ordinary soldiers and policemen.

The Thaw brought these antagonisms to a head. Some of the ill-famed favourites of the A.V.H. officers now made a parade of their defiance. There were two brothers, both from the Nazi branch of Horthy's political police, who for years had been the pets of the leader of the Operative Unit at Gyüjtö. One was a prison barber, and the other the chief domestic prisoner supervising the stores, the cleaning of cells and passages, and the distribution of food. Especially the latter. When the great cauldron of soup arrived in the prison block, he took a canful of its fat, for frying. He took several cans full of meat for himself and his favourites on any occasion, and often only its gravy reached the ordinary prisoner. As he had got special facilities for frying, he and his friends could arrange Lucullan feasts while their fellow-prisoners starved. These circulated as scandalous stories: understandably, they shocked prisoners more than the actions of their gaolers. Then, like so many Thaw stories, the news spread that a gaoler had severely reprimanded the Chief Domestic for trying to skim the soup—and that was the end of it. The two brothers fell out of favour. In the Thaw period they were allowed, as other prisoners were, to volunteer for work in the mines. They did so. An Operative who attended the interviews intervened: "You are not allowed to leave." "Why am I not? I want to." "Shut your mouth, you. . . ." and an unprintable expletive followed. The former Chief Domestic, in a fury, reciprocated: "You persecute me because I am unwilling to act as your *vamzer*," he shouted. I am not aware of further developments, but as far as I know, no greater harm was done to him.

Another gaolers' favourite was, like many, a prison barber, and incidentally one with quite a good record in that trade. Before the war he had been a hairdresser and masseur in a fashionable beauty parlour in what could be called the West End of Budapest. He was a stout man with huge belly and remarkable muscles, a heavy body with light fingers—doubtless destined for the job. But he wanted something else. After the Russian occupation he emerged as an A.V.H. captain. Some of my fellow prisoners, now shaved by him, had been arrested by him. For his affiliation with the "Gábor Péter gang," he was imprisoned on account of financial rackets previously encouraged. My friends warned me about talking to him: "you know he is a *vamzer*." I never thought it worth being cautious when talking to suspected or real *vamzers*. I knew they would report whatever they liked, and a suspicious reticence would only induce them to invent more lies about me. Besides, such a career interested me. I chatted to him in a friendly way. "Look here," I told him after an exchange of dirty stories about mutual friends, the actresses who used to be his customers, "you had in that beauty parlour quite an agreeable job, fingering the prettiest necks in Hungary and making quite a good living. What on earth made you leave that and change into that bloody uniform?" On such occasions he would lose his taste for ribaldries and answer pompously: "Fingering pretty necks was no ambition for a lifetime. History will vindicate us." I knew he had wanted an even better living and was a snob like so many "revolutionaries." He loved the captain's uniform. Even when imprisoned he could not conceal his pride in having worn it. Anyway he made no secret of his loyalty to Communism, even when the Thaw started. Everyone knew of his frequent interviews with the head of the Operative.

He was appointed Chief Domestic of the Gyüjtö hospital and granted a comfortable little separate room. His fellow domestics noticed he was scribbling all the time. In a tactful way, they drew the gaolers' attention to this. After all, gaolers had the right to search even a Chief Domestic's cell. They may not have dared in Stalin's time but now it was Socialist Legality. They read the handwriting found under his pillow, and the result was sensational. It contained denunciations not only of the prisoners but also of the prison staff. The head physician of the hospital was accused of harbouring "perfectly healthy reactionaries," and several officers and N.C.O.s were de-

nounced for lack of vigilance about the machinations of
Fascists, Social Democrats and other criminals. It was
not really very different from what might have been expected but the gaolers were shocked and—this was the
new feature—professed to be shocked. They formally
complained to the Commander who was known to detest
the Operative no less than they did. But he could not decide at once what to do.

Some of the gaolers decided without him. Particularly
one, called Pintér, mentioned above as a chief beater up.
A straightforward and single-minded torturer, he always
hated the Operatives. Besides, since the Imre Nagy
speech, he had shown willingness to make amends for his
past. What amends could he offer? Only another beating
up—this time of one whom the prisoners hated as much
as the ordinary gaolers. The *vamzer* thus caught was
beaten half-dead by Sergeant Pintér and his associates.
This was the sole spectacular instance of corporal punishment since its abolition *de jure*.

By the summer of 1954 most of the Communist prisoners had disappeared from Gyüjtö, and rumour had it
that many of them had been released, some solemnly rehabilitated and put into important posts. Kádár was
among the first to be set free, but the exculpation of Rajk
was still far ahead. That was a point, Rákosi felt, on
which he could not give in without detriment to himself.
He declared now that the Tito-Rajk conspiracy had been
a mere invention, concocted by the "Gábor Péter gang,"
but that the accusations against Rajk as a Horthy police-
spy and as an American agent were unfortunately true.
The levels of truth to be accepted were changing all the
time.

I was still frequently interrogated by the A.V.H., with
regard to Communists, but this time with the idea of
exculpating them. Mostly they were new interrogators,
speaking sardonically about the accusations extorted by
their predecessors. I was questioned about my former
cell-mate, and erstwhile colleague on the staff of the
B.B.C., George Pálóczi-Horváth. "Do you know of his
having had a share in the protest of writers against the

racial law in 1938?" Of course I knew. It had never been denied. But between 1949 and 1953, it used to be referred to as an act of divergency manipulated by the anti-Soviet bourgeoisie to deceive the working classes. "The Gábor Péter gang"—with a Jewish majority in its leadership—gleefully delivered the one-time protectors of persecuted Jews to its Nazi staff. The new interrogators were as a rule young gentiles of proletarian origin, and it was their task to do justice to the victims of that sordid mania. "Finally I have to ask you a question which you may find strange," the Interrogator apologetically said: "What was the connexion between the B.B.C. and the Secret Service?" I answered that the security agencies had their own observers, especially during the war, at the B.B.C., but to suppose that the Corporation had at any time been run by them was nonsense. "Of course, I know that," the Interrogator readily replied, "I just wanted to have this confirmed." Co-existence had been put on the agenda.

The rehabilitating interrogations often struck me as no less absurd than had been the inculpating ones. I was asked to reconfess about several people. The Interrogator drew up the minutes with ease: "My former confession on the subject was made under threats and as a result of physical maltreatment. . . ." My overgrown sensibility about accuracy induced me to contradict him: "On that particular occasion I was not maltreated." "But you were maltreated before, weren't you?"—he replied. "O, certainly." "Well then, OK. Why should it make any difference whether it was on that occasion or another one?" I agreed that he was after all right.

The saddest of my "rehabilitating" depositions concerned my late friend, the poet Endre Havas. He was the ugliest and most awkward charmer I knew. A horse-like jaw, a high and concave forehead, a slim and nervous body, its limbs scarcely fitted together, he hobbled about in life feverishly, driven by an incessant enthusiasm. The objects of his enthusiasm changed from time to time but not its substance: he wanted to belong somewhere and was forever making fantasies about the various camps he chose to join.

In the Horthy régime, as a young man, he joined the literary *avant-garde* and, shortly afterwards, the underground Communist movement. The political police caught and ill-treated him but as he was strong enough to be silent, he was released without trial. The *avant-garde* group, in the meantime, stopped being *avant-garde;* and he got disillusioned about Communism. The outbreak of the Second World War found him in Paris, an admirer of Roger Martin du Gard (whose novels he had translated into Hungarian) and a believer in the Fight for Freedom against Fascism. He was embittered against Stalin because of the Pact between Germany and Russia. Only the persecution of Communists then going on in France kept him from passionately turning against them; he could not let them down while they were persecuted. After the collapse of France, he succeeded in escaping to North Africa and later, assisted by British military units, in reaching London. At the time of his arrival, war had already been going on for months between Germany and Russia.

It was at that time that I became friends with him. He was an endearing personality, able both to convey his enthusiasm and amicably to share in a laugh at it. His limbs and voice trembling, his face and eyes shining, his emotions always at a temperature above average, he ran about between the various Free Hungarian headquarters, searching for the road of revolutionary salvation. "I've decided I'll join Károlyi," he reported; "whatever his errors, he is the man I can believe in." He became Károlyi's secretary and was to assist him, in various capacities for years to come.

The war going on, and the prestige of Russia growing, Havas rediscovered his Bolshevik sympathies. He was a man unable to support anything without engaging his heart; and who would not have supported the Bolsheviks at that time? He fell in love with the Red Army and, simultaneously, with a Hungarian refugee woman whose very existence drove him further towards Lenin. This was less from her personal influence, than her background. She was the daughter of a well-known Hungarian artist. Both her brother and her sister were artists. In her early youth, she had been involved in the underground Communist movement, as had her sister and brother and most of their circle. She had suffered from the political police, and from private sorrows. She landed in England as one making port after a shipwrecked youth. She was living in an English country town, working as a factory clerk, without showing any desire to be entangled in movements again, when Havas met her; and after marrying him she became, in the course of years, a flawless housewife and mother, concerned with politics mainly because her family interests had by then been vested in it.

Havas himself was a devoted husband and father, a man full of tenderness and coveting the atmosphere of home life. The more he became tossed about by fate, worn down by misadventure, and far from his homeland, the more he needed that. What we call home life is *bourgeois* home life. More or less everybody needs it because everybody is more or less a bourgeois, and Havas was fundamentally that. He would deny it but his most endearing ways gave him away. He had always been fascinated by Rimbaud; and as soon as he got hold of Aragon's Resistance poems he set about translating them, and would forever recite and quote them, his cheeks glowing, his chest panting. But in his own poetry, his best verses resembled neither Rimbaud nor Aragon; they resembled Francois Coppée. His vision of the Workers of the World Uniting was but an expanded substitute for family surroundings which he seemed to have lacked in early youth, for a home providing him with the sense of security, warmth, and self-respect. Those Workers of course were an abstraction; though he had as an underground Communist dutifully distributed leaflets in the Budapest factory districts, and later entertained charwomen and junior clerks in the London Hungarian Club, these were not the workers he was anxious to unite with. What he dreamt of was turners, bricklayers, and Maquis, converted to highbrow poetry-reading, and Villons and Rimbauds converted to virtue. Once exploitation of man by man was at an end, they would all settle down as breadwinners and join hands, and praise the Red Army happily ever after.

In keeping such high moral standards, one has to become either intellectually dishonest or mad. Poor Endre Havas was spared neither of these alternatives. After the end of hostilities, he woke up as one intermarried with the ruling political caste in Hungary. All his new relatives were about to drop, if they had not dropped yet, their pre-war Café Dôme manners and their Bloomsbury sneers at patriotic duties and military distinctions. Now they were all united in applauding the Liberators, in holding good jobs and, particularly from 1948 onwards, in Socialist Realism. Havas went all the way with them, and further. As he was fond of me, he resented my hesitation over the same path. My sceptical support for the Government was not the sort of thing he expected from one worthy of Uniting. I had no doubt about his pangs of conscience. They could only be silenced by adopting theories ever more obscure, together with devices ever less fastidious. In a way, and for a while, this helped him to display quite valuable faculties, hitherto unsuspected in him. As a Counsellor of Legation in Paris, assisting Count Michael Károlyi, he proved to be not only a punctual civil servant and amiable colleague, but, indeed, a good diplomat. His main task was to ward off anti-Soviet influences from his chief; but he did this so tactfully and showed, when not prevented by Party politics, so much helpfulness to any honest endeavour that even the Countess, the anti-Soviet pole in the Count's surroundings at that time, had a tender spot in her heart for the man she called "our *Eminence rouge.*"

Diplomats have been defined as "respectable spies." Where a spy's respectability ends, may be open to argument. A diplomat submerged in Stalinism would certainly consider as respectable anything which was useful to the Party. The two Communist Counsellors of Legation, serving under Count Károlyi in Paris, Péter Mód and Endre Havas, rendered services, without the knowledge of their Chief, to some authorities concerned with collecting information of a not strictly diplomatic character. They had both been summoned to Budapest for reporting when, in the early summer of 1949, the Hungarian Minister in Paris was notified from the Quai d'Orsay that both were considered *persona non grata*. This coincided with the moment of Mód's arrest—as an agent of the Deuxième Bureau. He was one of "Rajk's accomplices."

Havas used to admire both Rajk and Mód; he regarded them as model Communists. Their arrest shook him. "That must be a misunderstanding; they must be released very soon, you will see," he stuttered. When I met him that summer in Budapest, he had already succeeded in persuading himself that "the Party knows what it is doing." In June, "they must have made tragic errors"; in July, "they must have been traitors"; in August, he said: "First I was sorry for them but now I have only contempt for them." He himself was to stay in Budapest, as a publisher's reader, in the self-deceptive happiness of "being at last united" with everybody he cared for. At the very beginning of September, I told him of the arrest of the London Hungarian Club leaders. His big jaw fell, and he gazed at the wall.

About one and a half years later, in Vác, we would now and then hear hoarse and frantic shouts: "Help! Help! Long live Stalin! Long live the Soviet Union! Help! Help!" Then the blows of truncheons, and inarticulate cries and moans. The prisoner was apparently either beaten or doped into swooning. That was my friend Endre Havas. After his arrest, he had gone mad. His madness consisted in an inability to believe in the madness of others. He was obsessed with a mania that his gaolers were White terrorists and that he was the victim of a counter-revolutionary plot. I was not astonished by such a delusion, as I had had similar ideas myself. At 60 Andrássy ut, in my underground cell, when recalling how keen my hearers were on spotting "Trotskyites" among their comrades and "liquidating" them, I wondered whether a White conspiracy had not surreptitiously taken over and, the following night, watched to see whether the saints of Marxism-Leninism, including Rákosi, were still visible on the walls. I found their portraits there unharmed, and later recalled this mad guess of mine with irony.

Havas waited in vain for the relieving detachments of the Red Army. Instead, he was visited by the gaolers, most incensed by such "impudent provocation," and by their Nazi assistants, the prison barber and chief domestic, who were only too glad to thrash a Communist. Havas, with his conspicuous appearance and the typical awkwardness of an intellectual, was a tempting target. They dragged him about and played football with his body. He was left lying in his excrement for days. Officers and N.C.O.s and privileged prisoners all agreed that he was just pretending. After being transferred to Gyüjtö he calmed down but got no saner. He would mumble some incoherent sentences; such as "Farkas wanted me to . . . but I refused. . . ." He also mentioned "Károlyi"; apparently, they had wanted to extort a confession from him inculpating his former chief. Then, for two or three days he would mumble "My lips will be sealed." He kept to this. He got quite apathetic. The gaolers tired of beating him and let him lie about on the bunk. Once Péter Mód, doing some domestic work, succeeded in calling in to him: "Hello, Endre." He seemed not to recognize him and gave no answer. In 1952, the Authorities concerned came at last to the conclusion that he might not be "pretending." He was taken to a prison hospital. After minor troubles— hunger strikes and attempts at suicide by throwing himself on the floor—he seemed to have improved. But when the Thaw came, he was already dead.

And now, face to face with a young proletarian who had to rehabilitate by dozens the victims of Personality Cult and of deviation from Legality, it was for me to explain what an impeccable Communist the late poet had been. It was the routine procedure. "A poet, a Communist of deep convictions" he put down on his typewriter, respectfully and with some spelling mistakes. He prompted me with what to say, and I readily complied; his widow and two orphans should at least enjoy the benefits of Communist rehabilitation. What an ordeal the past few years must have been for them, in an environment where people were unwilling to believe in the innocence of anyone imprisoned.

"So he didn't work for I.S.," the Interrogator said after concluding his minutes.

"Of course not."

"But you said he was your friend, and you certainly were an I.S. agent, weren't you?"

"Of course I was not."

The Interrogator made the angry face which A.V.H. officers thought compulsory even when offering a gesture of good-will: this was an aspect of discipline. "Well, weren't you condemned as an I.S. agent?"

"I was, but on false charges."

"Then why the hell didn't you apply for a revision of your trial?"

"I wondered. . . ."

"If you don't do it at once it may be too late." Obviously it was a message from higher quarters.

Indeed there had already been rumours for months that it was now the Social Democrats' turn, and then the Smallholders would follow . . . Imre Nagy would leave no fake sentences unaltered.

"Thank you for your advice, sir; I shall hand in my application to the Prison Commander."

At the end of October, 1954, together with a load of Socialist convicts, I was dispatched in a lorry to the political police headquarters, "P.V.," for the revision of my case.

Chapter 10

God, Sex, Immortality

THREE defences have been invented against death: belief in God, in fame, and in birth. An agnostic by nature, I have never shared these beliefs. Many of my fellow prisoners discovered the Infallibility of the Pope, or the existence of a Divine Force above the Universe, or immortal souls in themselves, when nothing else, not even wishful News, was forthcoming to alleviate their suffering and despair. My good-natured friend who had once been a colonel in the traffic police, found solace in spiritualism and theosophy; and thanks to the interest shown by certain Marxist-Leninist gaolers in the messages arriving through a shaky prison table from deceased relatives, his indulgence in illicit research among the spirits was benevolently ignored. But this did not prevent him from killing himself when he found that his wife no longer loved him. My scientific friends in the Engineering Unit told me that the more they learned of the construction of the atom, or of the behaviour of the galaxies, the more they were induced to share the faith of one or another pious and uneducated flock; but when I asked why, they repeated the neat and distant arguments of some modern physicists and astronomers—about particles too tiny for men to predict their moves, or about the finiteness of the world, or the impossibility of proving the non-existence of God. I should have liked to be convinced by them; not only because a celestial consolation would have been welcome at that moment, but even more because I like to agree with the persecuted. But my sense of logic protested.

I have remained equally sceptical about the two secular creeds which ought to reconcile us with the idea of disappearing from life. Posterity may for a while remember a name, and children and grand-children may wear it; genes may outlast a hundred generations, and statues of stone may survive their creators; all this does not save us from dissipating into unconsciousness. So why bother about either moral or biological survival? Why take so much care with such symbols as a poem or a child? My scepticism about them was enhanced by natural laziness and a liking for independence.

In the summer of 1949, shortly before my arrest, when I felt my end might be approaching, I suddenly caught myself reacting differently. My opinions remained unaltered but not my desires. Verses started moulding themselves in my brain. I regretted that there would be neither a *magnum opus* nor a small baby left behind if I were to vanish. It was of course a stupid desire and I knew it to be so. It was also utterly irresponsible as far as the baby was concerned; it would have been an orphan. But I could not help longing for it and was sorry to have had no children in England. I was determined to have one in Hungary. I became passionate about it, and could not decide whether it was my disintegration or my rebirth which had begun; but I felt interested enough in myself to decide that I should go to the end of it. Previously, however much I loved a woman, I never thought she might bear me a child. Now I watched all women as potential breeding mares. I picked out a young girl who I thought might do perfectly though I was far from being in love with her. I had an appointment with her for the day following my arrest.

Prison life strengthened this longing. My coevals got photographs of their grandchildren. One baby was like another to me, all were charming and impersonal pictures, of token lives rather than human beings. Symbols, tokens —but what else had been left to us? The female sex itself had shrunk to an algebraic formula. I could also use the word "grown" instead of "shrunk," it had acquired both the unreality and the greatness of dreams.

Dreams are fairy-like and carnal. In the promiscuity of the prison cells, it is their carnal nature that gets more conspicuous. It starts with the crisp patches on blankets distributed by the storekeepers, continues with dirty stories, told often in a shy and avid *tremolo,* and ends in confidences. "I confess I masturbated . . ." a friend once started telling me but I pretended not to hear him, and he shut up. What is the use of learning what one could guess anyway? The frequency depended on age, and the opportunities to do it unnoticed, and on certain personal factors. But psychologically it was too much needed to be dispensed with by anybody. It could be done without guilt; without, at any rate, any feeling that it was the unwillingness of suitable partners that had prompted it. For some, it must have been quite a relief. Others, and perhaps most, were crippled by the years passed in artificial seclusion. A sturdy young Jugoslav, a lady killer second to none, was near committing suicide when, after his release, he discovered that he was impotent. As his testicles had been beaten hard by the A.V.H., he thought his deficiency might be organic and could perhaps never be cured. But it turned out to have been psychological; and once the difficulty was overcome, he went on "killing ladies" happily ever after.

Sex life in prison was nearest to normal among the homosexuals. They were a special group, who, though raided and dispersed several times, managed to get together again and again, either in the dormitories or the workshops. I presume they must have suffered a good deal because of their inclinations; the gaolers were glad to double their cruelty with anyone in whom they discovered a corporal disability or abnormality, and they must have trebled it when they had a right to do so on "moral" grounds. But this is just my assumption. What I came across was two or three youths with chubby cheeks, wagging hips, in the best clothes obtainable from the depot, allowed to grow longer hair than the rest and making ample use of this permission. One was a storekeeper, the other a Deputy Chief Domestic; they had frequent opportunities to meet; according to public opinion, they were all *vamzers,* accomplices not in sexual offences only. This may not have applied to all homosexuals but it certainly did to some.

Incurable heterosexuals, like myself, were confined to erotic symbolism. They lived in dreams and recollections. They would glare at a uniformed female, a gaoler or a nurse, and wonder whether these could be female beings indeed. Most of them were extremely coarse, in looks, manners, and feelings alike. But not all. I have mentioned one pleasant exception and could mention more. They were not, as a rule, ugly; an extremely pretty blonde, known to be cruel particularly with women prisoners, had been a street prostitute until that calling was officially abolished. The prisoners would say about all of them that they had been prostitutes, but in such allegations allowance must of course be made for spiteful thinking. Some of the women gaolers struck one as ideal lower-middle-class housewives, with broad country accents and precise manners. Such was, for instance, the supervisor of the depot at Gyüjtö. Suddenly she was removed: her superiors had found out that she had betrayed her husband with a handsome Chief Domestic. But such cases were rare.

Altogether the A.V.H. uniform worn by women acted as a deterrent, or at least as a question-mark for male prisoners.

Then, there were the female fellow-prisoners. They could hardly ever be seen but their existence was constantly emanating from day-to-day trivialities. We knew they were in our neighbourhood. Everything we knew about them made them appear dirty, humiliated and denaturalized, even more than ourselves. What must they have suffered! How strong they must have been to survive! Their very wretchedness transformed them into mythical personalities in our minds. Now and then, on the day when clean linen was distributed, one of us would get a pair of woman's pants by accident; a coarse and ragged piece of underwear, a pathetic caricature of the sex for which it was destined. Giggling and reveries started at its sight. "I decided," a prison barber told me (one who, unlike many of his colleagues, was surely no *vamzer*) "to marry no one but a woman prisoner." Many felt like that. There was some pity in this feeling, and comradeliness; but more of a nostalgia for the miraculous. Women as our equals in that state were a miracle even greater than the whole world outside from which we had been cut off.

There were odd minutes when they could be seen. When led to and from the hospital, one would see four or five women in frieze turned with their faces to the wall. For hours after one would try to guess what they looked like. In the hospital, facing the Little Hotel, women were treated as well as men. One prisoner doctor was caught by the cruel blonde woman gaoler when he was about to deliver a letter from a female prisoner to a male comrade. A tragedy followed; not only because all three of them were punished but because the letter-writer had already promised by the same channels to be the faithful wife of another male comrade. This amounted to adultery.

There was a period when, in two groups, some eight or ten women prisoners of the hospital made their daily walk in the courtyard visible from the Little Hotel. Before this started, the gaolers shouted "All windows to be closed, everybody off the window." Needless to say, everybody sneaked to the window. It was indeed an exhilarating and at the same time a weird sight: that they did exist indeed. Despite the watchfulness of both men and women gaolers, partnerships developed through the air. The most untiring creeper-to-the-window was the deaf young painter. He quickly fell in love with a Jugoslav girl, alleged to have been a spy. His love story became a matter of common knowledge, talked about and made fun of by gaolers and prisoners alike. Notwithstanding the ban on peeping, he drew a coloured picture of the women prisoners walking in the courtyards. The gaolers were delighted with it and turned a blind eye to his peeping. They thought art more important than vigilance.

That was the limit of the prisoners' share of everything which in the world outside could have made them lechers, lovers, fathers. It was a universe of sex-substitutes. I do not say that it was uninteresting; it revealed the skeleton of one's own feelings. I wish everyone could be spared the ordeals which led me to that experience, but I feel it was an experience worth having. It was like discovering religion in my flesh. My vision, a condensed projection of prison dreams, was fairy-like and carnal. It was a wish to be united with someone who would come. A wish to be born again by being united.

Chapter 11

"I Voman"

At "P.V." after my transfer for the revision of my case . . . I was alone in my cell, but no matter: I was offered books to read, and pencil and paper to make notes if I liked. The electric bulb above the door had to be on all night, as this was the regulation in all police prison buildings; Thaw or no Thaw, prisoners before trial could not be trusted not to attempt suicide. But the gaolers assured me that in my case that was a mere formality, I should be allowed to hide my face in the pillow at night. I was given fifteen cigarettes and matches per day, and the same food

as the gaolers—"sanatorium" once again. This time, even
the gaolers behaved as though they were my hired atten-
dants rather than my masters. No wonder: many convicts
who had in the last eighteen months arrived in circumstances similar to mine, were subsequently released and
now serving in high posts. Kádár stepping from solitary
confinement, as it were overnight, into the Party secretary-
ship of the most important industrial district . . . The
gaolers were not keen on running risks by bullying those
who might emerge as their superiors next week. "If you
want anything, kindly tell us" was how they received me.

In spite of the prospects of release, I went on training
myself in caution. I must not allow myself to be carried
away by dreams lest I should be disappointed. Let me
concentrate on the benefits of the moment—readable
books and edible food. My neighbour turned out to be a
friend of mine, waiting for his release like myself. He was
waiting less patiently. Knocking over the wall, he would
ask, "Opinion?" Our signature tune was the V-sign,
∪ ∪ ∪ ___, and our question mark a seemingly more
complicated but strikingly rhythmical couple of bars
∪ ∪ ___ ___ ∪ ∪ ___. I confined myself mainly to ex-
changing experiences about books and food. As my friend
had applied for light diet, we had important things to tell
each other. For instance, after lunch. *I:* ∪ ∪ ∪ ___,
He: ∪ ∪ ∪ ___, *I:* "Stuffed paprika tomatosauce poppy-
seed noodles." *He:* "Semolinasoup grillveal mashpotato."
I: "Enjoying Confessions" (by Rousseau, sent in by my
relatives at my request). *He:* "English books obtainable
here, got a Linklater quite amusing." "News ∪ ∪ ___ ___
∪ ∪ ___," *I:* "None. ∪ ∪ ∪ ___," *He:* ∪ ∪ ∪ ___. And a
pause followed till after supper.

My cell was the last in the passage. But I should have
liked to know who my neighbour's neighbour was. "Try
find out," I asked my friend. "Tried he doesn't know how
knock," he replied. In the meantime, we agreed that confidential messages between us should be exchanged in
English rather than in Hungarian though we should keep
to the Hungarian alphabet; *x, y, w* and *q* should be dispensed with. And doubling of vowels and consonants

omitted, whenever possible. "Vont be dificult. Kuite easi inded." My absentmindedness made me a slow knocking-partner. But, thank the Thaw, I could sit quietly on my bunk, paper and pencil in my hands, absorbed by literary notes which I was authorized to make. In such comfort, even our special Hungaro-English was smoothly decipher-able.

A post-meal exchange of, I think, "Sausages" on my part, and "Boiledegs" on my neighbour's, was inter-rupted by an aggressive signature tune, hitherto not in our use. It was the couple of bars most popular with Hungarian football-match audiences and juvenile ap-plauders: __ __ ∪ ∪ __. As it could not come from a neighbour, where could it have come from? One should beware of *agents provocateurs*. My neighbour seemed worried. He turned to English. But the new would-be partner was adamant. "Vho are" we heard over the wall, and then, a succinct introduction: "I voman."

This was enough for us to overcome our reluctance. More detailed introductions followed. She was an old ac-quaintance of my neighbour's, and accommodated now in the cell above his. She said she had met me once in the Hungarian Ministry of Information, but I did not remem-ber, and I was glad I did not. The unknown entity ex-pressed in knocks that arranged themselves on the pattern of "voman"-hood—that was just the thing that appealed to me. It was the living symbol of the sex which I wanted to bear me children.

I had a clear vision of her, clear though partly mistaken. In any case, I tried to check it. I asked both my neighbour and herself about her looks. I was sure she must be a brunette, and she turned out to be ashblond. I was right in assuming that she must be middle-size and slim. I was sure she must have an impertinent little nose. I should have liked to inquire about the matter but since impertinence, as far as noses are concerned, is not identifiable on factual grounds, I refrained from asking questions about it and trusted my imagination.

Impertinence was, at any rate at the onset, her main appeal. It was a challenge for me to break it. It was also a challenge which I felt was made on my behalf, a gesture of comradeship, challenge to the prison walls, to the authorities, and to fate. Not-giving-in consisted in getting round the regulations. It is no easy task to praise her now that she is my wife but I must confess she did it admirably. She chatted with unremitting *élan*. It is fantastic how temperaments reveal themselves in a language as abstract as knocking-over-the-wall. I do not mean the texts; but the technique. Hers was fast and astoundingly self-confident. She would interrupt any sentence by fast knocks suggesting that she knew what the end of it was to be. She either knew or did not. And more often than not, it was hopeless to interrupt her narrative by a "Rep" (eat from . . .) as was usual when one had missed a part of the text; she would not hear anything until she had finished. Communication with me was of course more difficult than with my neighbour right under her cell; and in the first days of what I should call her company, I was just dumbfounded by the shower of her knocks. I thought I might stop listening in from time to time, and go on reading or writing; I could not. I wished she would go to hell. Her proximity permeated me.

Florence had been imprisoned for more than four years. Her story was heartrending. Her mother was an Englishwoman by birth. She herself had never been in Britain but she as well as her mother used to be on friendly terms with some members of the British diplomatic staff in Budapest. After the war, she worked as the secretary, first, to the Minister of Foreign Affairs, and later, to the Minister of Information. When Hungary turned into a People's Democracy she was dismissed from Government service, and when spy-hunting reached its peak, in 1950, she was detained as a British spy. So we were colleagues. But she had been maltreated much more cruelly than I. Her toe nails stamped out, her body almost crippled by beatings, she had first been given a satisfactory but short hospital treatment and then dragged about in the filthy cellars of women's prison camps. When the Thaw started her turn came, and after being transferred to P. V. she could not believe her eyes when books and cigarettes and sausages for breakfast were offered her. But her gratefulness for the "sanatorium" boarding did not last long; once encouraged to hope for an early release, she became impatient with the interrogations and cross-interrogations still going on about her "spy contacts," and vented her feelings in a hurricane of knocks.

When facing the bravery and impertinence of a female one's natural reaction is to break it. The strength of mind of a girl may be impressive but it impresses even more when it is faltering. Strength unbroken is vulgar; it is its lapses into weakness which make it human and feminine. It was the touch of broken-heartedness and the palpable craving for a surrender which made me feel that that girl must be mine. The knocks were showering and showering and I was unable to put aside my pencil and paper on which I reconstructed her words. Now and then I just joined in with some clumsy coquetteries. "Blodi" I heard from her about someone and then let her know that "Mi future vife mustnt talk so." She gave a facetious reply, travestying a well-known love-dialogue from a Hungarian classic play. The joke went on for weeks, undisturbed by the fact that I did mean it. When she had been allowed a visit from her mother I inquired about my "Inlav"; and she after having been given a cell-mate, a recently arrested woman, who had arrived with some wishful news that the Russians were planning to withdraw from Hungary altogether, passed this piece of information on to me as "Engagement present." Once the ball was set rolling it went on its own way. We chose as our special signature tune when knocking to each other a double anapaest ∪ ∪ __ __ ∪ ∪ __.

She told me: "Darling I must confes Ive a child." Love or no love, that was too much. "Iou joke?" I asked. *She:* "No shes caled Dinki and is a dachshund." *I:* "Cheek, gave me a shock." *She:* "Vil iou like mi dogi?" *I:* "Ies and iou never think of other babies?" *She:* "Im mad about real babies." *I:* "Nov seriously Flo do iou vant child bi me?" *She:* "I do." Facetiousness had given way.

It was love at the first lack of sight, as I put it to myself. I had never been able to throw in my lot with anyone I knew; when very much attracted to one or another it was the power of attraction which my nerves resisted. Only the unknown could make me as brave as that. But I had some anxieties. I was twenty-three years her elder. "Sili girl" I told her. *She:* "Vhi am sili?" *I:* "For loving me." *She:* "Dont hurt mi felings." *I:* Could be iour father." *She:* "I dont vant veri ioung husband." Not "very" but I was already 53. Surely not the age of an opera *amoroso.* I felt I was ridiculous but did not care.

Technical hitches often interrupted our interchanges. Apart from stopping after a quick danger sign whenever we heard the boots of the gaolers approaching, voices from outside were frequently too loud for us to out-knock them. There were military exercises in the courtyards. There were madmen or pretenders in the prison-block who would burst out shouting in animal sounds. Most disturbing was the lavatory plug which was pulled in our neighbourhood in the middle of one or another devoted declaration of love. It was a blessing no longer to have the buckets but everything has its disadvantages.

While I tried to explain and to define my own feelings she was concentrated on more practical issues. For instance, how to make use of the fact that we had our weekly shower baths in the same premises—Saturday morning women, Saturday afternoon men. "Betven first and second ribs of radiator vil be a boks for iou" she told me. It was an empty matchbox, only with a lock of her hair in it.

Our main concern was from then onwards the "Bokses." It was no easy matter to exchange them. We needed luck which we did not always have and adroitness such as I had never possessed. Luck was needed because there were two bathrooms. If for three weeks successively she had bathroom No. 1 and I No. 2 our boxes piled up and we could not get hold of them. In No. 2 there was no radiator; the venthole was used instead. That hole was fortunately filled with filthy straw in which the box could be hidden. But one got dirty right up to the elbow when searching for it. Besides, it was only the gaolers' laziness or "lack of vigilance" which enabled us to do so. They should have watched us all the time, and would call in every second or third minute: "Hurry up." I started every shower bath in

No. 1 by slipping a piece of soap under the radiator so that I should be able to pretend I was looking for it if I were caught mucking about underneath. Because of my clumsiness in any manual performance I walked in a stage-fright to these feverishly expected excursions and am still astonished that I got away with it. After one or another successful venture I felt I was a hero; but surely Florence was a greater heroine as on one occasion she sacrificed her bath to get at the depth of the vent-hole and was glad she could at least clean her arms by the time her lady gaoler arrived. One of our boxes had disappeared and, as it happened, the following week no boxes of matches were given to us. Did they discover it, we wondered? We only learned later that this had been due to quite a different thing: an embittered prisoner had set his mattress on fire. This is why the gaolers were ordered not to distribute matches but to give light to the prisoners themselves. As it was too boring a procedure they managed to restore the *status quo ante,* and with it our means of communication.

My first box to her contained a poem, in strict metrical form and rhyme like all my ventures in that branch of literature, but I give here a literal translation:

Through railings, walls and prohibitions
I am grasping her hand
As one who through a nightmare is hearing
Some soft memories,
Memories of a continent never seen before
Where there is no departure but arrival,
And delight rips in the flesh as though it were a pain,
And wakening soothes one's nerves like a dream.
It was the curve of destiny that threw me to her,
It was its whip which chased me to her,
It was destiny turned into my blood which wants me
Never to leave her,
To stand by her in disgrace and blows,
To rest her head on my chest
And to see my face turning beautiful
In that of the child she will bear me.

Mostly the contents of the boxes, as could readily be

guessed, were letters. There was but one exception, on New Year's Eve, when I received a little piece of Palmolive soap just sent in by my "Inlav." I acknowledged it by knocking: "I start this iear vith iour soap and finish it vith iour babi." In spite of my caution I hoped in some months we would be free.

As to the letters I can only say I am glad to have no longer got them with me. I might feel it my duty to print the parts which would make me blush most. My memory will I hope select from them only what makes me blush a little.

I wanted to know about all details of her life, particularly as it was at that moment. How does she dress, how does she wash, does she get hot water and shampoo for washing her hair? Her reply was reassuringly ungrammatical. "My dear Pasha, you have rather unrealistic imaginings about Slaves in prison. Shampoo, here? Cold water and ordinary soap, one can quite well get used to it. At home I used to pull my nose whenever I had to wash something but here I have become quite a wash-bear." The word Slave did not stand for prisoners, but for women. She was Pasha's Slave. Very cheeky in this capacity as I often had reason to point out, but insisting on that qualification. She was, as she said, prepared to serve me but at the same time took it for granted that I should give her the orders which she had ordered me to give.

"I must know all about you," she wrote, "your favourite colour, your favourite authors and composers, your favourite dishes, your favourite fruit, your favourite drink." She also inquired about my "favourite slave" but I dismissed this question by allowing her "three guesses." As to the rest, I tried to give her an honest answer but I am not a man of Yes or No in so far as favourites go. "I am rather an eclectic," I wrote to her, "both by nature and philosophy. Dishes of course are a grave problem. I used to love English breakfasts if properly prepared, with bacon and eggs, and Oxford marmalade, and toast and strong tea. But a *café crème* in Paris with fresh croissants is not contemptible either. In my youth my favourite meat was *rántott csirke* (spring chicken *pané*) with green peas and cucumber, and my favourite sweet dish was *szilvásgombóc* (a Hungarian speciality: dumpling stuffed with plum). But there are so many other meats and other vegetables and other sweets competing with them. My mother used to be a marvellous cook and particularly excelled in preparing *vágotthus*—rissole, as it would be called in London, but I should think it a blasphemy to call it that. She used to make it of goose, veal, beef and pork, with a little goose-liver, and slices of hard-boiled eggs in it. The best fried *scampi* of my life with enchanting green salad, I ate in a modest restaurant at Viareggio (not the spa, but the old village). I have tender recollections of Chinese pancake rolls (stuffed with fried vegetable) though I made their acquaintance in war-time London where they may have been *Ersatz*. Black coffee of course nowhere equals that which you get in any Italian *café-espresso*. I like practically all sorts of alcoholic drinks except those made of mint and the very sweet ones. Fruit: some apples in Britain, such as Cox's Orange Pippin, or plums in Jugoslavia are delicious, but about peaches, apricots and mainly grapes I am rather a jingo. Which to prefer must depend on what is around. At this very moment my wish would be rather modest. I should like to walk out with you from P.V. to the *Lukács fürdö* (an open air swimming pool) five minutes hence, and have a swim either in your company or if you don't feel like it leaving you for a quarter of an hour alone. Then we should go to the next *tejcsarnok* (a kind of milk-bar) and have some white cheese with sour cream and a plateful of scrambled eggs. In the meantime I might wonder what my favourite colour is—the green-grey, which you say is that of your eyes, or that of your hair. At the moment I decide for the latter, for obvious reasons."

We agreed that to lessen the dangers involved we should not write anything of politics or of A.V.H. cruelties. But otherwise the register of our subjects was unlimited. Florence, once in her stride, crowded the sheets so much with tiny letters that I was sometimes hardly able to decipher them in the scanty light of the electric bulb. Recollections of her family and details of her everyday life varied in her letters with most serious problems. Herewith an example of the latter: "Please don't laugh, but I worry a lot about a problem which I can't settle without you. What should the baby be called? I hope you will agree that only a girl-baby can come in question. I don't mind twins, a girl and a boy, but I must have a girl-baby." The names which I subsequently suggested horrified her. Slave rebellion started at once.

One night after a long knocking dialogue a gaoler called in with a broad grin: "Knuckles on your fingers, I suppose?" I pretended not to understand but it was in vain. He had overheard me. "Why the hell do you do such things?" he said. "All right if you think it worth knocking him a Good night, but to go on for hours . . ." I promised him never to do it again. He pretended to believe it. Whether he was an honest chap or simply anxious to avoid controversy with one who might be released as a new Kádár the following day, I cannot decide. As I pointed out, statistically speaking, the decent amongst them were very few but I had never known him before and ought not to pass judgement. His reprimand was really meant to be a warning for caution. My neighbour got the same warning: we did not disclose of course that we had not simply been knocking to each other. "Really I promise, Sir, I shan't do it any more," I said. And then added with a smile of complicity, "Or at any rate not often, it is really not worth while. It was only family matters. But what's the use of taking risks for that. It may be if it were a girl. . . ." The sergeant waved his hand: "O you old men and the girls. Your time has long passed for it." "You are right," I said, "so I promise. . . ."

So we decided to be cautious. We reduced knocking to the minimum. Instead Florence invented another prison language, far more lengthy and cumbersome but it seemed to us safe at that moment. The pushing of the chair would be our signature tune. Three kicks on the wall would be a signal that we could listen. And then we would start walking letters. With awful big bangs we walked all day. After *a* or *b* one had to stop as though petrified and scratch one's head as in a fit of deepest abstraction, lest it should look very unnatural to the gaoler if he happened to peep in.

Z of course gave opportunities for a long though some-times emphatic walk, and then one was most careful to step so that, if possible, one stopped by the window or the door: again, to avoid unnatural gestures. Florence I knew was not a great walker; she regularly shirked the solitary morning walks in the courtyard (fifteen minutes of these were allowed to each prisoner). It amused me that she had now to walk for hours all the same. It was noble of her. For me it was a sacrifice for different reasons. However spoiled we were at that moment of our hoped-for release, I was unable to get a pair of boots which fitted. This was due to inefficiency rather than ill-will but it could not apparently be helped. There were nails sticking up from my heels. This made my pleasure somewhat painful.

More painful, I was again almost caught. My benevolent sergeant showed me a sheet of paper. Some incoherent words were written on it but some I could nevertheless decipher. "Mi love" for instance. "Now what's that?" the sergeant asked me. "No idea," I answered, "these don't make sense." The sergeant, needless to say, did not know English. It was up to him and his fellow gaolers to pass it on to quarters who might know. "Well, I don't know, but you'd better be careful how you walk, you are not alone in this prison and some complain about how loud you do it." He banged the door on my nose. I thought of re-warding him by an invitation card to my wedding later on but I did not know his name.

We could assume we were surrounded by *vamzers* but could not decide to give it up. Our more detailed ex-changes were by now confined to the "Bokses" but infor-mation about the whereabouts of the boxes themselves and other urgent messages had to be delivered at once by stepping hard. Such was my message, after a slave's mutiny, that I would "smack" her. "I don't sugest iou dare" she walked and, on that evening, we went to bed without walking Good Night.

In the first half of March, 1954, she told me about the most recent promise made to her by an Interrogator. She would be released under an amnesty on April 4th (anni-versary of Hungary's liberation from the Nazi rule) and would later have a chance of applying for a revision of her case. I was of course very glad. But farewell is a melancholy affair. I wrote my first and presumably last poem in English:

How can I bear
Losing Washbear?
In three weeks' time, I learn, she will be free;
Within three months she'll have forgotten me.
Forgotten all our calls
Through ceilings, floors and walls;
Our kisses and our talks,
By knocks, by kicks, by walks;
The meetings of our souls,
Through boxes, ribs and holes;
Our arguments and cracks
Concerning hits and smacks;
Our intercourses pending,
And still with happy ending . . .
Her love in solitude arisen
Will vanish once she's left the prison,
Its memory will turn to dust and ashes
Eclipsed by young, and smart and handsome Pashas.

So spoke a voice internal
Sneering with grins infernal
But don't think I believe a word
Of what I heard.
O no, I know for sure,
That that's but nonsense pure,
And that my rapping-stepping pet
Won't me forget.
And so we'll have in June
Defacto honeymoon,
Followed by babies, girl and sonny,
Bright as fullmoon and sweet as honey,
(Presumably though somewhat funny).

This at any rate is the recollection which makes me blush very much; but it has to be printed, not only for the person who inspired these rhymes and surely deserved something better, but for the truth of the record.

In prison I had difficulties with my teeth. Some had to be extracted. As I was careless enough to report them I was several times taken to hospital. On the day I learned of Florence's hopes for release I told her that, as I had heard from the prison doctor, I might be dispatched to the hospital any moment. Danger or no danger, we were walking in a rage. *She:* "In Easter cake vil be leter." *I:* "Dont im afraid it mai involve mi sister." My sister would have brought the cake to me after Florence had been released. I could not finish the sentence as the guard called in for me.

Chapter 12

Hunger-Strike and Mona Lisa

MY shuttle-trips between various prison-blocks reflected the tug-of-war going on between the de-Stalinizers and the Stalinists. It was thawing and freezing, re-thawing and re-freezing all the time. The A.V.H. was a Stalinist stronghold; it did not openly oppose Socialist Legality but sabotaged its implementation. On the morrow of my arrival at P.V. I was interrogated by a young officer, who tried to persuade me that I should now freely confess—if not to the whole, at least to some of the charges for which I had been sentenced. "I confess I am not a Communist," I said, "but this I suppose is no crime under the laws of the People's Republic." "I agree it is not; but I did not ask you about your opinions. The question is, what were your reasons for gathering information about Hungary. . . ." After two such sessions, nothing more happened in that direction. The interrogator very politely reassured me: "The fact that you are here means that your case is to be taken up. But you mustn't be impatient. You must understand that things are very complicated . . ." I did "understand" but I am sure he did not. He just repeated what he was told to say. The Rákosi clique was temporizing; of the Socialist convicts, Anna Kéthly alone was released, obviously as a sop to her comrades in the West. Dozens of others who had been sentenced as her subordinates in the "spy-ring" remained in gaol. I was taken to the Gyüjtö hospital, and then taken back to P.V., and then again to hospital. It was there that the re-freezing of my case became apparent to me.

A gaoler at the hospital received me with the coarse shouts to which I had not been accustomed since the revision of my trial. "What's all that dirt," he grumbled pointing to my belongings, and started fumbling in my papers. I had a shock: Florence's letters were among them. But impertinence is on such occasions the sole chance. And again, reliance on the literophobia of political policemen. "I warn you, sir, that I wrote all this on instructions from the Commander at P.V. If one single sheet goes astray it will be your responsibility." "Shut your bloody mouth," the gaoler answered but he left my papers alone; one never knew . . . Next he wanted to confiscate my cigarettes. "I warn you, sir, that I received them from the guards at P.V. and was explicitly told before being transported to this place that here too I should get the daily ration of fifteen cigarettes and the same food as the A.V.H. staff. If you deprive me of them I shall refuse to eat, and it will be your responsibility." After an unprintable reply he left the cigarettes and left me altogether with a furious bang.

My next quarrel arose about books. The people in charge said that for three or four days no books would be distributed and until then I could not get any. I started banging at the door and said I would repeat this every hour unless I got something to read. Amidst the most threatening shouts the gaolers refused to grant my request but after some hours' time a domestic worker entered with a huge volume in his hand: "Now look here, keep quiet. That sergeant woman (at that time it was a woman) would not allow this but I managed to get you . . ." I knew this was a face-saving manoeuvre but I accepted the volume with thanks. I was punished for my violence: it was *Communists* by Aragon, one of the dullest books I ever read.

I was given the ordinary prisoner's food which was bad as always, and the cigarette ration was not forthcoming, however often I asked for them. My reserves had run out. Some fellow prisoners clandestinely sent cigarettes to me through the prison doctor but the day came when I had nothing to smoke. That had of course happened frequently before but now I was no longer willing to put up with it. Indeed I was ashamed of caring so much about smoking—more than about the quality of the books, or the quality of my food, or the chances of my liberation or the delay in the revision of my case. A smoker is a slave. Could I take the risk of a hunger-strike? Apart from anything else, it might give them the idea of searching my papers thoroughly. I felt it would be irresponsible in the circumstances to provoke them; yet I was at the end of my tether. The following morning, when the door opened with the can of dark, lukewarm liquid they called coffee, and a piece of bread, I told the domestic worker: "Will you please report that I refused to accept food and shall go on doing so until I get the ration of cigarettes promised to me?" I repeated this at midday and in the evening for two subsequent days.

Of course, it was very disagreeable. Stinking food is bad but no food whatever is even worse. But I felt I could not give in. Now in a state of stubborn hunger I paced my cell all day long. On the third day, the Deputy Commander of the Gyüjtö dropped in: "Is it true that you refuse to eat?" "Yes, sir." In a very irritated but not particularly rude tone he asked me a dozen questions and then abruptly said: "I order you to eat. You can't make conditions. But I promise your case will be taken up. I promise. This has nothing to do with your hunger strike. You should be grateful that on this occasion we shall not punish you for it. Now start eating at once. I promise . . ." I knew it was the utmost he could do without openly giving in. The semolina boiled in smelly sunflower oil was quite welcome at that moment. I took care not to eat too much at once after almost three days of fasting. A few days later I was transferred to a special wing of the Gyüjtö—the section for those prisoners whose case had been accepted for revision.

My solitary confinement ended for a while. During the courtyard walks we could exchange messages with the inmates of other cells and with some new prisoners peeping out from their windows. We got the guards' diet again and our daily ration of cigarettes. We shared them with whom we could; we went out for walks with half-loaves of bread hidden under our jackets and, when not observed by the guards, threw them into one or another window. Between upper and lower floors, a post by string was developing which worked quite tolerably with our assistance at dusk. Traffic in cigarettes and matches was strong, in spite of strict prohibition. Even more, in fag ends, surreptitiously picked up from the court; the contents of three average fag ends, rolled in a piece of toilet-paper, made a good strong cigarette and no prisoner was so fastidious as to refuse it. To some, we threw paper and pencil—and this was not merely for unselfish reasons. We hoped that someone recently arrested might provide us with up-to-date information. One or two of them, not more, were intelligent enough to do this properly.

The most striking information was that Imre Nagy had resigned. His successor as head of the Government was a fairly unknown young man, András Hegedüs, from a People's College and with what was called a "Hungarian popular" background. How to evaluate this? The wishful thinkers believed it must be a good thing: not even Imre Nagy, they thought, had been national enough for the new era as he had after all been a Moscow-trained man. This interpretation was supported by the fact that the former Minister of Defence, Mihály Farkas, a leading figure of the anti-Tito terror campaign, had been pushed aside.

But we found out gradually that the opposite had happened. Rákosi had succeeded in torpedoing Imre Nagy at the Kremlin. Nagy was forced to resign. His successor, Hegedüs, was Rákosi's puppet. The eclipse of Mihály Farkas had a private cause. When de-Stalinization started, Farkas suddenly changed sides and turned against Rákosi. He experimented with Fouché's trick; for it was Fouché who, after acting as Robespierre's henchman, joined the conspiracy which overthrew and killed his master and thus managed to keep himself in high positions for later régimes. Farkas was less fortunate. Rákosi came back and took his revenge on him: he used him as a scapegoat for the illegalities committed. The Stalinists ousted him and later, in 1956, the de-Stalinizers had him arrested. Even treachery does not always pay.

We learned from a young prisoner recently arrested that Malenkov had resigned and made "self-criticism" because of his right-wing deviation. Imre Nagy, we gathered, was expected to do the same but refused. The Government cry was "back into the co-operatives"; the Imre Nagy Government was blamed for its willingness to abandon the plans for huge capital investment and to concentrate on consumer goods. In spite of this Rákosi made repeated gestures of friendship to Tito and received one snub after another. The Jugoslav prisoners felt this and became increasingly courageous—and even, to their credit, impertinent. Some of them had always been rather daring. Now they organized loud demonstrations and hunger-strikes, and beat some of their own *vamzers*. They got away with fairly light punishments.

We Hungarian subjects were given increasingly harsh treatment. The release of prisoners did not altogether stop, and some events encouraged us to hope that our own turn was about to come. We learned, for instance, that Cardinal Mindszenty had "provisionally been released from prison"; would it then be possible to keep the masses of minor "criminals" in gaol? As events showed, it would have been possible if Rákosi had had it his own way. He was cynical enough for propaganda purposes to release Cardinal Mindszenty or Anna Kéthly and, at the same time, to keep in gaol their less known "accomplices."

The re-freezing was carried out gradually. One day we were ordered not to talk, even to one another, during communal exercise. Next, our diet was changed back to that of the ordinary prisoners. Then the distribution of cigarettes stopped, and surprise raids were made on our cells, resulting in the confiscation of tobacco, matches, lighters . . . Our "telegraph" decision, by knocks over the walls and whispers during exercise, was quick. About a dozen of us chose a deadline, and then collectively refused to accept food.

The prisoner who was keenest on this decision was a Marxist believer who took Socialist Legality seriously. He urged us to insist on the continuation of hearings concerning the revision of our case. This was one, and formally the most important, of our demands. But I did not deny that what interested me most was cigarettes. I believed in Socialist Legality less than in the possibility of soothing my nerves with nicotine.

A good hunger-striker always eats in secret. Not much, but enough to keep himself going while he is conspicuously losing weight. Some of us had already hidden some slices of bread and now soaked and ate them in little bits. Others were helped to a spoonful of vegetable by a domestic worker. I had hard luck. Two of my three cellmates were devoted supporters of the Stalinist régime; they refused to take part in the strike, and I could certainly not trust their discretion if they had seen me eating. Some who were in a position similar to mine, refused to go to exercise or to the weekly shower-bath, arguing that they were too weak to do so, and used this opportunity to take a bit unnoticed. But I could not decide to do this; I wanted the shower-bath too badly; and the walks with a chance of finding fag-ends in the courtyard, and getting matches from the engineers peeping out of their windows, were too tempting to be resisted. On just one occasion I managed to get a piece of bread from the domestic worker, unnoticed by my cell-mates. I chewed and swallowed it on my couch late at night.

This hunger-strike lasted about eight to ten days. For the first forty-eight hours I felt the sort of ferocious urge for eating which I had experienced on the earlier occasion, in the hospital. But later, hunger stopped. In fact, during my imprisonment, this short period was the only one when I refrained from day-dreaming meals; my appetite, even for scrambled eggs, had gone. After the critical hunger-days I simply felt nausea. I was weak, had a sickish taste in my mouth, but did not feel faint. I should have liked to vomit, as an expression of my view of the world rather than any other reason. The other thing I should have liked to do was smoke. Nothing could spoil my appetite for cigarettes.

Higher quarters for a while pretended not to know about our hunger strike. They thought we might get tired of it before the critical time. But we held out. At last an investigating commission arrived on the spot and we were summoned before them, one by one.

"Is it true, Ignotus, that you have been refusing to eat since. . . .?"

"That's right, sir."

He clapped his hands, as if by amazement: "You, such an intelligent man as you are, how could you have done so? You know that's a disciplinary offence?"

"I know, sir."

"How then could you have done such a thing?"

"I think, sir, that no man, not even a prisoner, should be expected to abide by regulations if these are violated by the very authorities which are responsible for their implementation."

"What do you mean by that?"

"I presume we live under Socialist legality. I know that was not the case when we were in the hands of the Gábor Péter gang. Then we had no right whatever. . . ."

"You know of course that Gábor Péter is under arrest?"

"I do, sir."

"You recognize that many a thing has changed in the treatment of prisoners since we got rid of those gangsters."

"Certainly, sir, it has changed first for the better and now for the worse."

"Now what are your complaints?"

"That promises made to me by the authorities were not kept, and favours granted, revoked, one after another, without reason given."

He shook his head disapprovingly but kept up his benevolent tone. He took his pencil: "Now tell me what those promises were and what you expect should happen."

"I was encouraged to apply for a revision of my case. After two hearings when it became clear that I had been sentenced on false charges the proceedings were stopped. I have no idea what is to happen to me. In the meantime, the privileges allowed to those prisoners whose case is under revision have all been withdrawn. In fact I am now worse off than I was before the revision of my case. Then at least I was allowed to work in the translating bureau and received cigarettes and pay. Now I am deprived of the rights of the ordinary prisoners simply because the falseness of the charges against me had become so obvious that I was selected for revision."

"Well, it is not for me to decide what was true in those charges and what was not. You know a great number of people have already been released but you are an intelligent man and will certainly realize that we can't annul all sentences because some indeed were based on forged evidence. The willingness of the Authorities to remedy past evils should induce you to show more self-discipline and not the contrary."

"Yes, if I knew that something is being done about my case."

"I assure you it won't be forgotten."

"In the meantime I am unable to accept a worse position than I was in before." I suddenly dropped the official tone and said in anger: "I tell you frankly, sir, whatever happens I shan't eat until I am allowed to smoke. That may seem ludicrous to anyone but certainly not to a smoker. I don't speak of our other requests or demands —call them what you like—of which I presume you have already a full list from my fellow hunger-strikers. As to myself, I can only tell you that if you don't let me smoke I shall die here. Artificial nourishment may save my life for one week or two but you know very well that it won't do more than that."

He shook his head, as it were, in benevolent despair: "You, such an intelligent man . . . now look here. I promise you, I give you my word of honour, that we shall take up the case, and look into the matter. But you too must co-operate. Please consent to eat from now onwards."

"Sorry, sir, not until the distribution of cigarettes is resumed."

"So you don't trust us?"

"It's not a question of trusting or not. My experience of the last few months convinced me that it is no good for me just to trust and carry on like that. I must insist that promises made to me should be kept."

"Well, I am sorry. You are doing a great disfavour to yourself." And he dismissed me.

A few hours later a domestic worker stepped into the cell with a can full of semolina boiled in milk—in milk, this time, specifically prepared for us in the hospital! "Now start eating, I'll bring you five cigarettes at once, unofficially. And tomorrow, everything confiscated from you will be returned. You need not worry."

"Do the rest of us accept it?"

"Of course. I wouldn't say so, if they didn't." It was a domestic worker we trusted. I started eating and indeed got the cigarettes. The following day "everything" (which meant some books, a pair of socks and some cigarettes) was returned to me. Only my lighter, handed in by my sister some months ago by the commander's special permission had disappeared for good. Later I applied again and again to get it back but it "could not be found."

So our status was for a while re-established. We went on waiting for new hearings about our case. But this did not last long. Several of us were taken away—in fact the whole "unit" was dispersed. When the gaoler stepped in and asked one or another to follow him the prisoner could not of course know whether he would be led to a place where his case would at last be taken up, or just sent into another prison. Against such orders, resistance would not only have been hopeless but might have turned out to be a protest against one's own liberation.

Without explanation, I was thus led into a tiny cell, in an overcrowded "wing for Social Democrats" whose case was not under revision. Hygienic conditions were atrocious all over the wing. I was huddled together with three others in a cell designed, at the most, for two; but twelve to fourteen prisoners were squeezed into some other cells of the same size. Our main pastime was to catch bugs and fleas. Some prisoners were so ill that they simply could not leave their dusty straw-sacks; their companions had to hand them the bed-pans. Such people had been kept for a while in hospital but now, apparently under the order that Social Democrats must be crammed together in one wing, such hygienic considerations were no longer valid. Through a domestic worker I still received some cigarettes and matches, sent to me by the engineers. Another domestic worker, one of the well-known *vamzers,* denounced us. Our cell was raided, the straw scattered out of our sacks and spread over the floor, we were left in a suffocating cloud of dust. An old fellow-prisoner of mine was mainly sorry for a booklet in which he had till then succeeded in preserving his prison-poetry. They were very bad poems but he had put his heart into them. I was sorry for my cigarettes. I protested to the sergeant who made the raid. He was a smart fellow, resembling the young Maurice Chevalier. At the time of the first Thaw he had acquired a reputation as a considerate gaoler. He was in charge of Cardinal Mindszenty's carefully isolated cell, and moved about in the prison-block with a genial smile. Since then he had refrozen, together with the Government. He was brutal with us too. Violating the regulations according to which (since regulations were vaguely supposed to be observed) the cells and belongings of prisoners must not be searched without their attendance, he ordered us to leave the cell and to stand, our faces towards the wall, while his favourite domestic worker was messing our things up and taking what he cared to keep. My protest was futile.

Winter came, my last prison winter. Inside our cell only our breath preserved some warmth, and it was bitterly cold outside. But I would never miss the communal walk in the courtyard, both for fresh air and a hope of hearing some news. Now it was in crowds, about eighty at once, that we went for our walk; and as there were always some surprising innovations, physical jerks were now introduced for the sake of our health. It was a pathetic sight and in a way quite amusing to see the worn down prisoners in their ill-fitting boots and ragged frieze uniforms, hopping about and rhythmically bowing to keep themselves fit. We were severly ordered to line up according to cells, but always managed to create a bit of chaos in which information could be clandestinely exchanged.

Though the ban on my seeing visitors was never lifted I got round it by ignoring it. When the turn came for names starting with *I*, I applied for permission to invite my sister—my half-sister in fact, my mother's daughter by her first marriage—as a matter of course. She had to queue from 1 till 8.30 in the evening but was at last allowed to see me, in the presence of the Prison Commander, a major well known for his stupidity.

This happened when I had not yet been thrown back into the mass of ordinary prisoners; my case was still supposed to be under review and, accordingly, I spoke to her with considerable optimism. She had aged of course during the past six years and so had I, though fairly fit at that moment through sharing the guards' diet.

It was the first face in which I could see a reflection of what had been happening while I was secluded from the world.

I knew I was not allowed to touch her but ignored this to exchange a quick kiss with her. The Prison Commander called us to order but was not rude; I still ranked with those of whom one could not know . . . It was a moving and embarrassing moment: how would we carry on after six years' interruption?

Most embarrassing for me was the loss of some of my front teeth. At the time of my arrest my teeth were in a sound state but after that a decline in number and quality set in—first from kicks in the face during interrogations, and later from more natural causes. They were neglected or badly mended, and ultimately a number of them had to be extracted. This made me feel awkward, not so much for my appearance but the fact that I heard myself lisping.

"Well, what really is your work now?" I asked my sister.

I knew she had had to leave the Floris restaurant, in the centre of Budapest, of which she had been manageress for many a year; but she had contrived to stay "in the trade," managing a little suburban cafeteria. I felt she had had a harrassed life. I only learned the details later. She had not declared that she was my sister. On the usual printed forms asking whether she had any relations in prison, or concentration camps, she answered No. She constantly feared that her lie might be found out. The concierge of the block where she lived was an extremely honest woman and told her, "Yesterday your boss called on me and asked about you. She asked whether you were in correspondence with anyone in Western countries. I said 'Yes, with her sister, Mrs. Erdös'; I did not of course mention that she was a Miss Ignotus. Then she asked me whether you were planning to go abroad. I answered 'Oh no, I don't think so, on the contrary, as far as I know she is trying to persuade her sister to return to Hungary.'" This is just an example of what life was like in the Rákosi régime. Every second night the lorries arrived under A.V.H. surveyance, collecting the people who were singled out for deportation. Many a person spent these nights sleepless, glaring out of the windows, trying to guess whose turn it was and wondering when it might be his own. Many of my friends were deported and some died before reaching their destination.

My half-brother, a doctor of some standing, a member of the Social Democrat Party, had died of heart failure. Whether he guessed that prison was so near for him as my interrogations suggested, we shall never discover. He was apparently worried, mainly because of my arrest, but behaved in a calm way, even pretending to believe what I wrote in the small ration of letters to my relatives, that my treatment was humane and satisfactory.

"And Mother?" I asked my sister. She was by then the doyenne not only of my immediate family but of our whole circle, approaching her ninetieth birthday. This made her livelier and more sanguine than anybody else. She had endured and seen so much, that nothing shocked her any more. Each new day of her life was a special gift for her, only spoiled by my younger sister's exile and still more by my imprisonment. "I just want to see you once more before I die," she scrawled on a letter to me with her trembling hands; her eyesight and hearing were failing but altogether, as my sister said, "she is a miracle, carrying on, interested in everything . . ." Through the worst years of the Rákosi régime it was her good luck, and that of her son and daughter, that the man in charge of the literary funds, György Bölöni, allowed her a pension on account of my deceased father; so she did not have to depend entirely on the support of her children and friends.

"And what about Flo? Did you see her?" I asked *en passant*. My sister was quick and answered with an unemphatic "No, I didn't." I learned this way that Florence was still in prison.

I had three more such visits from my sister, in ever harsher circumstances. She saw me always more and more haggard, more depressed. The two last visits took place in the hall designed for that purpose, with double railings between us, under the supervision of sergeants. She casually mentioned that she had met "Florka." So she had indeed been released, though later than promised . . . And what did she say, I inquired. She said "Still."

This had been a keyword in our knocking conversations. Once when I had been away from my cell for a fortnight she knocked after my return: "I onli ask iou one vord: Stil?" I answered "More than ever." But now my message was that she should give that up. I saw no more hope for my release. I could not expect her to wait for me forever.

The sergeants in charge just stupidly glared at us while we were talking. When I burst out in shouts "Ils mentent, ils mentent," hinting at the promises made to me and then broken, they did not take any notice of the strange mumbo-jumbo. My sister tried to reassure me: "Don't be desperate, Mona Lisa often inquires about you." The sergeant just behaved like an hour-glass; his job was to see that the visit was not to last more than ten minutes. That a girl called Lisa should have tender feelings for me was not a thing he would object to. I appreciated the kind message, but confess I did not know how to interpret it. A fellow prisoner solved the riddle: Mona Lisa was in Paris. Surely my refugee friends had stirred up the interest of French writers who were now agitating for my release.

I found this interpretation plausible and it proved right. I had already had signs of steps taken to help me. I knew that back in 1949 Michael Károlyi had approached Rákosi's deputy Gerö on my behalf. I learned even in the Stalin era that the B.B.C. had quoted my name beside that of Anna Kéthly when referring to Labour Party protests. Later, I was interrogated about my contacts with "the American agent Thomas Mann" and the "covering organization of I.S. which uses the covering name P.E.N. Club," and I could well guess from the questions that they had tried something on my behalf; in fact, as I later learned, Thomas Mann had written a letter to the "ideological dictator," József Révai, inquiring about me, but received no reply. The "Trotskyite leaders" Stephen

Spender, Arthur Koestler and Ignazio Silone used also to crop up among those plotters against the working class who must have been known to me (though in fact I had never met Silone before my arrest). The questions were tiresome but more amusing than those about people living in Hungary. And they were also flattering by implication.

Now such interrogation went on less crudely: I was just asked very politely to explain about British and French authors and scholars who were in my opinion the sworn enemies of the People's Democracies, and about others who might be won over to support the Peace Movement. They assumed I was a progressive man and sensible enough to realize that in case of a *détente* my chances of release were to increase . . . I could not guess the list of very distinguished French writers who, warned by my friends, had protested on my behalf; but putting little hints together it had become my conviction that I was not forgotten either in London or in Paris.

At this juncture it was this which saved me from death, or at least from mental collapse. Many things were hideous in the A.V.H. prisons. The systematic corporal tortures at the beginning, and the nightmare of interrogations about relatives and friends for years to come. Cold, hunger, lack of space and air, solitary confinement, and to be crammed together with fellow-sufferers were all terrible; but nothing, not even lack of tobacco, could be so bad as the sense that one was forgotten. It is worth emphasizing this because the question often arises, whether or not to take a moral stand for people suffering in political prisons. "Do we not do them more harm than good by showing our sympathy for them?" many would ask. The answer is No. First of all because there is hardly ever a tryant, however determined to defy world opinion, who would not be more easily prepared to victimize someone about whom nobody cares than one whose martyrdom, he knows, will go down in history. It was not an accident that Cardinal Mindszenty among the priests, and Anna Kéthly among Social Democrats, were released first; the chief culprits before their accomplices—for the simple reason that their imprisonment had aroused the greatest public indignation.

Can there be no exception to this rule? Has there never been an example of increased vigilance over the prisoner concerned, and even of maltreatment, on account of such protests? This is possible. But a prisoner is glad to endure such additional pains if he knows that they are due to the interest taken in him. This anyway was how I felt. Once I knew that British and French authors, journalists and politicians were asking about me, and that my chief-gaolers were nervous about these inquiries, I did not mind for a moment what additional troubles might be in store for me. It gave me courage, and made me feel my importance. There was perhaps some vanity in this, of which I should be ashamed; but without it perhaps life not only in prison but anywhere would be intolerable.

I did not spend long in the cell with the old Social Democrats. "Pack up your traps and come," the gaoler told me.

"Where?"

"You'll see, come at once."

He led me into the Small Gaol, a building within the great prison camp of Gyüjtö. It was famous for its various peculiarities. Next to it stood the scaffold, and prisoners could now and then hear the sounds connected with executions. On its first floor women prisoners were held. On its other floors were the cells for specially rigorous imprisonment. The windows were so high that prisoners could not look through them, and there was an extra iron mesh on them which made it impossible to climb up. Many of its prisoners were in solitary confinement but even those who shared a cell were most severely segregated from the rest. There could be no chance for anyone in the Small Gaol to receive extra food or cigarettes. The greatest privilege allowed to a few was books from a very poor library, and some ten minutes' walk in the courtyard under strict supervision.

My sojourn in the building started with the confiscation of my "traps," including four or five dirty fag ends which I had been planning to roll into cigarettes and light when I could get a chance. I was stripped and searched all over. A ragged vest which I had managed to keep till then was also among the confiscated properties. It was bitterly cold in the cell, and I received only one flimsy blanket for the night.

"So you want to take all this from me and leave me freezing here?" I asked the gaoler.

"Don't ask questions, do as you are ordered."

I started shouting: "You have no right to do this. You think you can still behave as you did under the Gábor Péter gang. I shan't tolerate this."

There were thick carpets on the passages of the Small Gaol; silence was compulsory. My howling, lisping voice cleaved the air. I dared this because I felt the British and French writers behind me, believe it or not . . . "If I perish here it shall be known that the successors of the Péter gang murdered me."

"Will you shut up or else. . . ."

"No, I shall not. People will know who is to be murdered," and I raised my voice as much as I could: "I am Paul Ignotuf!" I made another effort to pronounce it properly: "Ignotusss!"

The gaolers, three of them by then, were exasperated. One was a female from the women's department. They threatened, among other things, to take me at once to the prison lunatic asylum which was also situated in the Gyüjtö camp. I myself became tired of the melodramatic scene. "Well," I said, "it is your duty to report to the Prison Commander that from now onwards I refuse to accept food. Not until my grievances are remedied shall I eat."

"It's not your business to tell us what our duty is, you . . ." and the door banged.

So my third hunger-strike started. The following day when the gaoler arrived with the morning "coffee," I refused to accept it and applied for an immediate interview with the Prison Commander, and for a book. The door was banged again and even angrier abuse than the gaoler's was shouted by the assisting domestic worker, a former White Gendarme Lieutenant. I have the impression he was really angry. He was a believer in subordination, servile and cruel on principle as well as by nature. He did not care which people or parties one might be serving. He liked disciplined injustice for its own sake.

Change of shift took place as a rule at 9 a.m. At midday a comparatively mild sergeant popped in. I repeated what I had said early in the morning. "Oh, you are mad," he shook his head. "Now that you have started hunger-striking you haven't a dog's chance of talking to the Commander or getting any books. I advise you to start eating at once and think yourself lucky if you can get away without punishment. Then in two or three months' time maybe the Comrade Commander might receive you."

"Sorry, Sergeant," I answered, "I can't change my mind. . . ."

I fasted for about three days. I felt my backbone was bent and my ribs sharply standing out like a skeleton's. I felt it was a struggle for life or death. Let me see whether they can afford to let me perish. Suddenly a domestic worker whispered through the peep-hole "I say! The Commander said he would come and see you in your cell. Man, do behave. Never anything like that has happened."

The Commander really came along. He was extremely polite. "Well, I really don't know about your case," he told me apologetically after hearing my complaints. "But look here, I have instructions to keep you here and it is very much against the rule to allow anyone to smoke in the Small Gaol. But I promise I shall urge a decision on your case and you will get an explanation soon. And what else did you want? Yes, you will get two extra blankets. . . ." I agreed to eat. The more so as at least my reputation was saved in that torture chamber. Again I must confess to vanity. When I saw the gaolers and domestic workers from then onwards glaring awestruck at me, I felt I had won a victory—at any rate for some weeks.

I am not sure whether I started two or three more hunger-strikes later. In any case I knew it was worth making myself a nuisance. By threatening hunger-strikes, I managed to get transferred to hospital, hoping as always for some cigarettes and news, at least from the convict doctors. But I got hardly any. My main pastime was reading, but I did not always get any books. That is to say, not always the thing which I was interested in reading. Once the gaoler in charge could offer me nothing better than *By-Laws of the Chimney-Sweep Trade*. All right, I said, why not study these for a few hours? When at large I shall never have leisure to do so . . . For three weeks I could not get another book. The gaoler always gave me the stereotyped answer that "The library is being changed, and for the time being no books can be issued." Then he added to comfort me, "But look here, you have got a book to read . . ." I protested that I had already read and re-read it a hundred times and that I was not after all so much interested in the by-laws of the chimney-sweep trade. He could not understand my complaint. "All the same, it's a book," he repeated. Finally one of the convict doctors saved me from dying of boredom, by handing in some English volumes—plays by Shaw for instance, which he, as a great privilege, was allowed to keep with him.

As I pretended to be ill—which perhaps I was, though I am not sure of what—I was allowed to lie about during the day. Once an A.V.H. nurse came and ordered me to dress and go back to the Small Gaol. "Sorry, I shall not," I replied. She was flabbergasted. "What do you mean? You were ordered to." "I repeat I shan't. You do what you like, but I shan't go. If you want a row, you can have it." That happened before Christmas. I was left alone for some ten days. After New Year I felt it was not worth resisting any more. No news or tobacco. I occupied a cell among the prisoners again, under specially rigorous supervision. I found out that I was at that moment the only one in solitary confinement throughout the building. Indeed I was proud of it. *Vanitatum vanitas,* luckily.

For technical reasons, at that time male and female gaolers were on duty together. This turned out to be lucky for me. Since my release I have often been told by former women-prisoners that they had found the female gaolers more cruel than the male. This was not my experience. Apparently, and not for very mysterious reasons perhaps, men were nicer to women, and women to men. Altogether, as I have said, almost all were hideous. But one of the women gaolers, a pretty young brunette, really contributed to saving my life by her kindness then. Perhaps it was my privilege of solitary confinement which turned her sympathy towards me, or perhaps my skeleton-like figure at that time. She offered me as many books as possible to read and gave me double portions of bread—a great treasure in view of the rottenness of the meals which I was often unable to eat even without a hunger-strike.

I knocked on the wall and on the radiator as usual to get news from fellow prisoners. But I got nothing except some silly wishful news. Cut off from everybody and everything, I did not know where to look for hope. I was tempted again to start a hunger-strike, demanding an interview with the Commander . . . But was it worth while? I should only ruin myself without getting anywhere. I had to decide whether to live or not.

I remember the dawn of 29th March. I struggled to my feet from my dusty straw-sack, and made my bed as ordered and washed. I got the lukewarm pseudo-coffee and double portion of bread from my brunette patroness. I started pacing my cell and wondering what to do. Then I clenched what had remained of my teeth and made up my mind: whatever happens I shall try to get well. I shall behave and eat, for two more years. If I have endured more than six years and a half I shall be able to endure two more. I must note this date, 29th March. If by 29th March, 1958, I am not released I shall kill myself. I shall make a final hunger-strike or commit suicide in some other way. It is difficult to live in prison, but even harder to die without permission. But one manages with determination, and so shall I. For two more years I shall try. Two years more I shall invest in survival. No more than two, but until then no fuss: I shall eat.

Chapter 13

Released

AT THAT MOMENT my door opened, and the Young Chevalier sergeant burst in. His face was gleaming with humanitarian joy—apparently re-thawed. "Pack up your traps." "All of them or only my personal belongings?" I asked as usual. The reply was not so usual. "Come on my friend, don't ask a lot of questions." Friend? What quick promotion from his normal form of address! With a gesture of triumph, as though he had solicited my release, he showed the way.

I took "my personal belongings," chief of which were a toothbrush and a piece of lard, about one ounce, saved for the rest of the week from my Sunday supper four days before.

From his sudden benevolence I might have guessed that my captivity had come to an end. But I did not. I had trained myself so thoroughly in wariness against wishful thoughts that I did not allow myself to indulge that idea. I stepped automatically. In the central hall of the prison block I saw about a score of Social Democrat prisoners; some of them just being shaved by the prison barber, and the rest waiting their turn. I remember their faces less than the big wash-basin on the floor, covered with foam, and the gestures of the prison barber as he cleaned his knife and asked me to sit down, whispering: "Didn't I tell you the other day that you'd be released very soon?" In fact he had whispered it in my ears but I paid no attention. Even now I would not believe my own eyes. It could just be a hoax. Or, maybe, they would ask me to return when I reached the prison gates, explaining they had mistaken me for someone else—it had already happened to some. Nevertheless I was willing to take one risk—my slice of lard. My fellow prisoner Stolte had been longing for fat all the time. "Couldn't you hand this to him or someone else . . ." I asked the barber. "I can't take anything now," he answered, "ask the gaoler . . ." Before I had a chance to do so I found myself clean-shaven together with other clean-shaven prisoners in the "room of smiles."

This was what the prisoners called the room where those awaiting liberation were collected. My fellow prisoners dashed at me in a state of agitation. "You have been in solitary all the time? You don't know a thing?" It was then that I learned about the de-canonization of Stalin. The news of the Twentieth Congress had leaked through —as had always been the case, with some exaggerations. "Stalin's corpse was transferred from the Mausoleum into the common cemetery. All books of Party History, etc. have been withdrawn—and do you know, what a funny chap D . . . (a domestic worker) is! Pretending not to know about the whole thing he applied for Stalin's works, as he said, to complete his own ideological re-education. He was told to go to hell. . . ."

I had a last look at ourselves in frieze uniforms as we queued in the passage to be admitted to the office room. It was exhilarating and heartrending at the same time. Next to me an octogenarian, a former Social Democrat M.P., sitting on a stretcher as for years he had been unable to stand on his feet; one of the dangerous "plotters" who might never have been released if it had not been for the orders from Moscow.

In the office, a stereotyped text was read to me, about my provisional release from prison; and some money handed to me in an envelope, irrespective of the claims which I might still have. . . . In the prison store, a suitcase with mufti in it which I recognized with great astonishment: a suit which I had left in London before my return to Hungary in 1949. . . . How did it arrive here? I only later learned that my half-sister in Budapest had got it

from my sister in London as they had been preparing to
receive me. On the day before my release, my half-sister
had been notified of the coming event and asked to send
in some clothes. Practically everybody knew of my release
sooner than myself.

A last attempt, as I was changing, with my lard: "Corporal, do you know the prisoner Stolte or someone else
who needs fat badly. . . ." He was in too great a hurry to
bother. Before arriving at the gates, I just saw my brunette
patroness for an instant. "Kiss your hand," I called farewell in the old Hungarian fashion, and she reciprocated
with the Magyar version of "au revoir." With my little
suitcase in my hand, containing my notes and two or three
books from my confiscated belongings, I found myself in
a taxi which was to take me from the suburb where the
Gyüjtö was situated towards the middle of the city.

Shall I say I was happy? It would not be the right
word. I was simply unable to believe that it had happened.
It was a dull day, and we drove between shabby grey rows
of houses. I eagerly breathed the air so as to make sure
that I was alive. Dull existence, the dullest on earth, but
without a door locked on me: that was the thing I had
day-dreamed of for almost seven years. That was the very
thing which in my true dreams I knew to be unachievable.
Now it had been achieved.

We were approaching the main avenue of Budapest,
named since 1950 after Stalin. The driver turned back
and asked me "Do you know what the new name of that
Avenue will be?" And he cracked a pun at it. I had made
up my mind to be cautious about *agents provocateurs*.
And it would be only too logical to assume that a driver
ordered to the prison building to collect recently released
prisoners might report on what he heard from his passengers. But I answered his pun with a frank and uninhibited
laugh. It was too good to be resisted. It was the first word
which made freedom palpable to me. Under the dull sky,
I felt the vibration of hopes and complicities which at that
time penetrated Hungary.

Yet I felt I must see whether I really was free. Reaching the Grand Boulevard of Budapest I stopped the taxi:

would I really be able to cross the street unhampered and buy a ticket in the Metro as any ordinary human being, in the familiar stench of sweat and metal? Yes, I did. I had no idea how much a ticket was. I groped my way towards the seats as a provincial who had never seen anything like that. I glared at every face to see if I might find an acquaintance. No one took any notice of me.

As I had not heard of my mother for a long while I was worried about her. Where could I inquire? I called on a couple of concierges who knew her. "Oh Mr. Ignotus, is it really true. . . ." I shook their hands. "Please tell me only one thing. Is my mother still alive?" "Surely . . . she's been very ill but is much better now. Lying in a hospital. But why did you think that . . ." My half-sister was working in her cafeteria but the concierge let me into her small flat. He also gave me the telephone number where I could ring her, so that she could come at once. "Thanks, thanks." Before anything, I felt I must ring a dentist cousin of mine; it is absurd to see people if one lisps all the time. Before I could do so, the telephone rang. "Florence speaking." It was the first time I heard her voice. Another dream fulfilled. It was too sudden to be realized. "Look here, I really don't know, it's horrid for me to talk to you with such a senile accent. I must see a dentist. I am so sorry . . ." She took no notice of my apologies. "I want to ask you one word," she said: "Still?"

My half-sister arrived. A friend arrived. Florence arrived. The impressions were too crammed to be digested. The problems of the moment were overwhelming. It was well I had always prepared myself to face them once I got into the dreamland of freedom. Mainly the trivial problem of how to dispose of one's time. I must see X who had been helpful to my people in the worst period, and Y who had inquired so much about me, and must buy a tie and see a doctor and of course the dentist and call at the police. . . . On the first day, I could not spare time to visit my mother in the hospital. One friend rang after another. I must get a diary at once. . . . However small my luggage, it was some time before I found a few minutes to unpack it. My notes, including the letters from Florence, which were stored and returned to me unread; some two or three books, two or three pairs of socks, a vest and a pair of slippers which had been sent to me but never reached me in gaol; and a toothbrush; and a slice of lard wrapped in a dirty piece of paper. My sister glared at it horror-stricken. "You won't eat it, I suppose." I did not know what to do about it; I was not used to throwing away such treasures but I realized there would be no one to take it to Stolte by now . . . "By the way," said Florence, "don't you want to eat anything?" "Yes, how stupid of me," my sister intervened. "I ask you about so many things and forget to ask you about that." In fact I had forgotten myself. How could I now revive my day-dreams of meals? Lunch time had passed by. "What about some scrambled eggs?" I asked her.

I stayed with my sister, sleeping on a broad and comfortable divan, in clean sheets, under a comfortable Central-European eiderdown. Again an impossible dream fulfilled. I stretched myself and tried to clean my brains. How account for all that had happened? I recalled the night of my arrest, the glare of the yellow electric bulb as I lay on the wooden bunk and thinking: "that's the end of it . . . I shall never be free again." In the depths of despair I had fallen asleep at once. In this night of relief I was unable to sleep for a second.

I was unable to sleep and unable to believe that I was not dreaming. So my first few days outside prison passed. In the meantime it was anything but dreamlike. It was a struggle to work through my agenda each day. My weight was about twenty kilos below the normal, my stomach had been unused to human food. I must put on weight and save myself from indigestion and mend my teeth and see everybody I should, and for heaven's sake not offend anyone. Such were my problems. And where transfer my mother who could no longer stay in the hospital but was still too weak to live on her own? And how should I let my sister in London know about my release? She had been in touch with my half-sister during the last few years; but all the same would it be wise for me to write to her direct? Rákosi was still in power. He hated those he had released. Some few of his former prisoners joined and made common cause with him. The rest of us wandered about in the country as the branded enemies of a dictator who had been forced to tolerate them.

No one was allowed to move without an identity card in Hungary at that time. This was not an innovation; in the last twenty years there had hardly been any régime under which people could easily afford to leave their card at home if they went out for a walk. As a matter of course I had to report for registration, in various offices. It was quite amusing. I met a number of Social Democrat comrades, former fellow prisoners, on every occasion. In the antechambers of the police and other authorities we held gatherings without ever planning to do so. The very sight of these men whom I had only seen in frieze before was amazing as they turned up in their new outfits. . . . Most of them had no idea why this had happened to them. Should one take the promise of Socialist Democracy seriously? Socialist Democracy would inevitably bring us nearer to something like Social Democracy . . . Should we be grateful to Bulganin and Khrushchev for denouncing Stalin and compelling Rákosi to release us? "By no means" some argued; "they are no better than their master Stalin was. They were compelled to do what they did. The Soviet Union is on the brink of collapse. Do you think Bulganin and Khrushchev would invite themselves to Britain unless they had to? They wanted to please Gaitskell and Bevan, that's why they set us free." And so on and so forth. But it would be wrong to imagine that we talked mainly politics. We jubilantly congratulated a septuagenarian who had just married. When we walked out to the street and arrived at a tramway stop a staunch Socialist leader lifted his two hands as if in despair: "I can't get used to it . . . isn't it awful?"

"What?"

"At every tram stop to see these fat fag-ends lying about and not to pick them up. What a waste!"

For more than six years and a half I had prepared myself not only for death in prison but also for unhappiness on being released. I knew many of my friends would have died or grown old by that time; others would have forgotten me; and the young would not know me at all. It would be one disappointment after another.

It turned out much better than that. All my life pessimism had saved me from fatal shocks. In freedom I had chiefly to worry about reciprocating the kindness of people who remembered me. No doubt many of them revealed their kindness only after my release, but I was really too much concerned with the present to bother very much about reproaches for the past.

I went to see the director of the Literary Funds, Bölöni, to thank him for his generosity towards my mother in the worst years. He was friendly in his own reserved way but I did not even try to talk things over more fully with him; in spite of personal honesty, he was a diehard Communist. But he arranged that I should be invited to write a book which might have been a mixture of essays and autobiography. I am still sorry it could not have been written and published, but I enjoyed starting work on it.

I was invited to join the Writers' Association, and the Journalists' Union; I gladly accepted. I was invited to join the Party; I gratefully declined. I was invited to join the staff of the Government paper which was supposed to belong to the Popular Front, and I refused for the time being. It was agreed with a friendly editor, Géza Losonczy (later abducted by the Russians and killed in deportation), that I would join them if or when some of us got a chance to write as we liked.

I was asked to join the staff of the Institute for Research in Literary History, and accepted but the appointment was only confirmed six months later. Inviting and deceiving people like me were equally usual.

In general, everything seemed reassuring. There was no question of my having to be shy about my prison years. On the contrary, it was taken for granted that some amends must be made to us. The Stalinists were still in power, but we were in fashion.

There was a retrial. The nine of us who had been lumped together by the logic of A.V.H. at the end of 1950 and sentenced as British spies plotting against the international working class, were now summoned again to be rehabilitated as Hungarian patriots devoted to the international working class. Some of us had not known one another before meeting as co-plotters in 1950; and some had quarrelled so as not to be on speaking terms when we met as co-heroes in 1956. Our retrial, like our earlier trial, was held *in camera,* and this play-back of a farce was itself farcical. Yet this retrial, unlike the former trial, contained some elements of surprise—mainly from the just and legal manner in which the President of the Court, Mr. József Domokos, conducted it.

That we had all been sentenced on false charges, and had "confessed" under threats and tortures, was readily admitted by the prosecutor himself. Nevertheless some of the evidence about the kinds of torture surprised even me; it became clear not merely that my fellow prisoners had not exaggerated in describing their ordeals to me in prison, but that they had been afraid to tell me the whole story. Now, the cross-examination of former A.V.H. officers who were called as witnesses threw light on Grand Guignol details. One of the worst A.V.H. torturers, Ervin Faludi, by then dismissed from State Security service to a less conspicuous position as "Chief of a national enterprise," admitted everything with equanimity. That they had lied and had made us lie was a foregone conclusion.

There was just one important charge maintained against one of us. Ironically, he had done his best to please the Russians since their occupation of Hungary—Arpád Szakasits, former puppet President of the Hungarian People's Republic. Rákosi apparently dreaded his rivalry so much that he had ordered the prosecutor to insist on his guilt. The prosecutor admitted he had not been a British spy but maintained that he had been a police spy under Admiral Horthy. As proof of this a document was handed in, a report by the Hungarian political police chief to the Minister of Interior in the thirties, in which Szakasits was mentioned with benevolence as one who provided the police with useful information.

There could be no doubt as to the authenticity of the stamps and signatures on the document. Szakasits pleaded not guilty on the grounds that he could not say why the Police Chief had "talked such nonsense"; it did not occur to him to question the authenticity of the document. To the surprise of all those present, including Szakasits himself, Mr. Justice Domokos declared: "The Court is not satisfied that all sheets in that document were typed by the same typewriter and therefore orders that it should be examined by an expert." Indeed it was examined; and the page containing the sentences compromising Szakasits turned out to have been faked.

Before the verdict all the accused—or rather the justified—made their last pleas. Marosán, once sentenced to death by Rákosi's court, after which he had co-operated again with Rákosi in running the Party machinery, made a most fiery speech. He is a suburban play-boy type, not unattractive, touching and grotesque in his awkward response to what had happened to him. Apparently his first thought was far removed from revenge; it was rather a wish to prove to his forsaken Social Democrat comrades that he had been right all the time. "György Marosán is no longer a Social Democrat," he shouted dramatically, "György Marosán is a Communist." And then: "We must denounce the lie according to which we have to thank Western Social Democracy for our release. The Twentieth Congress alone has liberated us."

The President of the Court promulgated that the details of the trial were to remain secret, except for the fact that all defendants were rehabilitated. I wired it to my sister in London.

I married. The event took place about one year after the date we had planned in prison, and as simply as possible. Not that I dislike ceremonies or spectacular weddings, and though I did not put the question to my wife I do not think she had any such objection either. But a ceremony should be appropriate, and nothing to fit our particular case has yet been invented. It just had to come as a semi-colon; the second half of the sentence, the "*de facto* honeymoon" forecast in my prison-doggerel, was to follow. It was a matter of grammar rather than social or religious organization.

There we were standing, six of us, in a medium-sized room of the Registry Office in the Town Hall. The mistress of ceremonies was a kind and ugly woman with a broad red-white-green band across her chest. With automatic solemnity she read the legal terms to us and asked each the expected question. I glanced at Florence to my left. She wore a Cameron tartan costume, a present from her relatives in Suffolk. Her nose was tilted in the air with just the impertinence I had imagined from the knocks on the wall: "Vho are? I voman." She had told me her eyes were grey-green. This turned out to be true, but different from my fantasies. I had known her as a heroine of conversations; these eyes now had the shimmer of inscrutable silence.

The fourth person in the room was a professional photographer authorized to attend all weddings in the building. Immediately after the ceremony he dashed at me with his price list, with its details of pictures in various sizes, with or without the lady with the red-white-green band, with or without the two witnesses who stood behind us. "All right, send me some samples," I told him and had a quick word with the lady official. She complained about the great number of divorces. "No wonder," she added, "as I see how marriages are arranged it is not astonishing to see how short they last. The other day a young man asked me to hurry up because after the wedding he had to go back to his office."

One of the witnesses was my wife's uncle, a former judge, a man of much knowledge, humour and affection. He could hardly find a word to say and quickly left us. The other was an old friend of mine and of my deceased father, a most charming and witty Hungarian author with the habit (which he thinks more important than his literary work) of hiding a flute under his jacket and improvising strange performances on it when the right moment comes. He saw us to Florence's home, shared a cold meal in the family circle and made friends with the dachshund who had by then become my stepdaughter. In a few hours' time, my wife and I were in the train on our way towards a few days in the country.

The Stalinists kept in power but we did not disappear from fashion. The kindness showered on me became embarrassing. I had glances of envy and hope from people of the *ancien régime*: "I am sure it is *your* turn now . . . they won't be able to prevent that . . ." It was not always clear who they had in mind. I was trying tactfully to disenchant them. Khruschchev might not be a Stalin but this did not mean he was an Ignotus. Nor was Ignotus a Count Bethlen . . . Oh, they were sure Khrushchev would come round. He must see the moral and economic bankruptcy of a régime forced upon a people against everybody's will. And there was no question of their wanting a Count Bethlen or a Cardinal Mindszenty or anything like that, let alone an extremist of the Right. They wanted sound and enlightened people in power. They simply wanted to breathe freely and to earn their living.

Even more embarrassing were the fits of kindness from Communists. "When can I see you, when could you have dinner with us? Yes, I realize you are busy but perhaps one evening next week. . . ." And another: "Now you are told that I am a wicked Stalinist. But those who are clamouring loudest today for Socialist Legality and the like did not open their mouths before '53. I saw . . . the other day with you. Do you know what he said about you after your arrest? He said 'I have always known he is a dirty swine, a British spy.' Now he is playing the fighter for freedom." Even Rákosi's supporters talked like that. And there was a spark of truth in what they said. Every fashion, even the noblest, has its host of opportunists.

Of the Communist writers I met at this time, the most remarkable was Tibor Déry. We were old friends but had never really been on intimate terms. Before the war, we used to sit about in the same cafés and contribute to the same periodicals—and a strong link between us was our mutual friend the late Attila József, the great Hungarian poet from between the wars; but we had few interests in common. He was an experimentalist doomed, I thought, to refined immaturity for his life-time. Socialist Realism, some years after the end of the war, had a double effect on him; it induced him to make concessions to Party propaganda and vulgarity, and at the same time helped him to call a spade a spade—something from which he had been inhibited by his *avantgarde* tendencies. This new mixture of sincerity and insincerity could have been the end of his originality; as things turned out, it was his great stimulus. As he had been the best-known fiction-writer among the old Party members, the cultural dictators expected him to *Zhdanovize* without reservation; and the artist in him protested. A campaign against him was launched by the local Zhdanovs in the heyday of Stalinist dictatorship, and several of us in prison who had known him were pestered to disclose "Déry's contacts with Horthy's political police" of which we "must have been aware."

I cannot judge whether, without such Party pressure, he would have become the fighter for freedom and the eminent and mature writer he is. Maybe he is indebted to our local Zhdanovs for his glorious career. If he had been left in peace, as many a non-Party writer was, and appreciated as a highbrow eccentric without being taken too seriously, he might have remained one of the distinguished nonentities crowding every nation's literature. But he was forced by Party orders to look to the common man, and the discovery of the common man turned him against the Party. "Do you feel you were mistaken in trusting the Party?" I asked him after my release. "Yes," he said, "I was mistaken; but I don't regret it."

I never asked him to explain what he meant by this; I agreed. Not only because old Party membership at that time—just after the Twentieth Congress—enabled anyone to stand up for human rights more vigorously than if he had been outside the Party or a new recruit; there was also a deeper reason. To believe in Communism was an error, no less detrimental perhaps to millions of people than belief in Fascism; but, unlike Fascism, it was a fruitful error. From former Fascists humanity has learned nothing except perhaps the art of dissimulating their pasts. From former Communists humanity has learned the art of being anti-Communist intelligently. I know some intelligent people who have never been Communists—from Sir Winston Churchill to Paul Ignotus. But the anti-Communism of all of us, whether Tory, Labour or Liberal, and whether Western, Oriental, or Central European, was either a rejection of social revolution (Sir Winston's case) or of unintellectual dullness (my own) or, at the best, of tyranny and bloodshed in general. The basic error of Communism, its utterly retrograde system, more rigid than the one it abolished, was first grasped and laid bare by writers who had gone through its schooling—instinctively by Silone, in lucid though incoherent visions by my great countryman Attila József, to some extent by his friend François Fejtö, and later, in impressionist patches, by Gide, and quite articulately by Orwell and Koestler, and now by Djilas.

Revolution in Hungary in 1956 did not come from the anti-Communists but from the disenchanted Communists. Such Dark-Pinks as I am, or such Whites as Cardinal Mindszenty's adherents, may or may not have sailed in its wake or wished it well for their various reasons. I knew a number of near-Fascists, of die-hard Conservatives and, among the writers, some co-called Narodniks, mystic believers in Hungarian Blood and Soil, who refused to side either with Rákosi or the followers of Imre Nagy on the ground that this was "merely the struggle of two Communist factions, one no better than the other." I myself felt it was none of my business to play a conspicuous part in arguments which to a great extent ran round such questions as whether Imre Nagy or Rákosi had applied the tenets of Marxism-Leninism correctly. But whatever the past mistakes of those who worked towards democracy with Imre Nagy, they were taking risks and pains to make Hungary a country worth living in. Except the diehards of old or new caste systems, and the staunchest sitters on a fence which stood upon pure Hungarian Soil, the whole country was with them. So was I of course.

Literature was the means of that Revolution, and belief in free literature its touchstone. A discussion organized by the Petőfi Circle of young left-wing intellectuals, on 27th June, about the state of the Press and literature marked the climax of a mass movement. The meeting was held in a hall but was transmitted by loudspeakers to the street and a courtyard which was crowded with people for about twelve hours—from early afternoon till the small hours. My wife and I were lingering in the courtyard watching the photographers on the roof. Everybody assumed that many of the photographs were taken for the A.V.H., but I do not believe many of us were frightened away by this assumption. It was after all a "Marxist-Leninist" meeting, publicly announced and authorized; it included among its speakers the Zhdanovist editor of the Party daily. I interrupted my peripatetic listening with a walk out to a neighbouring restaurant for some fish in paprika-stew and a glass of beer. But I did not miss Tibor Déry's speech. It was not really a very good speeech, but it was moving and impressive from its polite impertinence and its acoustic effects.

Déry has a deep and sonorous voice, modulating in long waves of tenderness, emotion, irony and pathos. He also articulates clearly and puts his verbs in the right tenses—less usual in my country than it should be. At the start of the meeting the audience was warned not to interrupt the speakers. They were nevertheless interrupted. Déry started with a simple sentence, the most effective possible at that moment. "Comrades, I only wish to tell you that I shall not be at all annoyed if you interrupt me." The battle was won by this invitation. In most of his speech Déry dealt with the attacks made on his novel by the Hungarian petty-Zhdanovs and their followers, the Minister of Culture among them. He referred to these only by way of example, adding "I am not moved by a thought of revenge." It might have been more convincing to hear other examples, but the ordeal which a Communist writer had to endure if he wanted to be faithful to his people had become clear. And it was a shattering moment when the man who had once run amok among the visions of Chagall and the prose of Proust, summed up his creed in the simple sentence: "I am a writer and cannot see people suffering."

Déry was expelled from the Party. My wife and I were due to have supper with him and his wife in their villa in the outskirts of Buda. Would he still be at large by the time we were expected there? I did not know whether it was very clever of me to visit him just then; but I felt it would be disgraceful not to do so. We chatted with him till late at night. We had missed the last bus. Rain was pouring, and there seemed no hope for a taxi. Then he rang a cab-rank himself, and said: "This is Tibor Déry speaking. . . ." "Oh, God, the writer? Are you free?" We got the taxi at once.

Ten weeks later the Writers' Association held its annual meeting, to elect its Presidential Board—a pompous name for its Committee, inherited from the Stalin era. But its election was a landmark, a real election with candidates and counter-candidates, with secret ballots such as had not been seen in Hungary for nine years. Déry was among the three newly elected members who had got the greatest number of votes. All the Muscovite writers, all supporters of Rákosi and all their agents, including the Minister of Culture, had failed.

To my surprise, I was nominated while away at my dentist's and elected. Less than half a year after my imprisonment this was quite a sensational event. An old Stalinist dashed at me and pressed my hands affectionately: "Cheers, so we have won." The secret votes in my favour were quite impressive; but the open handshakes were unanimous. It would have been rude not to drink a glass with my colleagues after such an event. I owed my first domestic row to this glory of mine. "For heaven's sake," my wife received me, "why couldn't you tell me that you were elected; somebody rang me with congratulations about it and I made a fool of myself by not knowing. Meanwhile your supper has got spoiled."

It was an era of hopes for happiness. Nobody was satis-

fied with existing conditions but everybody recognized
their improvement and felt excited at the prospect of
further improvements. Rákosi had been overthrown—
Mikoyan on his visit to Budapest had chucked him out
and replaced him by Gerö. This may not have been a very
substantial improvement but was symbolic enough to be
encouraging. One of the most relaxing features of the
Thaw was a series of group excursions to the West, notably Vienna. There was a special steamer on the Danube,
carrying groups of actors, printing workers, or whoever,
for about a week to the Austrian capital. Visitors had got
drunk with what they saw. The wonder of eating a
banana, which for a decade they had only heard about!
Many dashed at the first milk bar to have a glass of Coca
Cola. Its reputation in Hungary arose from its reputed
link with American bourgeois culture. The Communist
press had never been tired of sneering at the American
way of life symbolized by Coca Cola. "Oh, we must taste
it," the visitors sighed. And they were very disappointed
indeed. "I can't understand why they run it down so
much; it's really not so very good."

But the universe of Coca Cola and the multi-party system had its appeal. From all these excursions some of the
tourists had disappeared and had refused to return to
Hungary. The melting Iron Curtain was still too solid for
them to take the risk of staying behind it. Stalinist propaganda used such defections as an argument against further
facilities to tourists. The writers' excursion at the beginning of October was viewed with particular anxiety. Who
will return and who won't? When I applied for passage
together with my wife, I really did not believe we would
be allowed to go. The official in charge said at first he
could only grant permission to me. But I made a row and
succeeded in getting both tickets.

My sister from London came to see me in Vienna.
Hungarian Social Democrats from London sent messages
that I should by all means stay away: one could not trust
the Bolsheviks, however much they might be thawing at
that moment . . . I met a Hungarian journalist, by then
installed in the Austrian film industry: "What do you

think will be their reaction in Hungary when they learn that you have not gone back?" "But I *shall* go back," I answered. He was flabbergasted. My friend Fejtö rang me from Paris. When he asked whether I thought that the evolution towards Socialist Democracy would last I answered that I did not know but one had to try. It was a unique chance for my country and also for me. I could not fail my fellow-writers, who had vouched collectively for me and for us all. I wished to be with them while they were hoping and struggling.

When after our six days' visit, we were back on the boat, all of us listened to the transmissions from Budapest radio. We heard the speeches made at the ceremonial re-burial of Rajk. We heard the passionate attacks on "personality cult." One of the speakers is now Prime Minister of the Russian-appointed Hungarian Government. Another is, like me, a refugee.

Before the steamer started home, it was announced that all passengers without exception had returned on board. Tremendous applause followed. It expressed the conviction that Stalinism could and should be fought at home.

Chapter 14

London Again

I RETURNED from Vienna to Budapest—and am a refugee in London once again. That crowded interval in my story can only be told briefly and out of scale, for it includes a Revolution, of which I was witness. So were nine million Hungarians, including two hundred thousand who escaped to the West soon afterwards. So also were a large number of Western diplomats, journalists and others who arrived on the spot to see with their own eyes and eventually to help the distressed and wounded. Their eye-witness accounts have been included in official and unofficial Reports and in thick volumes published on the matter in most languages. What I have added to them can here or there be traced by students of history. Photographs and

documents of indisputable authenticity are available in
masses. What remains is to sum them up in fairness—
which not even the fairest mind can achieve while looking into open wounds. My endeavour was to help those
who might heal them. That is why I returned to Hungary
in October, 1956, and why I left not quite two months
later. I shall limit my story to explaining what made me
change my mind.

I remember the last night of the victorious Revolution.
In the company of my wife, then in the sixth month of her
pregnancy, I spent some hours in the house of Parliament.
Any visitor to Budapest will remember that huge building
on the bank of the Danube. It was built on the British
model and was meant to outdo its model in size, comfort, and beauty. Its huge and bulging dome, unsuited to
its delicate spires and pointed windows, bends like a protecting helmet over the population of the capital. It is a
part of nature no less than the mountains on the opposite
bank of the river, and since childhood I have got used to
considering it as no less inexorable than nature itself. I
used to walk under its arcades with my nurse, on fine
summer evenings. I walked there, though with different
desires and other women, in later years. In the era of
comparative liberalism, and particularly in the weeks of
parliamentary recess, thousands of young people used to
discover some substitute for a proper flat among its zigzags with their girl friends. Had there been less orna-
ments and more style in planning the majestic building,
it would have been less suitable for that purpose.

In its splendid lack of style, this enormous palace has
served as a factotum through the last outrageous decades.
Originally it was to serve as the seat of Lords and Commons as at Westminister. But nothing like that had been
there for years when the Revolution came. It had been
gunned and damaged. The park around it had been the
scene of mass demonstrations and bloodbaths. Some of its
chambers were just used as Government departments,
including the Prime Minister's office. The premises I vis-

ited were the temporary centre of the Free Kossuth Radio.

Muddle and enthusiasm were touching. It was a revolutionary headquarters at its best. We arrived in late afternoon, and had to cross the cordon of armed guards. No wonder: one had to be careful about spies and provocateurs, Soviet agents and Fascist plotters alike. Through its passages, as confusing as streets in London, I managed to find my way. I was to make a speech in Hungarian that day, and to start a series of talks for listeners in English some days after. I had ample opportunity to talk with the staff—one or two of them fellow-writers who had long been known to me, but mostly unknown young men, typical of the front line of the Revolution. They addressed one another as Comrade. "Are you a Communist?" I asked one of them, a young man who had just arrived from the revolutionary headquarters in Györ, the great city in the West of Hungary. "I am," he answered. He was quite clear that the Revolution which he supported wholeheartedly meant the end of Communist dictatorship in Hungary. "Never mind," he said, "our people must first be free and be allowed to discover for themselves that our theories were basically right."

I submitted my script to him. He was not altogether satisfied. "Of course you will say what you like, I have no right to censor you. But if you will let me advise you . . ."—and he had two objections. One, that some of my expressions smelled too much of middle-class democracy. Let us drop every phrase which might make people believe that an independent Hungary would be less socialist in spirit than the one dominated by Russia. Second he thought I was going too far in trying to protect the A.V.O. men hunted down by the outraged population. Would I not at least make it clear that I wanted the criminals to be punished severely. After some discussion we agreed on a fair compromise. My appeal to the Hungarians for unity and discipline, monitored and printed in various English publications, was the result of it.

My speech was recorded for broadcasting late at night. At the peak hour, Cardinal Mindszenty was to speak. I stayed to see him. It was a fantastic sight; the diehard Primate Cardinal arriving with an armed guard of honour amidst the Communist revolutionaries. He was received by a cabinet minister, once President of the Republic, originally a Protestant parson, Zoltán Tildy; later a political prisoner, released in April, 1959. The Cardinal walked in with swaying steps and glaring eyes the strange expression of which may or may not have been the result of his ordeal in A.V.O. imprisonment. I listened to his speech. Its text can be read and checked in several volumes of documentary literature. The spokesmen of Soviet policy on Hungary have since made a habit of referring to it as a counter-revolutionary incitement to restore the old *latifundia*. This is nonsense. The Cardinal's speech was moderate and cautious. But it was not appropriate to the extraordinary moment when it was made. One could not help feeling that a ghost was speaking from the past.

We hurried home through the pitchdark streets, and had just time to switch on the wireless to hear my own voice and, at the end, my wife's English announcement of my forthcoming talks. It was a quiet night, the quietest I could remember since the outbreak of the Revolution. We slept well but not long. We were woken by gunfire. It was 4 a.m. We switched on the radio and heard patriotic marches and anthems, one after another. It was patriotism to the extent of panic, and the Prime Minister's announcement followed. The Russians were attacking Budapest, our troops were engaged in battle. A leading member of the Writers' Association appealed to the intellectuals of the world: "Help, help, help."

The familiar sound of tanks roaring along mingled with the sounds of the guns. We peeped out through the window: Soviet tanks had arrived. Free Kossuth Radio had stopped. My wife's reactions were quick: she tore up the manuscript of my appeal from the night before. We have often recalled this moment with amusement.

The revolutionary battle and strikes went on for weeks after. Again, there is no need for me to tell their story. But one aspect of it all has perhaps not been made clear: the tides of changing moods and guesses, starting in my own case with the destruction of my manuscript, and ending when we decided to escape the country.

A friend rang and told me he had morphia ready. Rákosi's return was almost taken for granted. Unless the Russians could be persuaded to withdraw either by the West or by the Hungarian people, it was felt that a wholesale campaign of extermination would start against all who had opened their mouths. When the new Prime Minister, Kádár, as head of a "Workers' and Peasants' Revolutionary Government" first spoke over the wireless, the response was bitter because of his treachery and the Russians' lack of principle in thus violating the Hungarian people—but there was also a sense of relief. He paid lip-service to the Revolution. He did not say a word against the left-wing intellectuals who had started it, or against the masses of industrial workers, mainly Socialists, who continued to resist the invaders. The Rákosi clique, attempting to return to power, was denounced in the new government press. Discussions about the ending of the strike and battles between the Kádár Government and the Workers' Councils were fairly transmitted by the newly established radio. The Russians, it seemed, were trying to come to terms with the Hungarian people. Kádár and his associates started negotiations not only with the Workers' Councils but also with non-Communist leaders of the former coalition government.

If freedom of speech means that people speak freely, it had never existed to a greater extent than in those days, immediately after the Russian re-occupation of Budapest, in the streets under the threat of machine guns. Badges of the national coat of arms were worn ostentatiously by masses of people. Leaflets were distributed and posters read without the slightest notice taken of the Russian patrols and their potential agents. The destruction in the city was heartrending. News of more and more bloodshed was distressing. As the frontier between Hungary and Austria had been opened, many hurried to get out of the country. But those resisting the Russians stayed on.

The authority of the Writers' Association was not challenged by anybody. Our central office in Bajza Street was a headquarters for the revolutionary intelligentsia. The delegates from various revolutionary councils dashed in one after another and discussed consecutive plans, and issued manifestoes emphasizing their loyalty to the Revolution (and not to the "Revolutionary Government" of those days). It had other attractions too. In the middle of a city which looked as if it had suffered siege, this seemed an oasis of plenty. Some of its premises had been transformed into huge larders. Peasants from all over the country sent their goods freely, in one of the offices dozens of live chickens were twittering amongst the writing-desks. In another enormous bags of potatoes, carrots, and eggs were awaiting the authors and their spouses who carefully called for their rations.

Meetings went on incessantly. What should we do and what could we achieve? Should we repeat again and again our unwillingness to accept the *fait accompli* and insist on the "immediate withdrawal of all Soviet troops from Hungary" which was the main demand of the population? Or should we try to bring about a tolerable compromise between the occupiers and the people? Armed fights were dying down but the general strike still went on in the industrial suburbs of Budapest and in other factory districts and mining areas. The general cry was still everywhere "Ruszkik haza"—"Russians go home." But obviously it was the very thing which the Russians would not do—at any rate, not entirely and not immediately. Would it not be cleverer to demand something within reach than to ask for the moon?

Opinions were divided but the general atmosphere favoured intransigence. Despite Russian military occupation, people feared their own response more than they feared their master. Some recent events, however, tinged determination with panic. Crowds of young men had been rounded up in some districts, a number of them deported to Soviet territory. What should be done about them? A delegation went to see both the Russian-appointed Minister of Interior and the Russian *Kommandatura*. With the Minister, they had some passionate exchanges. The talk at the *Kommandatura* was more polite and more alarming. There was no doubt that the Russians considered the prisoners as hostages. They would allow the writers to intervene in their favour, if in return they would support the new Government, call for peace and order, and urge the resumption of work.

It was a tragic moment when any decision had to be irresponsible. Should we try to save the lives of thousands of young men, or the honour of the Revolution? The majority decided for a middle way. It was a touching and futile experiment. I remember the harassed and worn-down face of Gyula Háy, arriving at a meeting after a sleepless night when he had drafted the manifesto which was to vindicate the Revolutionary ideas and at the same time appease those who had crushed the Revolution. Surely this was more sensible than to have followed the advice of those who still called for "complete and immediate withdrawal"—and who since then have come to quite tolerable terms with the Russian-appointed Government. Gyula Háy meanwhile has been sentenced to six years.*

I disagreed about some details, and took a line which many appreciated but none followed. I wished we had dared to be less transigent in one way and more flexible in another. I suggested we should make a clear offer, telling the *Kommandatura* and the Government that we

---

* Both Déry and Háy were imprisoned from the beginning of 1957 until April, 1960, and then released under an amnesty. Amongst the intellectuals trying to bring about understanding with the Russians, the most important personality was a noncommunist member of the Imre Nagy coalition government—Professor Istvan Bibó, the legal historian, who at that time drafted a compromise plan, i.e., for the gradual withdrawal of the Soviet forces. Bibó was sentenced to life imprisonment *in camera,* and is now (May, 1962) in gaol.

were willing to take a stand clearly and firmly for the conclusion of the strike; provided the deportations stopped and those held were released, and provided the U.N. investigators were allowed entry to Hungary. My colleagues thought we must not provoke the Russians by urging the admission of the U.N. commission, or risk upsetting the feelings of the people by speaking against the strike unless the general demand for total military evacuation (which I thought quite unrealistic) was achieved.

We were hoping against hope. What if the Russians were to agree to withdraw gradually? What if a network of Councils could be established on a roughly democratic basis, as a step towards real parliamentary government—a network of Worker, Peasant, Intellectual, Army and Youth Councils, for instance? Could democratic parties, socialist and non-socialist alike, be expected to take part in such an arrangement? From the Government, approaches were made to Smallholders, Peasant Party representatives, Social Democrats and all sorts of liberals and Christian democrats.

What about the uncompromisingly anti-Stalin Communists who had started the Revolution? They would certainly be willing to join; but it was no secret that the Moscow emissaries suspected them more than anyone else. To deviate had in the Bolshevik doctrine always been a greater crime than to oppose; and though the Twentieth Congress seemed to put an end to heresy-hunting, the passions underlying heresy-hunting had never disappeared. The Hungarian people and mainly the workers were worried about Imre Nagy and his associates who, after the Russian onslaught on Budapest, had taken shelter in the Yugoslav Embassy. The question was not whether one agreed with them in doctrine; they had acted as the vanguard, and so had become symbols of the hope for independence, freedom and neutrality. The Russian-appointed Premier Kádar—himself a former member of the Imre Nagy coalition Government—was questioned about the relation between his Government and Imre Nagy. The answer was firm and unequivocal; the "Workers' and Peasants' Revolutionary Government" was willing to negotiate with Imre Nagy and his associates as soon as the latter left the Jugoslav Embassy. There would be no question of prosecuting them. They would not merely have safe conduct but would be considered as partners.

Then, a bolt from the blue. My sister had just spoken to a journalist friend of ours and ran to me: "Have you heard the news? Imre Nagy and his wife, and his daughter, and son-in-law, and grandchildren, and the Losonczys, and Lukács, and all the rest, you know . . . As soon as they left the Jugoslav Embassy they were caught by a Russian military detachment in the street and abducted . . ."

I rang the Writers' Association. A colleague who took the receiver confirmed the news with an agitated stammer. It was the end. Many felt infuriated with Kádár, but he seemed to me almost a figure of pity; especially when I heard him over the radio explaining that what the Russians had done was right, because after all the safety of Imre Nagy and his party had to be safeguarded. There had never been a Premier in such a pathetic position—compelled so conspicuously to spit in his own face.*

It seemed clear at that moment that my presence would be of no use whatever. Later I learned that I had been blacklisted by the organization which succeeded the A.V.H. I did not think it likely that they would imprison me again, but they would suspect and harass me. My attempts towards a sensible compromise, and my wish to do literary and scholarly work, had alike been frustrated. With a pregnant wife, could I take this risk? Besides, my old hobby of acting as bridge between the Hungarian and the Western Non-Communist Left overwhelmed me again. In 1949 that hobby had induced me to return to Budapest and expose myself to the A.V.H. At the end of 1956 the same thing induced me to escape as soon as possible.

---

* As will be remembered, Imre Nagy and his three comrades, General Pál Máleter, Miklós Gyimes, and József Szilágyi, were subsequently tried *in camera* and executed, according to a Budapest Government communiqué issued in June, 1958. This also announced the deportation and death of Géza Losonczy.

But how were we to set about it? I am very clumsy in such matters. I am no legalist, but perhaps for that reason most helpless when it comes to illegalities. I simply did not know whom to approach. Thousands and thousands were crossing the frontier every day, and Radio Free Europe transmitted for hours the messages of Hungarians who had just "arrived on free soil." It was a mass exodus, and the subject talked about everywhere and by everybody. A friend of my wife, a nice and simple woman, who shall be called Ann, an indifferent office clerk and excellent tennis player, came along to see us with her ten-year-old daughter. "Don't you think of escaping? I wish I could." Ann had a boy friend in Hungary and another in Australia. The more unbearable Russian terrorism seemed, the stronger the Australian *amoroso's* attraction grew as against the local one. But she knew as little as we did about how those tens of thousands went to it. We were just sighing.

Kádár repeatedly said, as reported later, on 27th November, in the Party newspaper: "We have promised not to start any punitive proceeding against Imre Nagy and we shall keep our word." Again a pledge. But who could believe any promise now? No hope either for improvement at home or escape to the West. It was a day of apathy until 3 p.m., November 26th. Then it changed to a day of melodrama.

The telephone rang, and Ann said excitably: "I met a dispatch carrier. The luggage must not include more than six boxes. It costs a lot of money and I am so unhappy, oh my God, I have got only half the amount . . . We must talk it over with . . . at once. If you want to send your things you must see those people without delay. It can't be postponed. The last load is to go tomorrow." A telephone censor would not have found it difficult to guess the meaning of such words. But everything was too much in a muddle for efficient terrorism. In fact, the suggestion that one should use special means to send boxes somewhere was credible. Very little railway traffic went about the country, and hitch-hiking was a substitute for it. In the city, the trams had not yet been brought back; which meant that most people had to walk. It meant walking in mud and over ditches—the city was in a shambles. Streets were dimly lit, and the curfew came into force after 8 p.m. If we were to embark on the venture, we had to start at once. But should we?

I could not decide, but I said we must act on the assumption that we were to leave. We must not leave the chance unexplored. We went to see our friend. Could we raise the money for her as well as for ourselves? I still had some cash from my compensation money which I had been paid after my re-trial. Four thousand florins were needed for each of us—the sum spent by an average Hungarian family in three months. We hurried along, first to Ann, and then to the flat from which we were to start. It was already getting dark. "Hello, hello," a cheerful stout fellow shouted at us. It was the former Prime Minister Dinnyés. I hardly knew him but had always liked his unpretentious, friendly and gay nature. He had fought the Nazis heroically as a member of the Smallholders' Party. After the war, he felt he had been heroic long enough. He fellow-travelled without visible scruples but, as far as I know, without harming anyone. He kept his good humour and his luxurious car. On this occasion, however, he was walking.

After his volcanic Magyar embracements, he told us a torrent of anecdotes. We were not in a mood to listen to funny stories but he was not in the mood to let us go. He broached the subject most current at the moment: "What do you say to those thousands of fools rushing abroad now?"

"Damned fools," we answered in chorus.

"Aren't they? Of course, it's no easy matter to live in Hungary. But, my God, to go abroad! My friend D used to say that everyone was a fool to emigrate unless he was less than thirty years old or more than thirty-thousand dollars a year."

"Of course, of course, how right he is. I am afraid we must hurry up because of the curfew. . . ."

He played about with his walking stick. His storytelling seemed endless.

"Sz., you remember, the old crook? He was a clever man. He had to leave Budapest because of his fishy dealings. But he returned. I asked him why. 'I am getting old, you know, and having the usual trouble with my bowels. You can't live at my age in a city, where you don't know the whereabouts of the public lavatories.' A wise man I say. Wasn't he?"

"Extremely wise," we assured him and dashed off. Stumbling and panting we called on the "luggage man" and went home, still undecided. We carried on with our preparations "as if we were going." At the peak of our nervousness, a cousin entered. "Oh, I wanted so much to see you. Could you come and have dinner with us tomorrow? Do you like *gulyás* done in the Székely way?" I had to tell him I was not free for the next days.

Until the last moment I never really decided we should go. I only decided we should carry on as if we were to go. In haste, we crammed the most necessary belongings into a little suitcase, a dispatch-case and two shopping bags. No knapsack was available.

We had just a few hours of sleep on the night of the 26th. We took our little luggage and trod the streets like sleepwalkers. "Let us behave as if we were going." We arrived at a flat where seven of us were gathered, ready to start. The party included a baby in its pram which was to be left at the frontier, and also our friend Ann with her ten-year-old daughter. She was weeping: she had only money enough for one person. Would the driver agree to take her daughter as well? . . . The driver arrived at about 10 a.m. He was rough and hasty. About the additional infant he just shrugged his shoulders, saying we would have to pay as the frontier guards must get their own share; but trusting us to find some money somehow, he took us all on his lorry. He explained how we should behave. Whenever challenged, we should name a country town in the West of Hungary as our destination, and each of us should have his own explanation of why he had to get there. We must pretend we had been picked up as hitch-hikers. So we were leaving Budapest "as if we were going away."

Indeed we were stopped several times. A security policeman climbed into the lorry. "Well, why do you all want to go to the West? You don't think I am such a fool as not to know. . . ." We insisted on our respective stories. "I shan't allow you *all* to go." He eyed a pretty girl, a dancer, who had some special connexion with the driver's party. Then he cast a glance at the baby. "How can you expose such a tiny thing to such an ordeal?" And he let us go.

At another post, near the great industrial city of Győr, in the West of Hungary, a soldier asked us: "Now where are you for?" Most of us said our destination was Győr. "So you want to go to Győr? Then good luck to you all beyond Győr, in the free world."

Beyond Győr came hard luck. A big detachment, including Russians, stopped us. We were ordered to return. So we did, as far as Győr. There the lorry drove through some muddy lanes, and after dusk we arrived at the frontier village of Mosonszentjános.

We turned out to be in the hands of liars and blackmailers. They were an exceptionally rotten crowd. Those who smuggled people over the frontier were paid for doing so, which in itself could not be objected to, considering the labour and risks involved. But most did so with moderation. Our guides were greedy and cruel. When we stopped at a peasant's house, the father and son responsible for that trade started shouting at us that they would be unable to undertake the trip unless we gave them more. They had to bribe the frontier guards. They had to risk their lives. On the chest of drawers, in the stuffy and dreary peasant's bungalow, wristwatches and banknotes were piling up. The guides really did not count them, they only argued. My wife and I refused to give up our watches. We even hid a small sum of money. "Give us everything," the peasant guide insisted; "beyond the frontier, it won't be worth a farthing. . . ."

Their story about sharing the money with frontier guards turned out to be nonsense. So did their whole promise to help us over the frontier. In Budapest, they had said we would only have to go about four hundred yards to the boundary, and that they would see us across. When we started the walk, it had grown to two miles. It turned out to be more than ten.

But it was not the distance that mattered. It was the land. We were dragging ourselves in mud, up to our ankles. Every step was an effort. Rain poured down, and it was dark. After about a hundred yards, I simply could not imagine how we would achieve it. I watched my pregnant wife: fortunately she wore a pair of high laced boots, but most of us had ordinary shoes. They stuck in the mud and had to be pulled out, full of muck. Some lost their shoes, which did not matter for a while but then we came to stubble. The barefooted were full of wounds on their soles and heels. The handle of my suitcase broke, and I took it under my arm. That made the journey even more painful. "Throw it away, you will not be able to take it over the frontier," the guide shouted at us. He gave this excellent advice to everybody. We knew he would pick them up if we did. I never knew I could stick to a suitcase with such fury.

It was pitch dark with only a few faint lights on the horizon when our guides abandoned us. We did not know quite where to go. We only knew where the bullets were coming from. Rocket flares went above us. We threw ourselves on our stomachs as a safety precaution. I was glad to have a rest even in such an uncomfortable spot, though I knew we should be almost too exhausted to get up. We came to a hedge where it seemed to us we could have a little rest. We decided we must already be in Austria. Anyway we made ourselves believe so—subconsciously no doubt, because we badly needed rest. It was about midnight. Then we heard steps. Torches were turned on our faces. We were still on Hungarian soil. Two Hungarian frontier-guards were approaching us.

"What are you doing here?" they asked. The question was correct but of course somewhat rhetorical. What could we be doing at midnight on the fallow by the Austrian frontier-line? "Well, I am sorry, I must escort you back to the next patrol-station." We appealed to their human feelings. We appealed to them as Hungarians. They argued with us, though with obvious reluctance: "Look here, it is our duty . . ." Some of us were already preparing to follow them. But my wife, in particular, was adamant. "My dear friends"—she said, "I do not mind anything by now, I do not mind what you do. You may kill me at once if you wish. But I shall not return. I have had enough after five years in prison. I don't want my child to be born for prison . . ." The two armed young men looked at each other sternly. Then one of them took my wife under her elbow. "All right, come with me, come all of you. We shall see you to the frontier."

So it happened. Having been left in the lurch by our hired guides, we were saved by those appointed to check us.

We arrived at a double plough-line. "Now that is the boundary line," the guard on my wife's left told us. He was a peasant boy, about 17 or 18 years of age. "We are all Hungarians," was the sentence repeated alternately by them and ourselves. It is an uninteresting truism but there were moments when it could work miracles.

Now I was particularly glad that I had not given all my money to the crooks in the village. Some hundred-florin notes had remained in my pocket. I handed them to the young man. He refused. "I did not do it for that. . . ." I insisted. "I know you didn't but I should be glad if you were to accept. You told me you had an old mother to look after and that was your reason for not coming over with us. Do me the favour of buying her a present with that."

We shook hands and parted company. The rockets were still visible. But we felt at least *de jure* safe, though not entirely. The frontier-line in that district runs in zigzags, and one may easily lose the way. We decided we should march until we reached an Austrian patrol-station. But tiredness prevailed. We saw a little stone hut in the middle of a great waste of land, and climbed in. We found straw there to rest on. We reassured ourselves that we must be safe, though at heart, we were still full of worries. Dear Ann was less inhibited than the rest of us in moaning. She had every reason to be upset. Her legs and feet seemed crippled for good. "I am afraid we may still be in Hungary. Oh my God, what are we to do if we are caught again. . . ." I apologize to her now by proxy for answering with something less than gentlemanly impatience.

We had run out of drinking water. I climbed out to find some. We remembered we had seen something like a well in the vicinity. Groping my way in the dark and the mud, I found it. Indeed it was a shadoof, a typical old well of the Hungarian country districts. This alarmed me a bit. As far as I knew, no shadoofs existed in Austria. All the same I set to work. I let the bucket down and pulled it up again, full of water. I took some in the thermos to the hut. So did another man. His conclusions from what he saw there were more optimistic. "Don't you see how different the shape of this bucket is from what they use in Hungarian shadoofs? This must be Austria. . . ." When day started breaking we got up and resumed our wandering. My wife had repaired my suitcase so that I was again able to hold it by the handle, which made a tremendous difference. Before carrying on, we called for another sip at the shadoof. We found the bucket full of corpses of frogs. We were nearly ill from the sight and carried on thirsty. How pleasant it had been to drink while we did not know what was there.

We wandered on between stacks of straw, only meeting refugees. We were still not absolutely sure of being on safe soil. Then we met a horse-driven cart, with an old peasant on it. We accosted him in Hungarian and German. He only knew German. He assured us we were in Austria. We begged him at least to take the women and children on his cart to an inhabited place. He refused at first: "I must hurry with my work, you see it's pouring. . . ." But then with a sudden change: "Kumts, alle." We all climbed on the dungheap in his cart, and were carried thus to the first village.

The sad and touching features of the reception camps have often been described already. I have myself published accounts of my experiences and expressed my gratitude and admiration for the people in the relief organizations out there. In general my refugee compatriots were

worth the attention and kindness showered on them. But
this does not mean that all were heroes, or even that they
were all honest. On the bus which took us from the frontier village to the Andau camp, we discussed the fates of
the leading Hungarian freedom fighters. What about Pál
Maléter, the leader of the Hungarian Army which resisted
the invaders? I said I was worried that he might have been
arrested by the Russians while negotiating with them, and
kept in prison ever since. As we know today, this was so;
and since then he has been murdered, together with Imre
Nagy. But a young swashbuckler in the bus firmly contradicted me: "Nonsense! I saw him two days ago. He is
leading our partisans in the Bükk forests. I was his aide-
de-camp and only left him because he ordered me to come
to the West and negotiate on his behalf. . . ." Later, in the
camp, I met two other youngsters who pretended quite independently from each other to be on the same mission.
One of them eagerly inquired as to the whereabouts of
Prince Esterházy, who was known to possess even then
quite considerable properties in Austria.

My wife and I spent the night on a straw-sack, crowded
together in a room with five or six other people. The
leader of the party was a dull and stubborn man, sitting
with a fur-cap on his head and not letting me open the
window for a moment. Stench and fug were unbearable. I
found out that he was a miner with his family, including a
baby three months old. The mother turned out to be a
slightly more intelligent person. "Why did you decide to
escape from Hungary?" I asked her. Conditions were bad,
no doubt, but these did not seem to be the people involved in any political imbroglio. Indeed they were not;
but that was just the trouble. "Well, sir, what's happened
to us is this," she said. "My husband went working. As he
descended the shaft and returned when his shift had
ended, the Freedom Fighter caught him there. 'Now my
man, if I catch you once again you won't get at the mine
gates alive.' Next day my husband stayed at home. Then,
the Russian patrol entered. The Russki said to him 'Isn't
it your working time? Look here, if I catch you once again
absent from the mine when you should be there I'll take

you to Zalaegerszeg, the internment camp, and you know people are not just imprisoned there but decimated. . . .' We simply did not know what to do. We liked it at home. We had just slaughtered a pig which we had reared, and we had enough to eat. But how could one live there? Death for working, death for not working . . . Then I said 'Very well, on the frontier we may meet death as well. But if we have luck we can get across. And so we packed as much as we could from the ham and sausages, and took our four kids, and set out . . ." I do not know what has happened to them since. They became submerged in the flood of 200,000 Hungarians fleeing over the frontier. But I do not know why anyone should be surprised at the fact that some 15,000 of the 200,000 have since returned. What could that dull peasant-miner have done in any country where the language, the way to rear pigs, the habits and outlook were completely unknown to him? Without being a traitor, he fled the Freedom Fighters no less than the invaders. When the Freedom Fighters were defeated, he had no more reason to live away from home. Perhaps he was too unimaginative even to return once he had escaped; otherwise it would really not be surprising if he had done so.

In the camp, a nurse asked us "Could you kindly act as interpreters for us with some children?" There was a party of about ten boys, the youngest 10, the eldest 15 years of age. Some came from Budapest, some from the country. We were to explain to them in Hungarian that they would get places in a hostel nearby. They were panic-stricken. "Oh, for Heaven's sake, don't let us be taken back to Hungary. The Russkis will catch us. The Russkis catch all children. . . ." We could hardly reassure them that by leaving the miserable, overcrowded camp in Andau they would not necessarily be returning to Hungary. That the Russians "took *all* children" was of course a legend. But facts making it believable were plentiful.

The rumour went round that I had arrived. Friends in Britain, France, Holland had been asking about me. A Danish journalist brought a message, and a lively, stout gentleman, Colonel Koenigsbert, from the World Veter-

ans Federation, offered my wife and me facilities to leave
for Britain as soon as possible. So we did, and travelled
quite comfortably from Andau to London. Enthusiasm
was exhilarating. Hungarian refugees all over Europe were
received with patriotic songs, and food and clothes parcels. In London, I was told, something like a fight was
going on for the care of Hungarian refugees; all were keen
to give hospitality to at least one Hungarian Freedom
Fighter. Our popularity was fantastic. I felt some doubts.
"I only dread the moment when I shall hear from someone that the Freedom Fighter he had sheltered pinched
his wristwatch."

Reality turned out to be more romantic than my fore-
boding. The first complaint of this kind that I heard about
concerned the Freedom Fighter who eloped with the
daughter of a wealthy host. But even this had its happy
ending in the form of paternal consent. After all, a hero—
even if a beggar—is no disgrace to an honest family.

It was the beginning of December, 1956. Only a few
weeks after our Revolution and its defeat, and the Suez
adventure and its failure. People felt the world was in an
impasse, and Britain in a crisis. What sort of crisis? I
asked. Moral crisis, financial crisis, political crisis . . .
I heard about the symptoms but what I saw round me
struck me as by no means depressing. Many of my friends
had aged, many had died. But most did quite well. The
city seemed cleaner, food better, people nicer than ever.
I was not perhaps an unbiased witness of all this. The
kindness showered on me and my wife was indescribable.
I felt I had arrived home abroad.

But all this could not comfort me for the alarming news
of my people at home. Nor for the sufferings of the person
who stood next to me. She was still with child when we
arrived. A day or two later, under the stress and calami-
ties of our escape, premature labour started. She became
the mother of a stillborn baby girl whom she had intended to call Beatrix. That little creature who had never
seen the sun paid with her life for ours.

Epilogue

I wrote the bulk of *Political Prisoner,* as a political refugee, in the French home for men of letters, "La Méssuguière," in Cabris, Alpes-Maritimes, from January to March of 1958. The book was first published by Messrs. Routledge and Kegan Paul, London, in October, 1959. When I learned that it was going into paperback, I went through the text again, bringing it up to date, making slight corrections and adding a few footnotes; but, I did not alter the essentials. My fundamental views have not changed since I wrote it, and the story strikes me today, even more than when I set it down, as rounded out by fate, with a note at the end which is sad but in the spirit of reconciliation. To alter it would be forgery.

But the time since 1958 and 1959 has not been uneventful, and I feel I should tell my new American readers about the way these events affected the *dramatis personae* —me, my family, and my homeland. I shall restrict myself to recording two instances only; first, adding a gay note to the sad note; and the other—adding some emphasis to the bitterness which has always accompanied my willingness to be reconciled with my fate and that of others.

The gay note is what might be expected, a Dickensian postscript. My wife, whom I need not introduce to the reader, gave birth to our son, Paul Imre, in a nursing home in Greater London, on July 31, 1958. On the eve of the event I happened to take a double dose of sleeping pills and was fast asleep when, in the small hours, she felt she should wake me up and tell me that I was about to become a father. She shook me in vain, but managed to drive herself to the nursing home. The following afternoon I was relieved to learn over the telephone that, however disgraceful my absence, it did not really matter. The condition of both mother and child was satisfactory. The mother's mood was even more so. "If you saw him how pretty he is," she told me before I could go and see them, "not that sort of purple other newborn babies are, you know. . . ." "Resigned to his being *he*?" "Even to that," she replied. My mother in Budapest, then about 90, had also, for some reason, hoped for a girl. On learning of the news she exclaimed, "Hang it all, it will be all right." And all right it was.

We live in an unluxurious but comfortable flat, facing Battersea Park, London, and Paul Imre spends much of his time feeding its ducks and climbing its trees, though with a bias for the swings and the rocking horse in its Children's Playground, where he has acquired a well-earned reputation as a bright, handsome, and lively representative of his age-group. It's a reputation too well-earned as far as liveliness is concerned! But as it is the very thing I was looking forward to, I must not grumble about it. I am happy watching him day by day, though I cannot help feeling this posture of belated paternal pride somewhat foolish. Maternal and grand-maternal pride is of course less inhibited and healthier. But life cannot be Dickensian, after all; surely not according to Dickens who knew and wrote a lot about the struggles to make ends meet. My wife works in an office; we have her English-born mother with us to look after the child. We also have my sister Elly who followed us to Britain some weeks after our escape. And we had for a while the intelligent but unheroic lady dachshund, Dinky. She had been helped to join us in this country, with more impeccable documents than we ever had, by the Royal Society for the Prevention of Cruelty to Animals. She has since died of old age, and a black kitten now fills the vacuum—not an altogether worthy successor, concerning personal relations; but, apart from its Baudelairean charm, quite a useful member of the household in keeping down the mice.

In the meantime, I am trying my best to be an English writer. The obstacles are almost insurmountable: My Hungarian is too strong to be forgotten. Language is for me a bond stronger than kinship, comradeship, business or political allegiance. I shall never lose my interest in Hungary. But I also know that those things which bound

me to the Hungary of 1956 have now disintegrated—
even more completely than I imagined while writing this
book.

I do not mean the military defeat of the Revolution.
That was a foregone conclusion once it had become clear
that the Russians were, and their opponents on the international chessboard were not, prepared to take up arms
on the issue. Many Hungarians hated the West for its unwillingness to fight. I rather reproached it for fighting to
the last Hungarian. "The West," of course, is an abstraction. However, the radio stations set up in some western
countries which transmitted Hungarian voices were tangible realities easily mistaken for "The West" especially
when they were more uncompromising than the Hungarian Freedom Fighters themselves in their defense of "Hungarian Freedom." But that is all over now, and what's
the good of crying over spilt blood?

Hungary, of course, had to capitulate: Her sole alternative was collective suicide. Most Hungarians accepted this
cruel verdict of history with the utmost cynicism, that is,
in the spirit most worthy of sensible people in circumstances where any hope of a reasonable settlement has
gone. They did not fool themselves nor one another
about the price they paid for survival. One of the cleverest
and most humane rulers history has ever known paid for
Paris "with a Mass." Afterwards, he made the best of it
as a king. The Hungarians had to make the best of it as
slaves. But slavery, too, can be leavened and borne in
good humour. I feel I made this abundantly clear in this
book, by talking about a much harsher variety of slavery.

What are conditions like in Hungary today? As travel
restrictions have eased, there are a large number of eye-
witness reports available. They converge in many details;
they conflict in others; and as to their final conclusions,
they are generally in accord with preconceived ideas, irrespective of the details reported. "It is better, no doubt,
far better than it used to be under Stalin and Rákosi,"
one reporter will say, "but still pretty awful." He is right.
"It is still pretty awful, no doubt," the other might say,
"but better, far better than it used to be under Stalin and

Rákosi." He is no less right. It simply depends on what you feel should be emphasized. What we call "cold war" consists of intermittent hot quarrels and lukewarm handshakes between the super-powers, and it is only natural that, in the heat of a clash, the memory of the blood shed in the streets of Budapest should be revived, only to be forgotten in the ensuing lull. Accordingly, the emphasis shifts from "pretty awful" to "better, far better," and back again. So much should be taken for granted.

What strikes me as most disheartening in all this is really a matter of style. The average Hungarian, honest enough to have turned into an outright cynic, is not guilty. The guilty Hungarians are the lofty Hungarians; not the hypocrites, not the prostitutes, but the self-deceivers. They are the sort of people who, as de Tocqueville observed, "are often accused of acting without conviction; but," he adds, "this was much less frequently the case than one might think. Only they possess the precious and, sometimes in politics, even necessary faculty of creating transient convictions for themselves, according to the passions and the interests of the moment, and thus they succeed in committing, honourably enough, actions which in themselves are little to their credit."* They are the sort of people who, in present-day Hungary, perform the ritual of capitulation enthusiastically and spectacularly though with loopholes left wide-open to convince themselves of their having performed an act of bravery. Such acts may be appreciated on both sides of the Iron Curtain; they are, in "Eastern" sloganology, "an honest conversion to sympathy for Communism by one known never to have held such sympathies" and, in "Western" sloganology, "the continuation of the brave resistance against Communism though by subtler means." However different the interpretations, there is a comforting spark of "co-existence" in them.

Really why object to such harmony? For one who considered the Hungarian Revolution as the beginning of a crusade to overthrow Bolshevism, it does not matter

* From his *Recollections,* Meridian Books, New York.

whether the survivors of its defeat do or do not know that they have been defeated. But it was both the attraction and the weakness of that Revolution that it could mean so many different things to such a wide variety of people. To me it meant a struggle for the right to call a spade a spade. This right has not only been violated but forgotten, practically everywhere where it might be remembered. But as forgetfulness is still preferable to revengefulness, we had better let sleeping dogs lie, and sleepy minds believe the lie.

P. I.

London, June 1962.

COMMUTE

TIME
TUNNEL

MURRAY LEINSTER

PYRAMID BOOKS • NEW YORK

TIME TUNNEL

A PYRAMID BOOK—First printing, July 1964

PYRAMID BOOKS are published by Pyramid Publications, Inc.,
444 Madison Avenue, New York, N.Y. 10022, U.S.A.

TIME TUNNEL

1

The affair of the time-tunnel began, so far as Harrison was concerned, with a series of events so improbable as to seem lunacy, but which appear to have been inevitable. In a cosmos designed to have human beings live in it, though, there would have to be some sort of safeguards against the consequences of their idiocy. The time-tunnel may have been such a safeguard. To some people, that seems a reasonable guess.

*****

It was a brisk, sunshiny Parisian afternoon when the matter really turned up. Harrison sat at a sidewalk table outside the little cafe in the Rue Flamel. He'd never happened to notice its name. He sipped at an apéritif, thinking hard and trying not to believe what he was thinking about. He'd come from the Bibliothèque Nationale a good hour before. Today he'd found more of the completely incredible. He didn't believe it, but he knew it was true. His series of discoveries had reached the point where he simply couldn't tell himself any longer that they were coincidences. They weren't. And their implications were of a kind to make cold chills run up and down anybody's spine. A really sensible man would have torn up his notes, gotten drunk to confuse his memories, and then departed

7

on the earliest possible plane for home. There he would
have denied to himself forever after that he had found
what Harrison had discovered in the dusty manuscript
section of the Bibliothèque Nationale.

But Harrison sipped at a drink and noted the small
cold chills running up and down his spine. He resented them
because he didn't believe in what caused them. But there
they were. They had to do with the cosmos in general.
Most men develop convictions about the cosmos and such
beliefs come in two varieties. One kind is a conviction
that the cosmos does not make sense. That it exists by
chance and changes by chance and human beings do not
matter. This view produces a fine complacency. The other
kind is a belief that the cosmos does make sense, and was
designed with the idea that people were going to live in
it, and that what they do and what happens to them is
important. This theory seems to be depressing.

Harrison had accepted the second view, but he was
beginning to be frightened because of what he'd found in
dusty, quill-pen-written pages in a library reading room.
And he didn't like to be frightened.

It was a very pleasant autumn afternoon, though. Leaves
had been falling, and they blew erratically about the pavement in appropriate fall colorings, and the sky showed
through the nearly denuded branches of the trees that
lined the Rue Flamel. There was nobody on the sidewalks.
For minutes there had been no traffic going past the
small cafe. It was just cold enough so that Harrison was the
only customer at any of the outdoor tables.

Around him there were houses which had stood in their
places for centuries and thereby acquired a self-satisfied air.
From high overhead there came a rumbling, distant thunder.
A jet had made the sound, but there was no use in trying to
sight it. It had left its noise-trail far behind. It was now undoubtedly hidden by roofs or chimney-pots.

Then, at last, someone did come down the street. It was
an extremely improbable occurrence, not that somebody
should walk down the street, but who it happened to be. The
odds against anything that actually happens are always enormous, when one considers the number of other things that
could have happened instead. But certainly the odds were
incalculably great that Pepe Ybarra, who had been at Brevard
University with Harrison and had shared one course in statistical analysis with him, would *not* be walking down the Rue

Flamel at this particular moment, when Harrison had come upon the preposterous and doubted his own sanity.

But there he was. He came briskly toward the cafe. Harrison hadn't seen him for four years. The last time had been in Uxbridge, Pennsylvania, when Pepe was being hauled out of the Roland River by an also-dripping policeman who was going to arrest him within minutes, but was forced to accept Pepe's warmly grateful handshake beforehand. Now he was walking down the Rue Flamel on an autumn afternoon. It was not a probable occurrence, but it was the kind of thing that happens.

He greeted Harrison with a glad outcry.

"For the love of heaven! What are you doing here? Where've you been? What gives? How long have you been in Paris? Do you know any interesting girls?"

Harrison shook hands and Pepe dropped into a chair opposite him. He regarded Harrison with approving eyes.

"I've been here for two months," said Harrison wrily. "I don't know any girls, and I think I'm going to try to forget what I came for."

Pepe rapped on the table. He ordered a drink over his shoulder. To Harrison he said warmly, "Now we have fun! Where are you living? What are you doing? Why don't you know any girls?"

"I've been busy," said Harrison. He explained. "I've an elderly aunt. She offered to stake me to a Ph.D. And she said that since I lived here when I was a small boy—until I was twelve—I ought to try to get back my French. And I had a crazy sort of idea that fitted into the proposal. It was something Professor Carroll said once in a lecture. Remember him? So I came over to get back my French and dig up the material for my thesis. My aunt is pleased. I wish I'd never thought of it." Harrison was silent a moment. Then he changed the subject. "What have you been doing?"

Pepe sketched, with enthusiasm, his activities since Harrison had last seen him. He'd been home in Mexico. For a while he was in Tehuantepec. She was a lovely girl! Then he'd been in Tegucigalpa. She was charming! And then he'd been in Aguascalientes, and the name fitted! She was *una rubaya*, a red-head. Mmmmmmmh! But there'd been trouble there. His family had sent him to France until the affair blew over. Now he was being very virtuous. Seriously, what was Harrison doing in Paris?

"I've been digging," said Harrison, "in the manuscript section of the Bibliothèque Nationale. Did you know, Pepe,

that a century and a half before Pasteur, there was someone
who described in detail the idea that living things too small
to be seen—germs, in fact—could be responsible for con-
tagious diseases?"*

Pepe accepted his drink, beaming. He nodded as he put
it to his lips. Overhead, the dull rumble of the jet-sound
died gradually away. A taxicab crossed the Rue Flamel at
the next corner. Blowing fallen leaves made faint whispering
sounds on the pavement.

"*Pues?*" said Pepe. He put down his glass. "What of it?"

"That's a freak," said Harrison. "But I just found in Cuvier's
notes—the naturalist, you know—that in 1804 a man named
de Bassompierre wrote him a theory which might be of interest to a savant concerned with natural history. And he out-
lined, very clearly and simply, the Mendelian laws of heredity.
But it happened to be more than half a century before Mendel
discovered them."

Pepe said, "That is not a freak?"

"No," said Harrison with some grimness. "Last week I
found in the laboratory notes of Ampère—the man who discovered so much about electricity, you know—that someone
named de Bassompierre wrote him in 1805 to tell him very
respectfully that there were such things as alternating currents. He explained in words of one syllable how they could
be generated and what they could be used for."

Pepe raised his eyebrows.

"This Bassompierre," he observed, "was quite a character!
You interest me strangely. In fact . . ."

"He was more than a character," said Harrison. "He
wrote to Laplace, the astronomer, assuring him that Mars
had two moons, very small and very close to its surface. He
also said that there were three planets beyond Saturn, and
that the one next out had a period of eighty-four years and
two moons, one retrograde. He suggested that it should be
called Uranus. He added that in the year 1808 there would be
a nova in Persis, (which there was!) and he signed himself
very respectfully, de Bassompierre."

"I am getting interested," said Pepe. "There is a de
Bassompierre in . . ."

*Note: This is historical fact. The theory was recorded
with derisive gestures by John Asdruc, physician to
Louis XIV of France. The germ theory was held by
Augustine Hauptman and Christian Longius, among
others M. L.

"Someone wrote to Jean-François Champollion," Harrison went on morbidly, "the Egyptologist. The Rosetta stone had just been discovered, but nobody could make use of it yet. The letter told him exactly how to decipher the Egyptian inscription. Champollion paid no attention for sixteen years. Then he tried the system suggested, but without referring to the letter, which he may have forgotten. It worked. But it had been described in 1806 by de Bassompierre."

"Evidently a universal genius," agreed Pepe. "But . . ."

"Lagrange, the mathematician," Harrison went on, distastefully, "had a correspondent who explained to him the principles of statistical analysis. He died before finishing his *Méchanique Analytique*, so there's no way to know if he paid any attention. But the description was so clear that you'd swear Professor Carroll wrote it. But it happened to be de Bassompierre. It was also de Bassompierre who around 1812 corresponded with the Académie des Sciences, and offered the interesting theory that atoms might be compared to miniature solar systems, with negatively charged particles orbiting complex nuclei of different masses. He added that all the elements heavier than bismuth would be found to be unstable, breaking down at different rates to other and lighter elements."

"Such statements," said Pepe with reserve, "are not easy to believe. After all, Madame Curie . . ."

"I know!" said Harrison fretfully. "It isn't possible. But this same de Bassompierre, who, by the way, died in 1858 at the age of ninety-one, also wrote to Desmarest, the geologist, and told him the facts of life about petroleum, including the products of fractional distillation. Do you see why I wish I'd never thought of looking up this stuff?"

Pepe sipped at his drink and put it down.

"I confess," he observed, "that I am interested in this de Bassompierre! I knew nothing of this! But where does it lead?"

"I'm afraid to find out," admitted Harrison. "But Talleyrand is said to have been his close friend, and Talleyrand never made a real mistake in guessing what would come next. Napoleon said he was possessed of a devil. Instead, he possessed the friendship of de Bassompierre. I can show you in Talleyrand's papers that he'd predicted the American civil war. Look, Pepe! De Bassompierre knew that there'd be a Maximilian, Emperor of Mexico, fifty years in what was then the future!"

He stopped. He felt queer. He had experienced a momentary

giddiness. It was almost unnoticeable, but it seemed as if the
street changed subtly and the branches of the trees were no
longer exactly as they had been. There was a doorway in a
house on the opposite side of the street which abruptly
looked wrong.

Pepe looked at him curiously.

"What's that?" he asked. "An Emperor Maximilian of
Mexico? What are you talking about?"

Harrison turned pale. He remembered saying the words,
"Maximilian, Emperor of Mexico." When he'd said them,
they'd seemed perfectly reasonable. They were meaningful.
But now they weren't. They were associated with somebody
named Napoleon the Third, to be sure. And of course there'd
been a Napoleon the Third, just as there'd been a Napoleon the
Fourth, and so on. But somehow it had seemed wrong. And
there had never been a Maximilian of Mexico.

"I suspect," he said in a sudden mixture of aversion and
relief, "that I've cracked up. I've been talking nonsense."

But Pepe's expression had changed, also. He looked puzzled.

"I am not sure, but now it comes to me. I have a memory,
a vague one. It seems to me that there was some story, perhaps a novel, about a Maximilian. His wife was named . . ."

"Carlotta," said Harrison.

"Pero sí!" agreed Pepe, relievedly. "Certainly! We read
the same novel at some time or another! There have only
been four Emperors of Mexico and none of them was
named . . ."

He stopped short. His mouth dropped open. There was
again a faint feeling of giddiness in the air. Again one could
not be sure that he felt it. The branches of the trees again
seemed changed, as if they'd grown differently from the way
they'd looked before. A door across the street looked right
again, where before it hadn't.

"Now, why the devil," demanded Pepe, "why did I say
that? Of course there was an Emperor Maximilian! He was a
fool! He spent his time compiling an official book of the
etiquette to be observed in his court, while he and all his
followers were being besieged by Juarez, who presently
had him shot!** And Carlotta went mad and lived in
Belgium until 1927! Why did I say there was no Emperor

**The writing of a book of etiquette was, histori-
cally, the principal interest of Maximilian while he was
being besieged in Queretaro, before his capture and
execution. M.L.

Maximilian? Why did I suspect that we had both merely read the same novel? And—*Dios mio!*—where did I get the idea that there had been four Mexican emperors? Am I insane?"

Harrison was still very pale.

"Let's find out." He rapped on the table. The waiter came. Harrison paid and tipped him. Then he said: "Do you know if there was ever an Emperor of Mexico?"

The waiter beamed.

"Mais oui! He was the Archduke Maximilian of Hapsburg, placed on the throne of Mexico by Napoleon the Third. He was shot by the Republicans at Queretaro. It is part of history, *m'sieur,* which I read as an amusement."

Harrison gravely doubled the tip. He said, *"Merci,"* and he and Pepe rose from the table. As they went down the street together, Pepe said ruefully:

"Now, I wonder how many waiters in Mexico could have told us that! And it is our history! But why did I make such a fool of myself? Why did I? Do I seem to act strangely? Should I see a doctor? A psycho-analyst?"

Harrison said with some grimness:

"Remember Professor Carroll? I'd like to see him! He said something that started me off on this business. Remember? He said that the cosmos as known is merely the statistical probability that has the value of unity? I'd like to see him analyze the statistical probability of de Bassompierre!"

"Ah, yes! De Bassompiere! I . . ." Then Pepe stopped. After an instant he said, "I also thought of Professor Carroll today. There is a shop, a very curious one. The name is Carroll, Dubois et Cie. The window says that they are importers and exporters *d'ans* 1804. They display incredible objects, apparently from the Napoleonic period, but absolutely new and in perfect condition. They even offer reprints of the *Moniteur* of 1804. But they say, 'exporters and importers'!"

Then he said indignantly:

"But why did I make so insane a statement about four emperors of Mexico? For seconds I believed tranquilly that that was the history of my country!"

Harrison shrugged. He remained absorbed in his own problem. Presently he said with a sort of mirthless amusement, "Would you like to hear something really insane, Pepe? Make one impossible assumption, and the matter of de Bassompierre and his correspondence becomes quite impos-

sible. There is only one fact to make the assumption unthinkable."

"What is the assumption?"

"If it were possible to travel in time," said Harrison, "and
one had evidence that a man in the early 1800s knew about
Mendel's laws, and that alternating current could be useful
—when at the time even D.C. was of no use to anybody
—and facts about astronomy the telescopes weren't good
enough to find out, and how hieroglyphics could be deci-
phered, and perfectly valid principles of statistical analysis,
and the real structure of atoms, and radioactivity, and what
could be done with petroleum. *If* it were possible to travel in
time, all those bits of information could be known to a man
of Napoleon's era if he happened to be moderately well-
informed and had traveled back to then from here and now."

"But you don't believe that!" protested Pepe.

"Of course not. But it explains every fact but one."

"The one fact it does not explain," said Pepe, "should be
interesting."

"The fact is," Harrison told him, "that there was a man
named Bassompierre, and he was a friend of Talleyrand's. He
was born in 1767, he travelled in the Orient for several years,
and he returned to France to discover that an imposter had
assumed his identity and looted his estates. The imposter attacked him when he was unmasked, and was killed. So de
Bassompierre resumed his station in society, corresponded
with men of science—all this is in the official biographical
material about him—and he was useful to Napoleon on one or
two occasions but was highly regarded by the Bourbons when
they returned. You see?"

Pepe frowned.

"There was a man named de Bassompierre!" said Harrison
harassedly. "He was born two hundred-odd years ago! He
died in 1858! He's authentic! There's no mystery about
him. He couldn't be a time-traveller!"

"Ah, I am relieved!" said Pepe amiably. "You see, I understood that if one travelled into the past, he might by bad
fortune happen to kill his grandfather as a youth. In such a
case, he would not be born to go back in time to kill his
grandfather. But if he were not born, he could not kill his
grandfather, so he would be born to kill his grandfather.
So he would not. So he would. And so on. I have considered
that one could not travel into the past because of that little
difficulty about one's grandfather."

"But in an exceptional case," said Harrison, "a case, for

instance, in which a time-traveller did not happen to kill his grandfather, that argument doesn't hold."

They went down the street together. Pepe made a grand gesture.

"Again, if one could travel in time, then even without killing one's grandfather one might change the past and therefore the present. Even the history books would have to change!"

"Yes," agreed Harrison wrily. "There might not be an Emperor Maximilian, for example. There might not be a you. Or a me. We might not ever have existed. I'd deplore that!"

"But do you mean," protested Pepe, "that because for a few seconds it seemed to us that an historical character did not exist—" He grimaced. "Because for a few moments we were confused, do you mean that during those few moments history was—was other than as it is? That something else was temporarily true?"

"No-o-o-o," admitted Harrison. "But if it had been, who'd have noticed it? I agree that we went through a freak occurrence, a shared delusion, you might say. But if it had been real, how many people would have been talking about a thing when their memories changed and they could notice it?"

"That is nonsense," said Pepe with decision, "and it is not even amusing nonsense. You don't believe it any more than I do."

"Of course not," said Harrison. But he added unhappily, "At least I hope not. But this de Bassompierre business does stretch the long arm of coincidence completely out of joint. It's all in the library. I wish it weren't."

They strolled together. Pigeons flew overhead, careened and came back, and coasted down to where two or three energetic flappings would land them lightly. They began to inspect a place where a tiny wind-devil had heaped fallen leaves into a little pile. They moved suspiciously aside when Harrison and Pepe walked by.

"No," said Pepe firmly. "It is all quite ridiculous! I shall take you to the shop I mentioned, which reminded me of Professor Carroll. It is foolish that anyone should pretend to be in the business of importing and exporting commercial articles between now and the year eighteen hundred and four! Yet if time-travel were possible, there would certainly be somebody to make a business of it! And I have a grandmother who adores snuffboxes. We will go to the shop. If the snuffboxes are not too bad, I will buy her one, and you will see if they still claim to import and export to 1804. But I will bet the snuffboxes are marked made in Japan!"

Harrison shrugged. He'd been worried. He'd come very close to being frightened. In fact, he had been frightened. But anticipations of modern discoveries had been made before. There'd been a bronze, planetary-gear computer brought up by a scuba diver from a Greek ship wrecked in the year 100, *B.C.* It could compute sunrise and sunset times and even eclipses. There'd been objects discovered near Damascus which were at least seven centuries old, and which were definitely and inexplicably electroplated. A craftsman presented a crystal goblet to the Emperor Nero, and then dashed it to the ground. It dented, but did not break. He hammered out the dent and gave it to the Emperor, who had him executed because his discovery would ruin the glass blowers of Rome. The goblet was possibly a plastic one.***

Yes. Anticipations of modern knowledge were not uncommon. But this was unusually disturbing.

It was a relief to have told Pepe about it, though. It was even reassuring for Pepe to have made that peculiar error about the history of his country. Of course the consequences of changes in the present brought about by time-travellers to the past would be horrifying to think about, if time-travel were possible. But Harrison now saw that it was wholly foolish. The evidence that had disturbed him wasn't explained away. But since he'd told about it he was able to be skeptical. Which was consoling.

Very, very thin and straight, a white pencil-line of vapor moved across the sky. It was the contrail of a jet, flying so high that even its roaring did not reach the ground. It was probably a member of that precautionary patrol which most of the larger cities of the earth maintained overhead night and day. There was no particular diplomatic crisis in the world at the moment—there were only two small brush-fire wars smouldering in the Far East and one United Nations force sitting on a trouble-spot nearer, with the usual turbulences in Africa and South America. A jet patrol above Paris did not mean that an unwarned atomic attack was more

***These items are reported in reputable histories, except the computer, which exists in an Athens museum and which I heard about from someone working on it from photographs, in the Princeton Institute for Advanced Studies. M.L.

likely than usual. But there was a jet patrol. There were also atomic submarines under the Arctic ice-pack, ready to send annihilation soaring toward predetermined targets in case of need, and there were NATO ships at sea prepared to launch other missiles, and there were cavernous missile bases in divers countries, ready to send intercontinental rockets beyond the atmosphere should the occasion require it.

But Harrison was used to hair-trigger preparations for mutual suicide by the more modern countries of the world. Such things didn't frighten him. They weren't new. Yet the idea that history might be changed, so that a totally different now might come about without warning, and that in that sub-stituted present he might not even happen to have been born . . . That was something to send cold tingles down his spine! He was consciously glad that he'd talked it over with Pepe. It was absurd! He was glad that he could see it as absurd!

A second contrail, miles high, made another white streak across the sky. Harrison didn't notice.

"The shop I mentioned," said Pepe, "is just around the next corner. I did not go into it, because I saw a woman inside and she was stout and formidable and looked like a shopkeeper. Truly practical shopkeepers should realize that even reproductions of antiques should be sold by per-sonable girls. But we will go there. We will inquire if they do import from and export to another century. It will be in-teresting. They will think us insane."

They turned the corner, and there was the shop. It was not a large one, and the sign, *"Carroll, Dubois et Cie"* was not conspicuous. The smaller lettering, saying that the firm were importers and exporters to the year 1804, looked strictly matter-of-fact. The shop seemed the most common-place of all possible places of business.

Harrison looked in the window. There were flint-lock pistols of various sizes. No two were alike, except a pair of duelling-pistols of incredibly fine workmanship. There were sporting guns, flint-locks. There was a Jaeger, also a flint-lock. But more than that, there was a spread-open copy of the *Moniteur* for April 7th, 1804, announcing the suicide of someone named Pichegru in his prison cell. He had strangled himself with a silk handkerchief. It was an amazingly per-fect replica of the official Napoleonic newspaper. But the paper itself was perfectly new and fresh. It simply could not be more than weeks old. At that, it would be a consid-erable publishing enterprise to find the type and the paper and make a convincing replica of any newspaper nearly two

hundred years old. And there were *Moniteurs* of other
dates in the window. Harrison suddenly realized that there
was seemingly a file for a month or more. And that was un-
reasonable!

He found himself reluctantly slipping back into the condition of mental stress and self-doubt that confiding in Pepe
had seemed to end. There had been a man named de Bassompierre back in the days of Napoleon Bonaparte. He had
given important people important, exact, and detailed information about various things that nobody knew until fifty
and a hundred and a hundred and fifty years later. So Harrison felt acutely uncomfortable.

When Pepe opened the shop door and a bell tinkled he
followed dismally inside. Then a girl, a very pretty girl,
came out of the back of the shop and said politely:

"*Messieurs?*"

And Harrison's eyes popped wide. Against all reason and
all likelihood, he knew this girl. Against all common sense,
she was somebody he recognized immediately. The fact was,
again, one of those that one evaluates according to whether
he believes the cosmos makes sense, or that it does not.
There were so many other things that could have happened
instead of this, that it was almost unbelievable that at this
exact moment he should meet and know this girl.

He said, startled:

"Valerie!"

She stared. She was astounded. Then she laughed in pure
pleasure and held out both hands to him.

And all this was improbable in the extreme, but it was the
sort of thing that does happen. The combination of im-
probability with commonplaceness seems to have been
characteristic of the whole affair of the time-tunnels. It appears that inevitability was a part of the pattern, too.

2

When Harrison woke next morning, before he opened his eyes he was aware of violently conflicting emotional states. On the one hand, he wished bitterly that he had never essayed to write a doctoral thesis that called for research in the Bibliothèque Nationale. On the other, he felt a pleasant glow in recalling that through that research he'd sat down to brood where Pepe would find him, and because of the research Pepe had carried him to the shop of Carroll, Dubois et Cie, where he'd seen Valerie, and that she remembered him with pleasure approaching affection.

Neither of the feelings could be justified. The only possible explanation of his discoveries required either the acceptance of an idea that was plainly insane, or that he abandon his belief that the cosmos made sense. In the matter of Valerie . . . But there is never a rational reason for a man to rejoice that a certain pretty girl exists and that he has found her. The experience, however, is universal.

When he was clothed, it was still hard to be sure that he was in his right mind. Still, when he had his morning coffee he felt a definite exhilaration because Valerie had remembered him. They had lived in the same building when they were children. They both knew people long gone to a better world. Valerie remembered the small black dog he'd owned more than a dozen years before, and he remembered a kitten she'd forgotten. They recalled

fêtes, they recalled a Twelfth Night celebration of which
Valerie became queen at the age of eleven by virtue of having the slice of cake with the bean in it, and they remembered the eccentricities of the concierge whom they had
occasionally outwitted. In general, they'd reminisced with a
fine enthusiasm. But it was not likely they'd have felt such
really great pleasure if, say, Harrison had married somebody
else in the years between or if Valerie had been less satisfactory to look at.

Now, today, Harrison finished his morning coffee and
was pleased to remember that they would meet presently,
secretly, because Valerie's aunt, Madame Carroll, did not ap-
prove of her knowing young men. The prospect made Harrison
feel fully capable of facing a new day.

Then Pepe arrived, fuming.

"The French," he said bitterly, "they are a noble race! I've
been asking about this Carroll, Dubois et Cie, and it's a
monstrous thing! You saw me buy a snuffbox yesterday. I
intended to send it to my grandmother. It would be just the
thing for her handbag, to hold her hay-fever pills. But I
examined it. And it is an outrage!"

Harrison blinked at him.

"What's the matter with it?"

"It is a work of art!" said Pepe indignantly. "It was made
by an artist! A craftsman! If it were an antique, it would be
priceless! But it was one of a drawer-full of similar snuffboxes, some inferior, to be sure, but others equally good. And
I bought it for peanuts!"

Harrison blinked again. "I don't quite see . . ."

"Somebody made it!" said Pepe. "By hand! He is capable
of magnificent work! This is magnificent! But he is turning
out things to be sold by Carroll, Dubois et Cie as curios!
Which is a crime! He should be found and told the facts of
life! Your Valerie says that her uncle, M. Dubois, is off on a
trip to secure more stock for the shop. She does not know
where he went. You may remember that I was enthusiastic
and asked where such things were manufactured. She does
not know that, either! Don't you see what has happened?"

Harrison shook his head. He was unreasonably pleased at
having rediscovered Valerie. It was something so unlikely
that he wouldn't have dreamed of it occurring.

"I've no idea what you're talking about," he admitted.

"I've made inquiries," said Pepe. "I'm told that workmanship like that snuffbox would entitle a craftsman to
plenty of money! If he made things of modern usefulness and

in the modern taste, he'd grow rich! But do you know what I paid for that snuffbox? Sixty-five hundred francs! Practically twenty dollars! Don't you see?"

"No," admitted Harrison again, "I don't."

"This Madame Carroll and this Monsieur Dubois have found a gifted craftsman," said Pepe angrily, "he is capable of masterpieces, and they have him making curios! Think of the skill and labor that went into this snuffbox! Think what they must have paid him for it, to offer it for sale as a curio for twenty dollars!"

Harrison blinked yet again.

"But . . ."

"The stupidity of it!" insisted Pepe, hotly. "The idiocy of it! As shopkeepers, this Madame Carroll and this *M'sieur* Dubois think only of how much they can get from miniature works of art they don't even recognize as works of art! They think only of a shopkeeper's profit! They keep a craftsman of the highest order turning out gems of skill and artistry so they can sell them to ignorant tourists! Like me!"

Harrison felt a very familiar depression creeping over him.

"Naturally Dubois would not let out where he gets his stock!" said Pepe scornfully. "Someone might find his workman and let him know what his skill is really worth! It isn't illegal to buy an artist's work for peanuts and sell it again at any price one can get. But it is an outrage!"

"The workmanship is that good?" asked Harrison forlornly.

"I spoke to an expert in such things," fumed Pepe, "and he said it could not be duplicated for ten times what I paid for it! But, he also said there is no large market for snuffboxes. I'll make a bet that these shopkeepers are too stupid to realize that work like this is different from any other curio product!"

Harrison swallowed. He felt a suspicion. But it was totally unrealistic to think that because there had been wildly unlikely coincidences in the immediate past, that there would be more wildly unlikely ones turning up in orderly succession. Yet . . .

"Pepe," he said unhappily, "you say it would take weeks to create that snuffbox. How many did you see, and how much time would be required to make them, by hand? And you saw the guns. They are not machine-made. They are strictly hand-craft products. How many man-years of labor do they represent? And there were some books in the shop, set in type of the Napoleonic period and printed on paper that simply is not made any more. How long to make the paper and set the type and print and bind those books? And how much investment in printing replicas of even one issue of the *Moniteur?* There are weeks of the *Moniteur* in the window, if not months! Do you think small shop-keepers could finance all this? And do you think that people who could finance such an enterprise would pick out Carroll, Dubois et Cie for their only outlet?"

Pepe swore. Then he admitted:

"I didn't think of those angles. But what is the answer?"

"I haven't the least idea," said Harrison unhappily. "It's ridiculous to believe in the only explanation that would explain it."

"That someone travels from now to then?" Pepe snorted. "My dear fellow, that is nonsense! You know it is non-sense!"

"I agree with you," said Harrison regretfully. "But I've never noticed that being nonsensical keeps things from hap-pening. Don't you ever read about politics?"

"I admit," Pepe conceded with dignity, "that foolish things are done by governments and great men, but I cannot do anything about them! But *if* there is a genuine artist working for a pittance so that a French shopkeeper can make a shrewd profit out of his commercial innocence . . . That I can do something about!"

"Such as what?" asked Harrison. Internally, he struggled against an appalling tendency to think in terms of the preposterous.

"I am going to the shop again," said Pepe sternly. "I won't talk to your Valerie, because you saw her first. But I shall say that I want a special bit of work done, only it will be necessary for me to discuss it with the workman. These shop-keepers will see the chance to make an inordinate profit. I will pay part of it in advance. They will gloat. And I will tell this workman what an idiot he is to work for what they pay him! I will advance him money to do such work for modern millionaires! If necessary, I'll send people to him who will pay him something adequate! Because he is an artist!"

Harrison stared at him in alarm.

"But look here!" he protested. "You can't do that!"

"Why not?"

"Why, Valerie! We were children together! And I knew this Madame Carroll when she was a skinny virgin, trying desperately to get herself a suitable husband! She's Valerie's aunt, and she was a tartar then and she's worse now!

Valerie lives with her! She doesn't want Valerie to know anybody because if she married, her aunt would have to pay a decent wage for somebody to help in the shop!"

Pepe snorted.

"You talked to her for fifteen minutes and you have a complete picture of the difficulties to romance with her! One doesn't learn such things unless there's some thought of evading them!"

Harris said indignantly:

"But she's a nice kid! I liked her when we were children! And dammit, I've been lonesome! I'm not interested in romance in the abstract, Pepe. You have to be a Frenchman or a Mexican to do that! But Valerie's a nice kid! And I don't want to make trouble for her!"

"She is not allowed to know young men," said Pepe in a detached tone. "Have you arranged to meet her, ah, privately?"

"Well . . . yes," Harrison admitted.

"And you do not want to make trouble for her!" said Pepe sardonically. "Ah, you rascal! In fifteen minutes you made her remember you, you learned about her tragic and unhappy life, and you made a date! You're a fast worker, my friend!"

Harrison said angrily:

"Look here, Pepe! I won't have that! I . . ."

Pepe waved his hand.

"Oh, I am helpless! I admit it! I've taken upon myself to rescue a skilled craftsman from peonage to French shopkeepers, than which there could be no worse slavery. But you can spoil things for me. You could tell Valerie of my noble purpose, and she could tell her aunt, which would spoil my altruistic scheme. So I'll make a deal with you."

Harrison glared at him. Pepe grinned.

"We go to the shop together. Again. Maybe Madame Carroll won't be there. In that case you can talk to Valerie. A bribe, eh? All I'll do is plant the idea of a specially-made article. If she or Dubois are there, I'll set up the idea of a fine swindle of which I'm to be the victim. Then they'll be amiable to you because you are my friend. They may even try to enlist you to help them swindle me! They . . ."

"It won't work," said Harrison.

"But I shall try it," said Pepe, still grinning. "You can't keep me from trying. But I'll let you come along if you like."

Very grudgingly, Harrison stood up. He was very far from happy. He was again unable to dismiss the completely foolish ideas stemming from dusty, elaborately shaded hand-written documents in the Bibliothèque Nationale. They were too fantastic to be credited, but he needed badly to find some excuse for dismissing them. He needed the excuse more than ever today, because he'd been trying not to think of the possibility that if the past could be visited, it could be changed, and if it were changed the present might follow and he, in person, could vanish like a puff of smoke. And Valerie could vanish too!

"I'm crazy," he said bitterly, "but let's go!"

Pepe walked beside him with a splendid, self-satisfied air. Presently they walked down the Rue Flamel and past the little cafe where they'd encountered each other the day before.

"If Valerie tends the shop," Pepe observed, "I ask if I can have a special article made, and then I'll browse among the objects on sale while you chat. If her aunt is there, I'll do all the talking."

"We're fools!" said Harrison. "Morons! Idiots!"

"If you speak of my altruism," said Pepe cheerfully, "I agree. But if you speak of your interest in a very pretty girl, then I point out that nobody is ever as happy as while he is making a fool of himself over a woman. When, in addition, his intentions are honorable . . ."

They reached the corner. They came to the shop. Only Valerie was inside. She greeted Harrison with relief.

"I am so glad you came!" she said breathlessly. "Something happened, and I won't be able to meet you as we agreed! And you forgot to tell me where you are living, so I couldn't have sent you word!"

Pepe said benignly:

"Providence arranges that I benefit all my friends! I am responsible for your friend's presence, *Ma'mselle!*"

Harrison found himself yearning over Valerie. The idea that anything could happen to her was intolerable. The most imaginary of dangers, if it might affect her, was appalling.

"My aunt was called to St. Jean-sur-Seine," explained Valerie, looking at Harrison. "Her husband, *M'sieur* Carroll, was . . . difficult. A crisis in the business developed. He and my uncle *M'sieur* Dubois were unable to agree upon a course of action. They actually telephoned by long-distance! So she went to St. Jean-sur-Seine to decide the matter. And I cannot leave the shop. So we would have missed our appointment."

Harrison was elated that Valerie hadn't wanted to miss seeing him.

"Let us to business," said Pepe profoundly. "I wish, *Ma'mselle* Valerie, to arrange for an especially designed object. The workmanship of your manufacturer is superb. Can it be arranged to have something especially made for me?"

"My aunt will tell you," said Valerie politely. But her eyes went back to Harrison. "My uncle attends to buying the stock for the shop, *M'sieur* Ybarra, but my aunt really directs the business. You will have to consult her."

Her manner was strictly commercial, except when she looked at Harrison. Then she seemed glad to be alive. He knew the exquisite anguish of a young man who wants to be all-important to a girl, when he cannot believe that she is just as anxious to be all-important to him.

"Then," said Pepe, "I will look around the shop, if I may. These are very skillful reproductions."

"But they aren't reproductions," said Valerie. "They are all originals. No two are exactly alike. They are all made by hand by, as you said, very skilled craftsmen."

"But where?" demanded Pepe. "Where are they made?"

Valerie shrugged.

"My uncle, M. Dubois, keeps that information to himself. He goes away, and he comes back with the articles the shop deals in. I do not know where he goes. My aunt has never mentioned it. It was M. Carroll who determined that the business should call itself a business of import and export with the year 1804. My aunt conceded that it gave the shop individuality."

Pepe said, "Hm." He began to prowl about. He examined a shelf of brocades and fingered them with a knowledgeable air. Presently he was looking at the books Harrison had mentioned. There were not more than a dozen of them. He fingered the fly-leaves and muttered to himself. He looked at the guns. He tested the balance of a sporting weapon. It was a flint-lock, but it balanced as perfectly as the most modern of sporting rifles. Presently he was reading a *Moniteur*. The paper was fresh, like the paper of the books. He became absorbed.

Harrison found his tongue. It is, of course, characteristic of all people in highly emotional states that they want to talk about themselves. Harrison and Valerie had material for just such talk. They had shared memories of a reasonably happy childhood, but they did not confine themselves to that topic. Harrison listened while Valerie explained that the death of her parents had sent her to boarding-school, and when that was ended there was only her aunt left to supervise her. Her aunt was then furiously occupied in directing the affairs of her brother, M. Dubois, but very suddenly there was a romance. Her aunt married, and there was a *ménage à quatre*, with Madame Carroll firmly directing the affairs of her husband and her brother as well as Valerie. And things did not go too well. But then, abruptly, the import-export business with the year 1804 began. The shop was opened and was immediately prosperous, but Madame Carroll ruled sternly that there must be the strictest of economy until it was thoroughly established and of course Valerie must help.

"M'mselle," said Pepe in a curiously muffled voice, " I take it that this issue of the *Moniteur*——."

"But of course, *M'sieur* Ybarra," said Valerie. "All of them are for sale. At one hundred francs the copy. You will find there the months of March and April, 1804."

"This one I buy!" said Pepe. "Of April second."

"They run, I think," said Valerie helpfully, "to the twenty-fifth. But when my uncle returns there will be later ones."

Pepe made an inarticulate sound.

"My great-great-grandfather Ybarra," he said after a moment, "visited Paris during Napoleon's time. He fought a duel with the Compte de Froude, and had his ear sliced. The account of the affair is here! I did not know the details, before."

"Indeed?" said Valerie politely. "That is doubtless interesting!"

She turned back to Harrison. She asked questions about what he had done with himself and what had happened to him in the past dozen years. He told her. He asked about Madame Carroll. He recalled her without affection. She'd been an acid personality, even then, with no patience with children. But since she was now Valerie's whole family—he did not think of her brother—it would be well to be informed.

Valerie explained with faint amusement that a small inheritance had fallen to her aunt, a tiny cottage in the town of St. Jean-sur-Seine, and that her aunt had gone there to make sure that she was not cheated of a single franc or centime. She left her brother in Paris. Then something happened. *Un Américain,* said Valerie, had been taken ill in the town. There was no hospital. There was no one to tend him. Since her aunt had to stay in St. Jean-sur-Seine anyhow, she undertook to care for the sick man for a reasonable fee. It would be so much clear profit. Eventually she came back to Paris, married to him. He was a M. Carroll, and Valerie liked him very much. He was most intelligent. In fact, in *les États-Unis* he had been a professor in a university. But now he had no post. He possessed a small income, to be sure, but he would not attempt to secure a position in a university or even a *lycée*. Still, he was a very pleasant man. Valerie regretted that he remained at St. Jean-sur-Seine while Madame Carroll operated the shop in Paris.

Harrison came out of the absorption with which he'd listened.

"Wait!" he said uneasily. "This M. Carroll! He would not be called Henry? He would not be a professor of methodology? The university would not have been Brevard?"

But it was. He was ex-Professor Henry Carroll, formerly of Brevard University, who had given courses in methods of research, including statistical analysis, when Harrison and Pepe were undergraduates. He was married to Madame Carroll, who was Valerie's aunt, who was the sister of the M. Dubois who attended to purchases of stock for Carroll, Dubois et Cie, importers and exporters to the year 1804.

Harrison found the news startling. When Pepe disturbedly said that he would come back later about the thing he wanted made, Harrison hastily made arrangements with Valerie for the meeting that for today must be deferred. He went out of the shop with Pepe.

"This," said Pepe in an irritated tone, "this has me standing on my head! I have read the account of my great-great-grandfather's duel, and you are quite right. I have seen nothing that could not be explained away if you had not found those insane particulars in the Bibliothèque Nationale! But I no longer believe those explanations. I displease myself! I cannot tell you why, but I no longer disbelieve in anything, or else I believe in everything! I am not sure which!"

Harrison said:

"The Carroll of Carroll, Dubois and Company is Professor Henry Carroll, late of Brevard. We took a course in statistical analysis under him, as you recalled yesterday."

Pepe stared. Then he said slowly:

"He was thrown out of his job, as I remember. There was some scandal which would not have been scandal had it happened to us, but was a very grave matter for a professor of statistical analysis and allied subjects."

"He's at St. Jean-sur-Seine," said Harrison, "wherever that may be!"

"He was a good guy," said Pepe. "He didn't flunk anybody without good reason."

"A very good guy," agreed Harrison. "What made you change your mind about the stuff in the shop?"

"I did not say, but—you are right. I have changed my mind. I cannot tell you why. Cumulative evidence that not everything that is insane is necessarily untrue. More than that, I feel that action of some sort is necessary. We have credible proof of the starkly incredible. What do we do?"

Harrison frowned. He was at least as much upset as Pepe. But besides, there was Valerie. Unless the shop could be explained completely, past all suspicion that it existed upon the impossible, Harrison would be uneasy for himself but desperately uneasy for Valerie. He would be wondering in panicky fashion if his—and Valerie's—having been born might not be rescinded.

"I think," he said uncomfortably, "that we'd better go to see Carroll. It seems to follow. We found each other, by accident, which led to my finding Valerie, by accident, and brought it about, by accident, that she told me where he was. It seems to make a sort of pattern. I think we ought to follow it along."

"I didn't know you were superstitious," observed Pepe.

"Anyhow," said Harrison without conviction, "as former students of his, it would be only natural for us to pay him a visit. Pay our respects, so to speak."

"Oh, yes!" said Pepe ironically. "Oh, definitely! I spend much of my time looking up professors who used to try to educate me, to thank them for their efforts and display their lack of success. But in this case I agree. Absolutely!"

"Let's get a cab," said Harrison. "The American Express can tell us how to get there."

They walked until a raffish Parisian taxicab hove into sight. They climbed into it, with dignity. It took off at that hair-raising speed all Parisian taxicabs affect.

On the way, Harrison said reflectively, "Do you know, Pepe, this is a silly sort of thing for us to do! Carroll will probably think us crazy!"

"If he will only convince me of it," said Pepe, "I will be grateful to him forever!"

He sank back in his seat. The taxicab hurtled onward.

Somewhere very high overhead, a jet-plane dove and circled and dove again. Somewhere on the high seas, the multi-nation crew of a NATO rocket-carrying surface ship went through a launching-drill, theoretically getting away all their missiles at imaginary targets at intervals of twenty-two seconds each. There were atomic submarines under the arctic ice-pack. There were underground silos ready to fire transcontinental rockets if or when they received properly authenticated orders to do so. It was officially admitted that enough atomic warheads existed to make, if detonated, the very atmosphere of the earth lethal to all animal and vegetable life.

In a universe designed for human beings to live in, there would have to be safety-devices. People being as they are, it would be necessary. Harrison and Pepe found out where St. Jean-sur-Seine happened to be and promptly arranged to be transported there. They did not feel any high sense of mission, or that they acted with particular wisdom or to great effect. Perhaps there was no reason for any such sensations. Perhaps their journey was just another thing that happened.

A decision on whether or not the happenings that gave them so much concern amounted to a safety-device, of course, would depend on whether one considers that the universe makes sense, or that it does not.

3

The town of St. Jean-sur-Seine was remarkably like very many other small municipalities over the length and breadth of the French republic. When—as rarely happened— tourists stumbled upon it, they found it both unspoiled and unattractive. Some ate one meal at the principal cafe. Very, very few returned for a second. It had once had a foundry which had cast some guns for Napoleon's army. The guns were unsatisfactory, and the foundry closed down. For a time there had been a traffic in truffles, found by misguided pigs and subdued trained dogs for the benefit of men. But truffles, whose mode of propagation has never been satisfactorily settled, did not propagate with much energy near St. Jean-sur-Seine. That traffic died out. In the 1880's there was an epidemic of measles in which the entire civic body, including the mayor and the whole municipal administration, was simultaneously incapacitated. There had been a murder in the town in the early 1900's. There was no other history to impress a visitor.

Harrison and Pepe Ybarra arrived on an asthmatic bus in mid-afternoon. It took an inordinate time to locate *M. le Professeur* Carroll. Eventually they found someone who made the identification of *M. le Professeur* with the pleasantly regarded *Américain* Carroll. *"Il fréquente le chien et le chat,"* explained the citizen who finally realized whom they sought. "He talks to everyone." And therefore he had not been thought of as a professor.

He escorted them to point out, helpfully, a not particularly trim cottage built upon the site of some former industrial complex. It could only have been the cannon foundry of Napoleonic times. By that time the hour was not far from sunset. There was a bed of flowers outside the cottage, badly in need of attention. There was a section of antique stone wall with the remnants of window-openings to be detected. There were piles of stone, once painstakingly separated from the walls whose upper courses they had formed. Now they were moss-grown and grass-penetrated while they waited for purchasers to cart them away for other structures. No purchaser had appeared. Perhaps no new houses had been built.

Pepe said:

"Dios mio! He lives here?"

"I think," admitted Harrison, "that we're making fools of ourselves."

"Nothing," said Pepe, "would give me greater pleasure than to find proof of exactly that statement! Let's hope!"

He advanced to the door of the cottage. He knocked. There was a rustling inside. He knocked again. Dead silence. He knocked a third time.

There were footsteps. They seemed reluctant. The door opened a crack. An eye peered out. That was all. Then a voice said irritably, within:

"Bien! Q'est?"

Pepe turned astonished eyes to Harrison. There are voices one does not forget and which one recognizes even when they are speaking in French and one has heard them speaking only Mid-Western English with the words "Mary," "marry" and "merry" not to be told from one another. Harrison nodded. He swallowed.

The single eye continued to regard the two of them around the barely-cracked door. The familiar voice said impatiently:

"Q'il est?"

The possessor of the eye did not answer. Harrison raised his voice, in English:

"Professor Carroll, my name is Harrison and I have Pepe Ybarra with me. We took statistical analysis under you at Brevard. Remember?"

Silence for a moment. Then the familiar voice said:

"Now, what the hell?" It paused. "Wait a minute!"

There were scufflings. A woman's voice. Carroll's voice said in an undertone something like, *"Il n'parle."* There was a grunting, and footsteps moved heavily away. Less heavy

footsteps went with them. The eye at the cracked door removed itself, but the door remained stationary, as if some
one had his foot firmly against it to prevent its being opened
by force. Carroll's voice said something indistinguishable—
again in French—and then there were sounds as if someone
had been impatiently brushed out of the way. Then the door
opened. Carroll stared unbelievingly at Harrison and at Pepe
on his doorstep.

He was tall and broad as Harrison remembered him, but he
was clothed like a Frenchman, which is to say as no professor of methodology and statistical analysis would ordi-
narily be clothed. He wore corduroy trousers, and his shirt
looked as if his wife had made it. He wore French shoes.

He looked from one to the other, and shook his head in
astonishment.

"It is Harrison!" he said profoundly. "And Ybarra! Who'd
have believed it? What in hell are you doing in France?
Particularly, what the hell are you doing in St. Jean-sur-
Seine? And what are you doing on my door-step? Come in!"

He stepped aside. Harrison entered with Pepe close behind
him. The room contained furniture of the sort an inhabitant
of St. Jean-sur-Seine would consider tasteful. It was atrocious.
It contained a short, plump Frenchman in a state of apparently desperate agitation. He was attired like a minor
and not-too-prosperous *bourgeois* of the year approximately
1800. His shoes were clumsy. His stockings were of coarse
worsted. The cloth of his major garments was homespun.
He seemed to be entirely unconscious of any oddity in his
apparel, and his costume had the look of having been
worn as a matter of course. It did not look like fancy-dress.
And he looked like a man in acute distress. As Harrison and
Pepe entered, he wrung his hands. A door to another room
closed decisively.

Carroll ignored the short man for a moment. He shook
hands with his two visitors.

"This is a surprise!" he said in a tone compounded of
curiosity and vexation. "I didn't think anybody knew where
I was, or would give a damn if he did. How on earth did you
happen to find me? And when you found out, why on
earth . . . No. I won't ask why you bothered. You'll tell
me."

Then he said abruptly, "This is my brother-in-law, M.
Dubois." In French he said briskly, "These gentlemen were
students of mine, some years ago. They have come to pay
their respects."

The plump Frenchman in the astonishing costume seemed a trifle, a small trifle, relieved, without being wholly reassured. He said uncomfortably, "*Enchanté, messieurs.*"

"Have a chair," said Carroll, with the same briskness. He continued to ignore the plump man's costume. "Tell me what you've been doing, and that sort of thing. I take it you graduated, and you're doing Europe, and somehow—but Heaven knows how!—you heard of me pining away in obscurity and disgrace, and you've called on me for some irrational reason."

Pepe sat down, rather gingerly. He eyed the man in the antique-style garments. Harrison said awkwardly:

"I'm afraid you'll think I'm crazy, sir."

"Not at all! Not at all!" said Carroll. "Why should I?"

"Because," said Harrison, "I have to ask you—and I can't justify asking—if you're acquainted with a—that is —do you know . . ." He stopped. Then he said abruptly: "There's a man named de Bassompierre. Have you ever heard of him?"

"No," said Carroll briskly. "I haven't. Why?"

Harrison sweated. The plump Frenchman said:

"*Pardonnez-moi, messieurs, mais . . .*"

Carroll nodded to him and he went out, with something of the air of a man escaping agitation in one place to go and be more agitated somewhere else.

"This de Bassompierre," said Harrison painfully, "wrote to Cuvier and explained the Mendelian laws of heredity to him. In detail."

"He probably meant well," said Carroll charitably. "What of it?"

"He also told Ampère about alternating currents," said Harrison, "and Lagrange about statistical analysis, and Champollion about hieroglyphics. And he wrote to the Academy of Sciences about nuclear physics."

"If they wanted the information and didn't have it," said Carroll pleasantly, "I don't see why he shouldn't give it to them." Then he stopped short. He stared. Then he said very carefully: "Did you say Cuvier, and then Ampère, and then Lagrange?"

"And Champollion," said Pepe wrily, "about hieroglyphics."

Carroll stared hard at Harrison, and then at Pepe, and then back again. He pursed his lips. Then he said with extreme care, "Would you mind telling me when this happened?"

"He wrote to Cuvier about the Mendelian laws," said Harrison, "in 1804. To Ampère, in 1807. To Laplace, whom I didn't mention before, in 1808. To the Academy of Sciences, in 1812."

Carroll remained conspicuously still for a long moment. Then he spoke more carefully still:

"And he told them, you say . . ."

Harrison repeated what he'd told Pepe the day before. The notes and correspondence of certain much-esteemed learned men, in the custody of the Bibliothèque Nationale, contained such-and-such items. One M. de Bassompierre had written to those learned men and had given them exact information which did not exist when he gave it. Harrison explained in detail, feeling the frustrated confusion of one who knows he is talking pure lunacy which happens to be fact.

But Carroll listened with intense and concentrated attention. When Harrison finished he said, distastefully, one abrasive phrase in pure Middle-Western English. It indicated that he was less than happy about what he'd just heard.

Then he said cagily:

"But why do you bring this news to me?"

Harrison stammered. Pepe spoke. He explained apologetically that the shop of Carroll, Dubois et Cie had aroused his interest. He'd taken Harrison there. He'd met *Ma'mselle* Valerie . . .

"Oh yes," said Carroll. "Nice girl. Pretty, too!"

Ma'mselle Valerie had known Harrison when they both were children. Telling him the news of her family, she'd mentioned Carroll, her uncle by marriage. Then Harrison spoke awkwardly:

"And I'd started my research because of something you'd said in class, sir. You said that the state of the cosmos at any given instant was merely the probability which under the circumstances had a value of one. And of course that implied all sorts of other probabilities which had cancelled each other out, so that a close examination of history ought to show some anomalies, things which once were fact, but whose factuality had been cancelled."

"I said that?" demanded Carroll.

"It follows from the first statement," explained Harrison. "It was interesting. So when I got a chance to go after a Ph.D. I started to do research on a well-documented period of history. I picked the Napoleonic era and started to look for events which at the time had really happened, but later on turned out not to have happened at all."

Carroll shook his head, frowning.

"I shouldn't have said it," he said irritably. "It wasn't good sense. It wasn't even so, though I thought it was. A fact is a fact! But there are some damned queer ones! Go on!"

Harrison explained his painstaking search through the personal papers of historical characters. He repeated that somebody named de Bassompierre had passed on facts that nobody could possibly have known at the time.

"Wait a minute!" said Carroll darkly. "I wonder . . ."

He strode out of the room. He practically filled the doorway as he passed through it. A moment later his voice boomed in another part of the cottage. He sounded angry. A woman's voice joined his. There was a first-rate squabble. It ended with Carroll shouting. A door slammed, and he came back. The woman's voice continued, shrill and muffled.

"It wasn't my brother-in-law," said Carroll irritably. "He swears he didn't peddle such information. He wouldn't have the brains to do it anyhow. And God knows my wife wouldn't think of it! This is the devil of a mess!"

Harrison suddenly felt numb. He'd been clinging desperately to the hope that his discoveries were deceptions. He'd been lured to the shop by that hope, and then to St. Jean-sur-Seine and to this present place and moment. Carroll's history had let him hope that it would all turn out to be eccentricity, or mild lunacy, or something equally reassuring. But Carroll took him seriously! Carroll did not think him insane! Instead, he accepted the incredible statements without question and had moved to find out if the plump M. Dubois in the antique costume was responsible for the facts of which Harrison had told him.

"I—I—" said Harrison. Then he was unhappily silent.

"It's the devil!" said Carroll, scowling. "Using the thing was against my better judgement to begin with! I was an ass to. I was an ass from the beginning! But how the devil . . ."

Pepe stirred. It seemed to Harrison that Pepe was paler than ordinary.

"Professor, sir," asked Pepe unsteadily, "do you mean that these things we've been trying not to believe are—are not our delusions? It was very comforting to believe that I was slightly cracked. You see, this de Bassompierre . . ."

"Delusions?" said Carroll irritably. "Unfortunately, no! You aren't cracked that I can see. But who the devil has committed the insanity that I *can* see? Who else listened to my lectures when I thought I was only casting pearls, and picked one up? You did," he nodded at Harrison, "and somebody else must have done the same. I may have played hell with the state of things in general!"

There were footsteps. The door to the inner room opened violently. A short, stout Frenchwoman with a red face entered with the stride of destiny. Her eyes were furious. Her speech, which began instantly, was a frenzied denunciation of Carroll, uttered with such speed and vehemence that individual words could not be distinguished. She waved her plump arms, glaring at him. She shook her fist in his face. She stamped her feet. Her denunciation reached a crescendo.

"Les flics," said Carroll sternly. *"Les flics—"*

She seemed to strangle. She subsided fiercely. She stood formidably still, her arms folded defiantly, her face crimson, her eyes snapping, breathing fast and furiously.

"The police," repeated Carroll firmly, switching to French to include her with Harrison and Pepe in the conversation, "would be interested to hear what you have just said of me. But these are my friends, former students from *les États Unis*. It appears that our enterprise has come to their attention, doubtless through some blunder M. Dubois has made. It is an emergency of importance. But perhaps it may aid in the solution of our previous trouble." To Harrison and Pepe he said, "I present you to my wife, Madame Carroll."

Harrison tried to bow politely. Pepe was more successful.

"And now," said Carroll firmly, "you will join your brother in watching over our other problem!"

He turned her around and guided her irresistibly back to the door. She squirmed. She resisted. He thrust her bodily into the other room and pulled the door shut. She made yelping outcries of fury. She went away, scolding shrilly. There was the apologetic murmur of the plump man's voice.

"I've made several mistakes in my life," said Carroll, "and I thought she was the worst. I seem to have been delirious when I married her. But this news you bring is really the very devil! We'll have to do something about it!"

He sat down, scowling. Pepe asked:

"Are we to understand, sir, that someone, somewhere, has made what one might call a time machine and is using it?"

"Of course not!" snapped Carroll. "A time machine is out of the question! But dammit, I must have said something that was more intelligent than I realized, and somebody must have used it to upset a sorry scheme of things and now is working busily to make it sorrier! But who the devil is it, and how did he get back there?"

"Where?" asked Pepe.

"To 1804!" snapped Carroll. He waved his hands. "Getting there is possible enough. We supply our shop with goods by doing it! But who else? And why the same period? Dammit, that's too much of a coincidence!" He stopped. "Oh. You think of a time machine. It's quite unnecessary. You don't have to build an elevator to get to the second floor of a building. You simply have to find the stairs. Then you walk up. That's all. But this—"

He swept his hand through his hair, leaving it standing on end. It had been a notable habit of his, at Brevard.

"There are so damned few of them!" he said in exasperation. "Damned few! You don't think I live in a hole like this because I like it, do you? I'd say the odds were ten to the ninth against anybody finding a second possibility to the same period! There are more than that, no doubt, but find them! There's the rub!"

Harrison drew a deep breath. Somehow the garments worn by the plump man had helped him to believe that Carroll, who had ignored them, was eccentric rather than an authority about anything. But . . .

"Professor," he said painfully. "I started out not believing this stuff. Then I did. Then I roped Pepe into the business, and I managed to stop, but he came to believe it and again I thought it was likely. You seem to understand it. I'm messed up for the third or fourth time. Will you settle it so I'll know what to believe?"

Carroll shrugged. He stood up.

"Come along."

He opened the door through which Madame Carroll had been thrust some minutes before. Harrison followed, and Pepe came after.

The next room was a dining room. Windows on one side let in a certain amount of dusky twilight. The sun had set upon St. Jean-sur-Seine since their arrival at the cottage, but through the windows one could see grass and the stones awaiting a purchaser, and part of the still-standing massive wall of something built very long before. In the wall opposite those windows there were no glazed openings, but there was a door, a new door, crudely made of planks and covering an unseen opening beyond it. It was self-evident that on that side the wall of the dining room was practically underground. Stained plaster proved it.

"There was a foundry here once," said Carroll, continuing to frown at his own thoughts. "They were casting cannon for Napoleon's army. But with the inspired incompetence of which some people are capable, they managed to cast them with huge flaws so most of them blew up when proof-fired. It looked like intended treason to the Empire, so they shut down in a hurry. They left one gun in the mould in which it had been cast."

He opened the homemade inside door. Earth did cover that side-wall of the cottage. But there was a burrow beyond the door. It was a man-height high and roughly as wide as the doorway itself. There were some stones showing through the dug-away dirt. In the doorframe itself there was a throw-switch with wires leading somewhere. It was turned on. At one side of the burrow a mass of rusty iron protruded. It could be identified as a six-pounder cannon, muzzle up, without the cut-off end which was the next step in cannon-founding after casting. It had been abandoned, undisturbed, when the foundry closed down.

"That's it," said Carroll. "It hasn't been disturbed since casting was abandoned here. In fact, it hasn't been touched since the melted metal was poured into the mould. I'm going through here. Follow me closely. You'll be sick at your stomach for a moment."

He moved confidently ahead. He disappeared. Harrison blinked and stepped after him. He felt an instant of nausea so intense as almost to be a cramp and a sudden violent dizziness which was peculiarly like the almost imperceptible giddiness that had accompanied talking with Pepe about Maximilian of Mexico. Then there was light before him. Carroll reappeared, waiting for him. Pepe came blundering behind.

They were standing under the roof of a completely intact stone building, which was obviously no longer in use. It had been a foundry. There were brick furnaces and a heap of charcoal plus enormous bellows to be operated by hand. Such equipment indicated that the system of iron-founding practised here dated from before modern processes were devised. Vividly bright sunshine came through the cracks of plank shutters that closed all high-up windows. There was no cottage. None. Instead, the great roofed enclosure went undisturbed to where there had been a ruined, largely torn-down wall. But now the wall was not torn down. It was erect and solid.

Harrison's eyes fixed themselves, fascinated, on the nearly vertical slivers of noonday sunshine. Out of the windows of the room he'd just left, the time was sunset.

Pepe said incredulously:

"This is—this is . . . When is it?"

The form of the question told of his complete, stunned acceptance of everything that common sense and experience still denied.

"This will be June tenth," said Carroll matter-of-factly, "and the year is eighteen-four. It's," he glanced at his watch, "eleven-forty A.M. Clock-time is different as well as calendar time at the two ends of the . . ." He shrugged. "I spoke of a stairway. It's more nearly a tunnel. A time-tunnel, which is a hundred sixty-odd years and some weeks, days and hours from one end to the other. We came through. We will now go back. I'm going to ask you to help me solve our current emergency, and then we'll set to work on the really big problem you've brought."

He motioned for Harrison to go before him. Harrison looked helpless. Carroll pointed to a small plank upon the ground. It looked like a threshold with no wall or door attached. Numbly, Harrison stepped over it and felt an intense digestive disturbance and a monumental giddiness. But he took one step more and he was in the burrow—the tunnel—with earth all around him and the home-made doorway before him. He stepped out into the cottage dining room. His forehead felt wet. He mopped it as Pepe came stumbling back, with Carroll matter-of-factly in his rear.

"I'm not going to ask you to not to tell anybody what you just saw," said Carroll casually. "You'd be an idiot if you did. But you've brought me a hell of a problem and I'd be foolish to try to be secretive with you. Come along!"

He opened another door, and they were in the kitchen of the cottage. The cooking arrangements were of that extreme primitiveness which an over-thrifty householder considers economy. There was a stair which evidently led to sleeping quarters overhead. There was a bench against one wall. The short, plump M. Dubois sat on that bench in his unbelievable garments. He held a remarkably large carving knife uncertainly in his hand. He looked woebegone. Beside him sat his sister, Madame Carroll, with a hatchet held firmly in her grip.

And, lying on the floor with his hands and feet securely

bound with cords, there was a third individual. He wore baggy corduroy trousers and a blue sash and a red-checked shirt. His expression alternated between extreme apprehension and peevish resentment. He looked at Harrison and Pepe with wide and at first scared eyes. But Harrison flinched when Madame Carroll burst into shrill and infuriated complaints, uttered with such rapidity that only one accustomed to her speed could have understood her.

"M. Harrison and M. Ybarra," said Carroll calmly, "are now involved with us. Not financially. They claim no share in the enterprise. Their interest is scientific only." To Harrison and Pepe he added: "Perhaps I should also introduce the gentleman yonder. He is a burglar. His name is Albert. He is our present problem."

Madame Carroll turned to them. Seething, she informed them that her husband was a fool of the most extreme imbecility. But for her he would be robbed, he would be destroyed, he would be murdered by such criminals as they observed had already made the attempt!

The bound man on the floor protested aggrievedly that he had not attempted murder. He had only intended a small, professional robbery. He was a burglar, not a murderer! They had only to ask the police, and they would certify that in all his career as a burglar he had never injured anybody but one *flic* who was standing eagerly underneath a window to trap him, when in his haste to escape he'd jumped out of the window and on him.

Madame Carroll silenced him with a wave of her hatchet. She was crimson with indignation, with desperation, perhaps with despair.

"What are we to do with him?" she demanded dramatically. "If we give him to the police it will become public! Our business will be revealed! We will have competitors thronging to offer higher prices than we can pay, and offering to sell for lower prices than we can afford! We shall be ruined, because of this scoundrel, this murderer!"

The bound man protested. They had held him captive for more than twelve hours, debating. It was illegal! Harrison said with a sort of stunned interest:

"The problem is that this Albert is a burglar?"

Carroll said vexedly that he'd been having a few glasses of wine in the town's least offensive bistro. This man, Albert, doubtless saw him there and considered it an opportunity. When Carroll went home earlier than usual, he found Albert ransacking his possessions. Albert struggled desperately when

Carroll seized him, but there he was. Carroll said ruefully, "And there he was, too, when Dubois came out of the time-tunnel. Which was unfortunate."

"Unfortunate?" cried Madame Carroll, in a passion. "It was a crime! You imbecile! This criminal . . ."

"Just a moment," said Pepe. "The gentleman is a burglar. He practises his profession privately, without witnesses. Perhaps he can understand that you prefer your business to be considered confidential, too."

The prisoner said shrewdly:

"Counterfeiting, eh? We can make a deal."

"For the sake of privacy," Pepe added, more nearly in his normal manner, "he can see that you might find it necessary to report to the police that M. Carroll was forced to injure him fatally in order to subdue him."

"That is not necessary!" objected Albert sharply. "It is not necessary at all! If I were a *flic*, perhaps! But since we are of similar professions . . ."

"The matter could be solved," said Pepe with a grand air, "by the use of professional courtesy and a gentleman's agreement."

"*C'est vrai!*" said Albert. "Naturally! I will pledge my honor not to speak of anything that has occurred here! That will settle everything!"

Carroll grunted. "Harrison, any ideas?"

Harrison moistened his lips. Somehow he was still thinking of those vertical rays of sunlight beyond the tunnel in the other room, whereas he could look out of a window here and see the deep-red glow of the sky above a just-descended sun. That bright sunshine bothered him horribly. It was appalling; upsetting!

"I think," he said awkwardly, "that I'd let him see what you just showed Pepe and me. I don't think it's likely that he'd tell about that!"

Carroll considered. Then he nodded. He picked up the bound man and walked effortlessly into the other room. Harrison heard the clatter of the opening door. There was silence.

Then Madame Carroll said bitterly, "It is unfortunate that one cannot . . ."

The hatchet in her hand moved suggestively. M. Dubois shivered. There was silence. A long silence. Then sounds in the next room again. The improvised door creaked and shut, and a moment later Carroll brought back the burglar. He laid him matter-of-factly on the floor. Albert's face was ashen. His eyes rolled. Carroll regarded him meditatively, and then took a knife out of his pocket and opened it. He cut the cords which bound the prisoner.

"I think," he said, "that he is impressed."

"M-mon Dieu!" said the prisoner hoarsely, *"M-mon Dieu!"*

Harrison saw Carroll bending to lift the small, scared Albert to his feet. He helped. The little man's teeth chattered. Carroll nodded.

"Let him out, Harrison. Good idea! He won't talk!"

Harrison led the burglar through the dining room and the room which opened toward the street. The small criminal wavered and shook upon his feet. His teeth continued to chatter. Harrison said, frowning, "You'll attract attention if you stumble and shake like this! Have you any money?"

Albert shook his head. Harrison handed him half a dozen hundred-franc notes.

"Here," he said distastefully. "You need a drink. Several of them. If I were you, I think I'd have about as many as I could find room for. I wouldn't mind joining you! But anyhow I advise you to keep your mouth shut!"

"Mais oui," gasped the former prisoner. *"Mon Dieu, oui!"*

Harrison opened the door for him. He watched as the little man went unsteadily out to the street and then turned to the left. There was a wine shop not more than a hundred yards away. The former prisoner headed for it. He walked fast. With purpose. Harrison watched him out of sight.

He went back to the kitchen. Carroll was saying briskly, "Get out of those clothes, Georges, and into something befitting a modern business man. Then we'll divide up the stock you brought back and Harrison and Ybarra and you will take it to Paris on the next bus out of town. If our friend Albert should be indiscreet, I'll be here alone and of course can deny everything. Naturally, I'll be believed."

He turned to Harrison.

"That's precaution. But you've brought a problem that's much more important than our own affairs! What you've told me is that most alarming news anybody could imagine! I don't think," he added, "that my brother-in-law can be responsible for what you report. He could take a modern scientific book back in time, but he wouldn't know where to place it. Anyhow, there is normally a sort of dynamic stability in the grand outline of events. But this de Bassompierre seems to be tapping at history like a stone-cutter tapping at a rock. Enough tappings, and the thing will crack! We've got to stop him! So we'll get this stock for the shop to Paris and set about handling this de Bassompierre!"

Perhaps an hour later, Harrison and Pepe passed the wine shop a hundred yards from Carroll's cottage. A familiar figure drooped over a table inside. It was Albert the burglar. He was comatose. He had no troubles. Under the circumstances, he was probably wise.

But Pepe shifted his heavy parcel and said detachedly:

"I observe one sane and admirable result of our researches so far. So far as you are concerned, anyhow."

"What?" asked Harrison.

"You have found this Valerie," said Pepe. "She is charming. She remembers you with affection. True, her aunt is as unpleasant a character as one could wish to find, but now she will not object to your friendship. She will not dare. You know too much!"

Harrison wasn't altogether pleased with Pepe's viewpoint, but that was the way Pepe's mind worked. He changed the subject as he changed his own burden from his right hand to his left.

"Carroll's right," he said uneasily. "Something's got to be done about this de Bassompierre trying to change all of past history! Apparently there's no great damage done yet, but if he keeps on passing out information a hundred-odd years before its proper time. . . ."

"Yes," agreed Pepe. "From one point of view he should be strangled. Yet that would be unfortunate, since history says he was not."

He seemed to hesitate for a moment. Harrison said gloomily, "I think Carroll will use the time-tunnel to try to fix things up. If one can import snuffboxes from a former time, one can certainly argue with somebody in the past! He needs to be persuaded not to mess up all the present we know and the future we guess at."

"The present," said Pepe, "is not intolerable, but the future is less than satisfactory. I regret that I have to remain only a bystander. I mentioned that my great-great-grandfather, Ignacio Ybarra, was in Paris in 1804. Later, after the independence of the colony of Mexico, he was Ambassador to France. But if I went with you and Carroll to argue with this de Bassompierre, it might happen that by some unhappy accident I might meet and cause the death of my great-great-grandfather. In such a case, of course, I would not be born to be the cause of his death. So he would not meet an untimely fate, and I would be born to cause his death. So I would not be born. So I would. So I would not. And so on.

I prefer not to try to solve this paradox. I shall remain unwillingly a bystander."

Harrison said nothing. They trudged on together to where the antiquated bus to Paris would be found. Presently Harrison ceased to think about Pepe, and Carroll, and Albert, and Madame Carroll, and even about whoever de Bassompierre might be and all the other things involved in the idea of a possibly—or certainly—variable history.

He thought about Valerie. He had a date with her for tomorrow. He cheered up.

4

Valerie smiled cheerfully at Harrison and said: "Shall we sit here?"

He agreed immediately, as he would have agreed to anything else she said. This was Bonmaison, and all about them there was the atmosphere of picnics and tranquil romance and all the natural and ordinary affairs which are the only truly important ones. Low down on the horizon, toward Paris, there was a white streak of vapor in the sky. It was unquestionably the contrail of a jet-plane flying so high that it was invisible. Only the train of moisture condensed upon flame-formed ions could be seen. The jet was part of that round-the-world patrol maintained over Paris—and London and New York and nearly all the great cities of the world—in case some person in authority somewhere should decide to start a war. But it did not apply to Bonmaison. It was a symptom of the insanity of human beings in a cosmos obviously designed for them to live in, but which they industriously prepare to make unlivable.

But at Bonmaison one did not think of such things. There, and at many similar places all over the world, people adhered to an almost universal conspiracy to pretend that international organizations and agreements had made the world really safe, and that the alarming situations of which one reads are actually only arrangements so the newspapers will have something to print.

Harrison could not fully act according to this conspiracy today. He'd encountered proof that possibilities existed which were more horrifying even than atomic war. If history changed, if past events were disrupted, if some day bygone events would cease to have occurred and other quite different events took their place, why, he might not ever have been! Much worse, even Valerie might not ever have existed!

Valerie had seemed to choose this spot for them to repose and talk comfortably, but she continued to look about her. People of no importance go to Bonmaison to sit on the grass and eat ices and solve such profound questions as to what degree unparalleled affection justifies recklessness, and to what degree one should be practical. Usually, the girls are the practical ones. But they are disappointed if the young men are not urgently impractical.

A carrousel made alleged music a little distance off. Children rode on it, gleefully. There were booths where young men were fleeced of five and ten-franc pieces as they tried to demonstrate to their companions their skill at complicated and rigged games. There were boats on the small meandering stream, and shirt-sleeved swains rowed clumsily while girls admired them. There were shrieks of laughter when Polichinelle behaved sadistically for the amusement of innocent childhood. There were other couples—many of them —who had either already settled themselves comfortably or still sauntered in quest of exactly the spot the precise development of their romance dictated.

"Perhaps," said Valerie reflectively, "over there might be more pleasant."

Again Harrison agreed. Pepe's prediction that Harrison would be tolerated as an acquaintance of Valerie had come true. Madame Carroll had smiled frigidly when Valerie presented him as a friend of her childhood. Now they were together at Bonmaison, and provided that Valerie returned very soon after sunset, they were permitted a temporary escape from Madame Carroll's direction.

Valerie looked contented. Harrison, of course, looked foolish. She sank gracefully to the ground and smiled warmly at him.

"Now," she pronounced, "now we can talk!"

And Harrison immediately found it impossible to find anything to say. He looked at her, and actually his manner of looking said many things Valerie appeared to find satisfactory.

"My aunt," she observed, ignoring his silence, "was very much pleased with this morning's business."

He managed to ask the obvious question.

"Why," said Valerie, "someone came into the shop and bought lavishly. Not as one buys for one's hobby or for curios, but in quantity! And he asked many questions about where such items were made. My aunt was discreet. He probed. He pumped. He tried to entrap her into revelations. She gave him no information."

Pepe had also had an idea of finding out where the shop's stock-in-trade was manufactured. Now he knew, and so did Harrison. Neither of them was much happier for the information. Apparently Valerie did not share it. She laughed a little.

"Ah, but he tried to find out where he could get such goods! He squirmed and sidled and tried innumerable tricks! He said he would like to have special items made. My aunt told him that she would take his order. Then he confessed that he was actually a dealer—as if she had not known!—and offered a price for information about the manufacturer!"

Pepe had intended something of this sort, too. Harrison listened emotionally to the sound of Valerie's voice.

"In the end," said Valerie pleasurably, "they struck a bargain. On my aunt's terms! He is well known as an art dealer in England and in America. It is a splendid bit of business. She will order such items as he desires. He will pay extravagantly. My aunt suspects that he will probably age them artificially and sell them as true antiques. She does not do that, because she does not wish for trouble with the authorities. But what he does with them is not her affair. Still, she put heavy prices upon them!"

Harrison mumbled. Valerie continued:

"He bought all the very best items in the shop. More than my uncle just brought back! It will be necessary for him to make another trip immediately to get more!"

"Maybe," said Harrison, "it was good humor brought about by a good business deal that made her agree to let us come here today."

"*Mais non*," said Valerie wisely. "It was M. Carroll! Anyone but my aunt would be fond of him. But he angers her. He is not practical, and above all things my aunt is practical! Yet even she dares to go only so far! He told her that she must not offend you. He said that you were important to probable developments in the shop. He said that if you were offended, he would take measures. Ah, but my aunt was angry! She brooded all the way back from St. Jean-sur-Seine! She likes to direct. She does not like to be directed."

Harrison did not want to think, with Valerie, of St. Jean-sur-Seine and the ghastly possibilities implied by the confirmation of all his most implausible suspicions. He wanted to think only of Valerie. But thinking of Valerie made him think of disasters that might come to her.

A soldier and a girl went by, and Harrison considered morbidly what could be the result of a mere few boxes of percussion-caps upon the history of Europe and the world, if they happened to be demonstrated ahead of their normal time.

Napoleon was not receptive to the idea of submarines, to be sure. The American Fulton had found that out. But he would grasp instantly the advantage of percussion-cap guns over the flint-locks his infantry used. Flint-locks, in action, missed fire three times in ten. Merely changing muskets to percussion guns would make the increased fire-power of his armies equivalent to two hundred thousand added soldiers. Napoleon would not miss a bet like that! There would be no trouble with manufacture. The technology of the early nineteenth century was quite up to the making of percussion-caps once the idea and the proof of its practicality was known.

Even one box of percussion-caps, put into the proper hands in 1804, would mean that the invasion of Russia in 1812 would be successful. The Russian armies would not be defeated, they would be destroyed. There would be no abdication. There would be no Hundred Days. Waterloo would never be fought. A million Frenchmen would not die before their reasonable time, and instead would live to become fathers instead of the left-overs from whom modern Frenchmen were descended. And of course the probability of exactly those persons marrying, who had married in the past that Harrison knew of, and of their having exactly those children they'd begotten in that same past, and of Valerie sharing his childhood and the two of them being here at this moment on the grassy sward of Bonmaison—it would be improbable past imagining!

Valerie talked, and he listened yearningly. Presently there was a movement nearby and someone grunted in satisfaction. Harrison looked up. There was Pepe, impeccably dressed, and beside him there was the much larger figure of Carroll.

"He was right," said Carroll largely, with a nod of his head at Pepe. "He said he knew where to find you. I didn't know where you lived, but he'd mentioned his hotel, so I hunted him up to locate you." He switched to French. "Ah, Valerie! I trust to your kindness not to remember having seen me. There would be a great squabble to no purpose. My intentions in Paris are most innocent!"

Valerie said tranquilly:

"But of course! Did you know that M. Dubois makes another journey immediately? Someone came to the shop, a most eminent dealer in art-objects, and most of the shop's stock departed with him. It is necessary to get more."

Carroll shrugged.

"No harm in that that I can see. Harrison—"

"What?"

"This de Bassompierre, I have to talk to him! That's why I came to Paris."

Harrison started slightly. De Bassompierre had been born in 1767 and died in 1858 at the age of ninety-one. But—

"I'm ordering clothes and equipment for the purpose," said Carroll crisply. "But I need someone to go with me. This whole thing is your baby. I hope you'll go with me. Will you?"

Harrison swallowed. Then he looked at Valerie. She looked as if she did not understand. He looked back.

"It is really possible to do anything?"

"Naturally!" said Carroll. "You and Ybarra had an odd experience, remember? About the history of Mexico? It's proof of two things, no, three. One is that history can be changed. The second is that somebody's trying to change it. The third is that even when it's changed it has a tendency to change back. There's a sort of elasticity to events. Your theory that things which at one time are facts can cease to be facts has a certain amount of cockeyed sense to it. If something happens, and in consequence a given fact becomes inconsistent with the rest of the cosmos, it stops being a fact. It vanishes. History closes over it as water closes over a dropped stone. There are ripples, but they die away. People sometimes remember and even write it in their memoirs, but it isn't true any longer."

Harrison listened. He looked at Valerie. She looked patient, as a girl does when talk is about something unrelated to her own personal interests.

"You were looking for items of that sort," Carroll went on, "and you found something much more serious—someone deliberately setting out to change the course of history. If he isn't stopped, he'll stress the grand design of things beyond its elastic limit and things will stay changed! So something has to be done!"

Harrison was suddenly anxious about Valerie's opinion of this talk. If she thought Carroll was out of his mind, she'd think him—Harrison—no less demented. But her expression remained placidly unconcerned.

"So, I'm going to argue with him," said Carroll. "I've got to find his tunnel, too, and see that it's collapsed. We can't have this sort of thing going on! Dubois would be of no possible use to me in an enterprise like this! I could never make him see what it was all about. I want you to come along. The number of people I could ask—as a gifted understatement—is strictly limited. Ybarra would be handy, but he says no. He had a great-great-grandfather—"

"In all," said Pepe apologetically, "I had eight great-great-grandfathers. The one I've mentioned was one Ignacio Ybarra who spent some months in Paris in 1804. He made acquaintances there which later, when he returned as the Ambassador from newly independent Mexico—"

"He doesn't want anything to happen to him," finished Carroll, "through his great-great-grandson. It's reasonable! But I want you to go get yourself measured for an outfit befitting a well-to-do American travelling in Napoleon's time. I've picked out a tailor. He thinks the outfits are to be taken to Hollywood for a television show. Do you need money?"

Harrison shook his head.

"I insisted," said Carroll with some humor, "that I must be able to draw on the bank-account of Carroll, Dubois et Cie. My wife will burst with fury when she finds out I've done so! I've ordered books to do research on de Bassompierre, memoirs, and so on. Ybarra is sympathetic enough to dig out the forms used for *laissez-passe* and the identity papers we'll need. Modern methods of forgery should take care of them. If you'll get yourself measured for clothes, we'll be all set. Right?"

Harrison nodded, more or less uneasily. Carroll said:

"Valerie, *mon chérie,* I count upon your friendship not to mention that I have come to Paris. It is agreed?"

"But of course!" said Valerie. She smiled at him.

Carroll strode away. Pepe followed. Harrison, looking after them, noticed for the first time that Carroll moved with a certain unconscious ease, so that he couldn't have passed as a man of no importance in any period of history.

Then Valerie said anxiously:

"You are to go to—where my uncle Georges goes to buy the stock for the shop?" she asked uneasily.

"It seems to be necessary," admitted Harrison.

"How long will you be gone?"

Harrison knew an irrational elation. That was the angle which first occurred to her!

There was no actual reason for him to seize upon such an item; to find his tongue working freely though his breathing became uncertain. He could have said the same things at any other time, and probably more effectively if he'd practised them beforehand. But he heard his mouth saying startling and impassioned things in a hoarse and quite inadequate manner. He overheard urgent insistences that he had remembered her from their childhood and had never been able to think romantically about anybody else, and a large number of other unconvincing statements which he believed implicitly as he made them.

Valerie did not seem to be offended. She listened, though, with every appearance of astonishment. And suddenly he was struck dumb by the realization that this was very hasty, and she might not believe any of it. He regarded her miserably.

"I—I hope you don't mind," he protested, panicked. "Only I—I would have had to say it sooner or later ..."

Valerie rose from where she sat.

"I do not think we should stay here," she said primly.

She moved away. He followed her miserably, not noticing that they were not headed toward the carrousel or any of the other more thickly populated parts of Bonmaison. He stumbled in her wake.

She paused and looked around her. She did not seem astonished to find that they had arrived where they were not in sight of anybody else at all. But Harrison was astonished. He stared at her. She smiled very faintly.

Incredulously, he reached out his hands. She displayed no indignation.

Presently they ate ices together and Valerie was composed, though her eyes shone a little. She said:

"My aunt will be furious! But we will tell M. Carroll and he will force her to agree."

In his then emotional state, this impressed Harrison as the most brilliant and intelligent and admirable of all possible remarks.

When he got back to his hotel, Pepe was waiting for him. Pepe frowned.

"Look here!" he said indignantly. "I've been thinking about my great-great-grandfather, who was here in 1804. If anything happens to him—"

"Pepe," said Harrison raptly, "I'm going to marry Valerie! We decided on it today!"

"If Carroll goes back to 1804," fumed Pepe, "nobody can tell what will happen! You know the theory about what if a man kills his grandfather in the past. But it doesn't have to be him! If *anybody* went back in time and killed my great-great-grandfather, I wouldn't be born! And Carroll's going back!"

"She knew," said Harrison blissfully, "she knew the minute she saw me again, that I was the one she wanted to marry! The very minute, Pepe! The instant she recognized me as her old playmate!"

"So I'm not going to take any chances!" said Pepe fiercely. "There's de Bassompierre, too! I could blow up the damned time-tunnel, but de Bassompierre does seem to be doing some pretty undesirable stuff. So I'm going along! And I'm going to see that none of my ancestors get killed!"

Harrison beamed.

"That's fine!" he said, not really aware of what Pepe had said. "We're not going to tell Valerie's aunt just yet. There'd be fireworks. And anyhow it wouldn't be fair to Valerie to get married before I've made that trip with Carroll. It could be dangerous. I don't want her to be worried!"

Pepe stared at him. Hard. Then he said irritably:

"*Dios mio!* As if this business weren't bad enough without having only lunatics to carry it out!"

Harrison went to bed in that state of emotional semi-narcosis which is appropriate to a newly-engaged man. He was literally unaware that any other important thing had happened in the world. The newspapers of that afternoon announced a new international crisis. He didn't notice. It appeared that the mainland Chinese had exploded their first atomic bomb.

The significance of the fact was, of course, that the communist Chinese were now added to the nations threatening the world's precarious peace. There were cabinet meetings all over the world, where heads were shaken and helplessness admitted. It had not been expected that the Chinese would have the bomb so soon. The individuals who seemed to know most about it guessed that they hadn't developed it entirely by themselves. There were indefinite surmises that somebody had defected from the Russians, on the ground that they were reactionary conservatives in their politics, and had carried information to Peking which made the bomb possible. It was even guessed that the defector had originally defected to Russia from France. There were despairing speculations where he—his identity was strongly suspected— would defect to next.

To people not newly engaged, the explosion of an atomic bomb by the communist Chinese seemed a very serious matter. Certain groups dusted off their "Better Red than Dead" placards to carry in new demonstrations of reaction to the news. On the other hand, much of the world grimly prepared to live up to an exactly opposite opinion.

But Harrison slept soundly. He waked next morning with an excellent appetite and in the most cheerful of moods. He tried to think of an excuse to visit the shop of Carroll, Dubois et Cie. and was regretfully unable to contrive one. He went to the tailors and felt remarkably idiotic while they showed him fabrics and styles and were astonished that a supposed television actor was not interested in clothes.

Later, though, M. Dubois called upon him.

"M'sieur," said the little man agitatedly, "my sister and I wish to implore your aid! The most horrible, the most criminal thing has happened! My sister is half-mad with grief! She is distracted! We implore your assistance!"

Harrison blinked at him.

"What's the matter? What's happened? What can I do?"

"You know of our business and its—unusual nature," said Dubois. His voice trembled, and Harrison found himself thinking that he must have had a very bad half-hour with Madame Carroll. "But perhaps you do not know that my brother-in-law has acknowledged that he plans a journey to the—ah—the place where I buy the stock for the shop! You did not know that? But you will see at once that it is unthinkable! It is horrible to contemplate! It would be ruinous! My sister is distracted!"

Harrison raised his eyebrows.

"I'm sorry that she feels badly," he said as soothingly as he could, "but after all it's not my business!"

"The arrangements for my journeying," protested Dubois. "They are most delicate! The business connections I have made—they should be cherished with the greatest circumspection! If the nature of our operations should become known, either here or—or at the other end, the result would be disaster!"

"More likely disbelief," said Harrison. "Nobody's likely to

credit the truth even if they hear it. They'll never guess it!"

Dubois waved trembling hands.

"I do not argue, *m'sieur*. I do not dispute. But I plead with you to help us avoid ruin! M. Carroll must not make this journey!"

"But it isn't any of my business!" protested Harrison. "There's nothing I can do about the plans Carroll makes! I've no influence."

"But you have, *m'sieur!* You are not being candid! He has spoken to Madame Carroll about you! He wishes her to treat you with distinction. He has commanded it! *M'sieur*, you do not realize the enormity M. Carroll has already committed, and who can tell what other enormity he plans?"

Harrison said nothing. Dubois mopped his forehead.

"*M'sieur*, he has withdrawn from the bank almost a fifth of the accumulated profits of the business! He has withdrawn money from the bank! My sister has now removed the rest and placed it where he cannot lay hands upon it, but *m'sieur*, if he will do this—" Dubois seemed about to strangle. "You should see my sister! She is pitiable! I almost fear for her reason! *Mon Dieu*, one is frightened by the violence of her suffering!"

Harrison rephrased the information in his own fashion. M. Dubois had been led by the nose through all his life by the tantrums of his sister, until he could imagine no more terrible an event than another tantrum. It was understandable that she would not want Carroll to travel where her brother had stolidly ventured. But it was certain that the worst of all possible crimes was the removal of money from where Madame Carroll controlled, to any place or person where she did not.

"Still," said Harrison, "I don't see what I can do."

M. Dubois wept. Literally, he wept. Madame Carroll must have terrified him all the way down to his toes.

"*M'sieur*, use your influence with him! My sister, in her despair, authorizes me to promise that it will be to your advantage. I open myself to you! I fear for my sister's reason if M. Carroll carries out his insane plan! Therefore, I speak of *Ma'mselle* Valerie! It has always been my sister's ardent desire to place her in a situation of security, with a substantial fortune so that she can live happily. M. Carroll has placed that desire in extreme danger! He has taken a fifth of the profits of the shop! He has, in effect, robbed *Ma'mselle* Valerie of a fifth of the fortune she should inherit from my sister! Do you comprehend my meaning?"

"No," said Harrison.

"*Ma'mselle* Valerie is the most charming of girls," said Dubois imploringly. "She is virtuous, she is intelligent, she is affectionate. She will be my sister's heiress. And my sister is convinced that with tact and gentle persuasion she could be induced to consent to a marriage which—"

Harrison started.

"Which would have the most favorable of financial prospects," said Dubois desperately. "All that is required is that you persuade M. Carroll to abandon his mad project, return the money he has taken, and let things go on exactly as they were before! Nothing more than that, *m'sieur!* And you will be established for life!"

Harrison counted ten. He didn't even bother to think of the fact that Dubois simply proposed that if he obeyed Madame Carroll implicitly in this and all other matters for the rest of his life, she might—might!—leave him some money and in addition would promote an arrangement that he and Valerie had already concluded on their own. It was almost humorous, but not quite.

"I will have to consider it," he said. He didn't want to send Dubois back to his sister with news that would infuriate her more. So he said, "I would have to talk to Carroll and find out how determined he is. I would have to— Let it rest for the time being, M. Dubois! We will talk of it later."

M. Dubois argued vehemently. Presently he rose to leave.

"Let me tell you, *m'sieur,*" he said desperately, "My sister is distressed to distraction! I fear for her health if M. Carroll should proceed with this ill-advised action. Even more, I fear—"

But then he stopped short as if he'd clapped his own hand across his mouth. He went away, confused. And Harrison realized that he was genuinely frightened. He hadn't the imagination to see the hair-raising possibilities that Harrison and Carroll and Pepe saw, alone among the human population of earth. But he was frightened. And Harrison suddenly realized that Dubois was actually scared by his guess of what Madame Carroll might do if her husband—Carroll—did use the money due him for the use of his time-tunnel for his own purposes. It is commonplace among the students of homicide that murders are committed more often over money than for any other motive. It is also a commonplace that the amount of money involved may be trivial. To Madame Carroll, the money earned by Carroll, Dubois et Cie was the object of passion as genuine if not as understandable as that of a jealous woman. She was capable of a crime of passion—over money.

So Harrison distastefully prepared to make another bus-trip to St. Jean-sur-Seine. He'd have to warn Carroll. He'd have to make Valerie understand . . .

But still something had to be done about de Bassompierre, back in the days of Napoleon Buonaparte! Something definitely had to be done! His activities could only be allowed to go on if one believed that the cosmos did not make sense; that there was no particular point in civilization, and that the human race didn't matter because it was only an accident, undesigned and without significance.

There have always been people believing this and earnestly laboring to create a state of things humanity could not survive. There will probably always be such people. Clearly, however, if they are wrong they won't succeed. If people are important, it has been arranged for them to survive. If the cosmos is designed for them to live in it, there must be some safety device built into it to prevent their extermination.

It didn't appear, though, that Harrison and Carroll and Pepe, and Madame Carroll and Valerie and M. Dubois together amounted to anything so important.

Quite the contrary.

5

The world rolled sedately upon its axis, and tides ebbed and flowed, and barometric highs produced winds flowing clockwise about their center in the Northern hemisphere, and counter-clockwise in the Southern. There were people who casually mentioned coriolis forces in connection with this subject. There were minor temblors in various places, and the people supposed to know about them explained that tectonic adjustments were their cause. There were forest-fires and forestry officials explained that the woodland floors had lacked humidity, and there were droughts and people spoke with exactness of water-tables and floods, when there was sure to be an authority on the subject to discourse on abnormal precipitation in terms of inches of rain-fall or acre-feet of run-off. But these were natural phenomena, about which it is always possible to speak with understanding and precision.

The Chinese, however, exploded an atomic bomb, and a spy-plane was shot down over Western Europe, and a U.S. anti-submarine force, having located a foreign submarine in Caribbean waters, zestfully practised trailing it in spite of its evasive tactics. They stayed over it—where they could have dropped depth-bombs if they'd wanted to—for seventy-two hours hand-running. Then it surfaced angrily and the squadron leader of the hunter-killer unit solicitously asked if it was in need of assistance.

It was not possible to make exact statements about happenings like that. They were things that people did. Unreasonably. Irrationally. On what seemed to different people
appropriate occasions. But what seems appropriate to humans
isn't necessarily reasonable.

There was the fact, for example, that M. Dubois came
gloomily to St. Jean-sur-Seine, carrying a very considerable
number of very elaborate small bottles of perfume. The
weather in St. Jean-sur-Seine was clear and mild. M. Dubois arrived on the last wheezing bus, nearly four hours
after sunset. He trudged to the cottage in which Carroll
endured the tedium of existence in a provincial small town
with no alleviation whatever. Harrison and Carroll greeted
him pleasantly. Tacitly, all argument was avoided. Carroll even cooked an omelet for his brother-in-law by way of
refreshment. To be sure, M. Dubois took Harrison aside and
asked him disturbedly if there were any chance of Carroll
putting his money back in Madame Carroll's hands and aban-
doning his mad project of a journey into France *d'ans*
1804. Harrison said that the prospects were not yet good.
Dubois sighed heavily.

The time was then well after midnight. Carroll went
casually through the improvised doorway in the sitting-
room and along the burrowed passage-way beyond. He came
back to observe that rain fell heavily in St. Jean-sur-Seine in
the year 1804 and it was deep night there, now.

M. Dubois went prosaically about his preparations. He
was deliberate and took a good deal of time about it. Harrison
went through the time-tunnel himself and stood for a moment
upon the plank threshold between centuries. The then-intact,
disused foundry resounded with the heavy drumming of rain
upon its roof. The air smelled of wetness. The blackness of
the night was unrelieved. Of course the foundry would be
particularly dark, but in the time at this end of the tunnel
there was nowhere outside of houses where there was any
light whatever. On the entire continent of Europe there was
no single room in which candles gave as much light as modern men considered a minimum for comfort.

Far away, over at the horizon, there was a dull rumble of
thunder. If anything moved anywhere on the earth it might
be a lumbering coach with twin candle-lanterns to cast a
feeble glimmer before it. But nobody moved faster than five
miles an hour—seven at the utmost—even in the daytime.
At night three miles an hour was fast travelling. Especially

in rainy weather the overwhelming majority of people went home at sundown and stayed there.

Harrison returned to the dining room of the cottage. Uncomfortably, he looked out of a window and saw stars in the heavens. And even in St. Jean-sur-Seine, in modern times there were street lamps. Occasional buildings had lighted windows in them. Desolate and dreary as the little town was in the world of today, it was infinitely more liveable than the same town of nearly two centuries before. There had been much progress in how to do things. It was regrettable that there was less progress in knowledge of things worth doing.

Dubois, presently, would walk heavily through the home-made doorway. He would move through the tunnel which in feet and inches was of negligible length, but which had a difference of a hundred and sixty-odd years, some weeks, and a certain number of hours between its ends. He would come out where there was no cottage; where a ruined, disused cannon-foundry was not ruined but only disused, and where Napoleon was Emperor of the French and all the world waited for him to lead an armada of flat-bottomed boats in the invasion of England.

It was not reasonable for so remarkable an achievement as a time-tunnel to be used only to deliver exotic perfumery to Paris in which very few people bathed. It was not reasonable for the return-traffic to be ornamental snuff-boxes, out-of-date newspapers and flint-lock pistols to be used as paper-weights. The fate of Europe hung in the balance at one end of the time-tunnel, where Napoleon reigned. At the other end the survival of the human race was in question. The tunnel could have been used to adjust both situations. But it was actually used to keep a shop going.

M. Dubois packed his stock-in-trade into saddlebags under the eyes of Carroll and of Harrison. He had already changed to a costume suited to another time.

"I notice," said Carroll, in the tone of one who politely tries to make conversation, "that you specialize now. At first you carried an assortment of products through the tunnel. Now you seem to take only perfume."

M. Dubois said depressedly, yet with a certain pride:

"These perfumes have no competition where I market them. I have a business connection and it is mere routine to deliver these and collect for them. These are the most valuable objects I can transport with strict legality."

"Ah," said Carroll pleasantly, "then as a member of the firm I must be getting rich!"

Dubois said painedly:

"Madame, my sister, considers that if the business is permitted to go on as it has done, some security for one's old age should be possible. But only if the business goes on as it has!"

Carroll shook his head. Dubois strapped up the second saddlebag.

"Georges," said Carroll. "You are a very efficient man in your way. Granted that you have a particular correspondent in Paris, who buys all you take to him, you must have an arrangement with someone in St. Jean-sur-Seine for horses and so on. And they simply must consider you a smuggler! Has it occurred to you that some day they may decide to rob you? You couldn't very well protest. Not to Napoleon's police!"

Dubois said indignantly:

"But I do not deal with law-breakers! My arrangements are with persons of discretion and reputation!"

"But you wouldn't tell me who they are?"

M. Dubois looked appalled. He did not answer.

"My poor Georges!" said Carroll kindly. "My wife, your sister, rules us both intolerably! She sends you back to eighteen-four when you have not rested from your last journey! She is prostrated because I want to use some of my own well-earned money, and takes elaborate precautions so I cannot get so much more as would buy me Caporals! What do we get out of this slavery of ours?"

Dubois said with dignity:

"I do not bandy words with you. I do what is appropriate. What is estimable. I have great confidence in the judgment of my sister. Her advice has invariably been correct. And I find that so long as I behave with circumspection, following the ordinary rules of prudence, there is nothing to fear in an occasional journey to—ah—the place where I conduct business."

He picked up the two saddlebags.

"*M'sieur*," this was to Harrison, "I trust you will continue your discussions with M. Carroll and come to a desirable conclusion."

He opened the crude door in the dining room. As it opened, there was a flash of light from the farther end. A roll of thunder followed immediately. The muted sound of rain could be heard. Air came into the dining-room from the tunnel and the year 1804. It was cool, wet air. It smelled of rain and green stuff and freshness.

"Georges," said Carroll, "is it wise for you to go out into such a storm?"

The sky outside the cottage was full of stars, but thunder again rumbled faintly through the time-tunnel.

"That," said Dubois reprovingly, "is one of the inconveniences of business. But no one will be about the streets. I should be well on my way before daybreak."

He went heavily into the time-tunnel, carrying his saddle-bags. Carroll grimaced. When Dubois had vanished he said almost sympathetically:

"He is not altogether absurd, this brother-in-law of mine. Except with his sister, he is even valiant in his own way. If she had married a Landru, who would have cut her throat, or if he had married a woman able to defend him from my wife, he might have been a poet or a psychoanalyst or perhaps a driver of racing automobiles. Something foolish and satisfying, at any rate. But—"

He shrugged and closed the door through which Dubois had vanished. Harrison was struck, suddenly, by the extreme commonplaceness of the transportation system between eras. He stirred restlessly. One expects the remarkable to be accomplished by remarkable means, but nothing out of the ordinary was apparent in this room or in the tunnel itself. There was no complex array of scientific apparatus. There was an ordinary dipole switch outside, just beyond the door. It was turned on. There was a door, which when opened disclosed a crudely-dug opening into heaped-up earth. It looked like it might be an improvised vegetable cellar. There was a mass of rusty iron sticking out of the dug-away dirt at one place. That was all.

At the moment Dubois went through, there'd been a lightning-flash which certainly wasn't from the sky outside the cottage. But it was only a flicker of brightness in the untidy excavation. Afterward, there was only the lamp-light from the dining-room on the damp earth of the tunnel. Now, though the door was closed, there came the muted, almost completely muffled sound of thunder which did not originate in the twentieth century.

Harrison stirred again. He was moved to ask questions. Carroll had shown no particular pride in what might be called a time-tunnel. Having made it, he seemed to accept it as casually as a pot or pan or other item of domestic equipment. It was used to keep a shop supplied with articles of commerce not otherwise available. It did not appear to matter to him that it should, if demonstrated, call for the redesign of the entire public view of what the universe was like.

Then Harrison suddenly realized a completely confusing fact. If Carroll did reveal his discovery of a process by which men of modern times could travel into the past, he might be much admired and he might contribute as much to human knowledge as was popularly credited to Einstein. But inevitably there would be other time-tunnels made. Inevitably, sooner or later someone would fail to consider the elastic limit of reality. Eventually somebody would change the past in a manner to modify the present. Ultimately, some modification would come about in which Carroll had not discovered how to make a time-tunnel.

Harrison tried to think it out. He arrived at pure frustration.

Suddenly there were sounds beyond the clumsy door. It pushed open. Harrison started to his feet. He was instantly convinced that somehow somebody from the past had stumbled on the tunnel-mouth and now came through it. Anything or anybody might appear.

But M. Dubois came back out of the tunnel. He carried the saddlebags, as before. But he also carried a mass of bundled-up cloths.

He looked at the fabric in his hand.

"I went," he said unhappily, "to the place where we arranged a door to the foundry that could be opened for our own use. I was about to open it and start on my journey when I stumbled on something that should not be there. This is it. I thought it wise to bring it into the light to look at it."

Carroll took the stuff from his hand. He spread it out. There was a pair of baggy corduroy trousers. They had been neatly folded. There was a blue sash. There was a red checked shirt. They were not garments worn by the lower orders in 1804. They were garments of the late twentieth century. They were, in fact, the clothes worn by the burglar named Albert when his fate was discussed in this same cottage's kitchen. But Dubois had brought them from the intact disused foundry of 1804.

Carroll swore. Harrison was alarmed. M. Dubois looked woodenly at the garments. Plainly, somebody had gone through the time-tunnel without authority. Somebody from the late twentieth century was loose in the early nineteenth.

That somebody was a small, reedy burglar named Albert. Anything—absolutely anything—could happen!

"Ah!" said Dubois. "These belonged to the burglar of the other day. He has somehow gone through the tunnel again. There he must have robbed someone else of clothing so he can mingle unnoticed by the people about him. My sister will be relieved."

"Relieved!" snorted Carroll. "Relieved!"

"My sister has been distressed," said Dubois, "that he might become drunk, tell strange things, and so draw attention to this house. Even attention is undesirable! But I have rented the foundry building, in 1804. I said that I wished it ultimately for the storage of grain. I can employ a watchman ... I will see about it."

He picked up his saddlebags and moved to the clumsy door again. He went through it. This time he closed it behind him. Carroll stared after him.

"The cold-blooded—cold-blooded—" Carroll searched for a word which was strong enough. He burst out with it, "Business man! But my wife figured that one out! I said I was going through. She figured out a watchman to threaten me that I couldn't get back. So I wouldn't interfere with her damned shop-keeping! Damnation!"

Harrison said uneasily:

"But there is that poor devil of an Albert marooned yonder. What'll he do? And how did he get the nerve to go through the tunnel, anyhow? He must have done it while you were in Paris!"

"No doubt," said Carroll furiously, hardly paying any attention. "But my wife has got me really angry!"

He paced up and down the room, kicking furniture out of the way. Harrison went to the tunnel door, and hesitated, and went through again. It occurred to him that so casually to change from one era to another was only less ridiculous than to do it for no better reason than to peer into the blackness of the foundry and to listen to the falling rain.

He stood, carefully with the threshold-plank under his foot so he could not fail to find the way back again. The rain fell and fell and fell. There was no sound anywhere except falling water. Then a lightning flash and after it a peal of thunder, and presently a lightning flash again. It was a wet night. Rain water beat into the shuttered foundry in the most minute of mist drops. Somewhere out yonder Dubois trudged through the downpour in the stygian streets of St. Jean-sur-Seine of 1804. He was firmly intent upon the con-

duct of business with whatever law-abiding and reputable
business men believed him a smuggler.

Then, above the drumming of the rain, there came the
booming of a fire-arm. A voice shouted loudly:

"Thieves! Burglars! Assassins!"

There was another explosion. Harrison believed it the
second barrel of a shot-gun. He was wrong. It was a second
flint-lock pistol.

He stood still. It would not be discreet for a man in twentieth-century costume to join the neighbors who would throng
to aid a fellow-citizen two centuries back in time. He had a
momentary feeling of anxiety that Dubois might be involved. But that was not too likely. It would much more
plausibly be Albert. If the small burglar had gone through
the time-tunnel a second time, after being carried through it
first by Carroll and being frightened horribly by the experience, he had probably made use of his professional experience. Certainly he'd abandoned his own garments as not
suited for the times, and he'd undoubtedly stolen substitutes.
He might be practising his profession for further aids to survival in a time which was not his own.

Nothing happened. Long, long minutes passed. Doubtless
there were angry citizens helping a fellow-householder search
for a burglar. Probably there was a humming of indignant
talk. But Harrison heard nothing. The rain drowned out all
lesser noises.

He stood still, listening, for what seemed an interminable
period. In theory, he was aware that this was a remarkable
experience. Albert or no Albert, here and sheltered in the
disused and wholly intact foundry, he was surrounded by the
France of Napoleon Buonaparte. Across the ocean Thomas
Jefferson was still alive, and Robert Fulton had not yet as-
sembled the inventions of other men to constitute a steamboat.
In Hawaii admiring warriors still dined on enemies whose
bravery in battle merited the tribute. The Great Auk was not
yet extinct, and buffalo roamed the Great American Plains
by the millions. Harrison realized that simply standing here
was a startling thing to do.

But it was not very exciting. The rain poured down, drumming on the foundry roof. Astonishing as being here might
be, it became tedious. Regardless of its splendid meaning-
fulness, nevertheless he was simply standing in the middle of
the night, while rain fell in a perfectly ordinary fashion. And
nothing happened.

He had actually turned to go back into the time-tunnel

when someone swore sharply in the disused foundry. The
profanity was strictly modern French. The intonation said
that somebody had barked his shin in the darkness and that
he did not like it.

Harrison listened with all his ears. The rainfall drowned
out minor noises. But more profanity came. Someone muttered peevishly.

Harrison said:

"Albert, if you want to get back where you came from,
come this way."

Dead silence, save for the rainfall.

"A few nights ago," said Harrison conversationally, "I
suggested to *M'sieur* Carroll that you be turned loose. I gave
you some hundred-franc notes and advised you to get drunk.
You did. Now if you want to get back where you came
from—"

A voice said in astonishment:

"Mon Dieu! C'est—Oui, m'sieur! I very much want to get
back!"

"Then come along," said Harrison. "You could get in a lot
of trouble, staying here!"

He waited. He heard sounds, which he realized were Albert's approach. The small burglar stumbled, and Harrison
spoke again to give him direction. Presently an outstretched
hand touched Harrison. Albert drew in his breath sharply.

"Right!" said Harrison. "This way!"

He withdrew, and went through the area of giddiness and
nausea. Then he went on into the dining room of the cottage.
Albert came stumbling after him. He was soaked. Saturated.
He'd been out in the rain storm in which Dubois travelled
now.

"Carroll," said Harrison, "here's Albert again."

Carroll scowled. Albert said with an air of immense relief:

"M'sieur, I am like the false coin. I return. I express my
regret that I am again a problem to you. And, *m'sieur,"* he
added gracefully to Harrison, "I congratulate you that I am a
burglar and not an assassin. I could have knifed you in the
dark. You should be more cautious. But I am grateful. I
thank you."

Carroll growled:

"I thought you had enough of—beyond that tunnel! How
the devil did you get back through it?" Then he said, "and
why?"

The little man shrugged. He looked down at his costume.
It did not fit him, but it had possessed a sort of *bourgeois*

splendor before it was saturated with the rain. The only thing that could be said for it now was that at a sufficient distance he would seem to be clothed for the early 1800's.

"There are your other clothes," said Carroll coldly. He pointed. "You won't want to be seen at this end of the tunnel in what you've got on. Change!"

Albert obediently began to strip off the elaborately be-frogged coat. There was a clanking, and coins rolled to the floor. They glinted gold. He looked fearfully at Harrison and Carroll. Neither stirred. He hastily picked up the coins.

"Better take a good look at them," growled Carroll. "They won't be easy to spend!"

The little burglar squinted. His mouth dropped open.

"But—*m'sieur!* These are not— There is the head of Napoleon, and there are the words "twenty francs" upon it, but—"

"Twenty francs gold," said Carroll, grunting again. "Before the franc was devalued. In money of today a gold napoleon is worth—hm—somewhere around twelve hundred depreciated paper francs. But you'll be asked where you got them."

Albert looked at him inquisitively.

"I'll buy them," said Carroll reluctantly.

"At what price, *m'sieur?*"

"Twelve hundred paper francs apiece," Carroll told him impatiently. To Harrison he said almost angrily: "They're stolen, but we can't send them back. And I'll need some gold-pieces presently! I didn't expect ever to become a receiver of stolen goods!"

"A most generous one, *M'sieur!*" said Albert profoundly. "It is a pleasure to do business with you!"

He counted the golden disks. There was a good double-handful. He put them in Carroll's hands and waited expectantly. Carroll counted them, in turn, and leafed out bills to a suitable total.

"How," asked Harrison, "did you get the nerve to go through that tunnel a second time?"

Albert tucked the modern currency away as he donned his present-day costume.

"I am a Frenchman, *m'sieur*," he said firmly. "I had an experience which was impossible. But I had had it. So I said to myself, *'C'est n'pas logique!'* So it was necessary for me to learn if it was true. Therefore I repeated it. But then there were difficulties. I could not find my way back until the *m'sieur* here—" he bowed to Harrison—"called to me."

"You may go, this time," said Carroll sourly, "but don't come back again! Next time you'll be in real trouble!"

"M'sieur," said Albert, "I shall not intrude again. But if you should need someone of my talents— It is a pleasure to deal with you!"

Harrison ushered him out and came back.

"I'll get the devil of a good lock," said Carroll, "and put it on that door! Maybe I'd better make the door stronger. I've no mind to be the sponsor of a crime-wave in St. Jean-sur-Seine in the time of Ybarra's great-great-grandfather!"

Harrison paced up and down the room.

"Things pile up," he said restlessly, "and we're getting nowhere fast!"

"My wife," said Carroll drily, "thinks I'm impractical. Maybe you do too. But we can't go hunting de Bassompierre in twentieth-century clothes! I've arranged for proper costumes. We have to wait for them. We'll need money of the period if we're to move about freely. I'm working on that, as you just observed. Also there's information about de Bassompierre. We need all we can get, if we're to persuade him to change his course of conduct and tell us where the other time-tunnel is. But still it's incredible that somebody else made another to the same period!"

Harrison stopped his pacing and opened his mouth to speak. Then he closed it and went back to restless stridings.

"You probably think," said Carroll evenly, "that I'm impractical about the time-tunnel itself. Why pick a hole like St. Jean-sur-Seine for my researches? Why bury myself here? Maybe you wonder why a supposedly sane man would marry the woman I did or how I came to be disgraced, discredited, despised in my profession?"

"I didn't mean—"

"I'll tell you," said Carroll with a fine air of candor. "I was stupid! I taught my classes that reality was the probability which had a numerical value of one. Remember? Then one day I overheard myself telling my students that time is the measure of things that change. And a little later I was astonished to hear myself say that an unchanging object is not affected by time."

"Yes-s-s-s," agreed Harrison. "That should be true."

Harrison's expression grew sardonic.

"It was a dogmatic statement," he said, "and I should have let that sleeping dogma lie. But I tried to test it experimentally. It looked like melted metal, solidified, would change at the moment it became solid. But if it wasn't moved, wasn't stirred, wasn't bothered, it shouldn't change again. It should—. I spare you the details, but it should be possible to make what I've called a time-tunnel back from now—whenever that was—for the number of hours, minutes, seconds, and so on between 'now' and the freezing of the metal. The trouble was that when that distance in time was short—days or weeks or thereabouts—the tunnels were unstable. They might last milliseconds. They might not. To prove that they existed at all required very special equipment. Like a fool I wrote an article about it. Foolishly, they printed it in a learned magazine. And then I caught the devil!"

"And?"

"You needed very special equipment to prove my results. Nobody else had it. But they didn't need it to discredit me! If time-travel was possible, a man might go into the past and kill his grandfather—"

"I know that one," said Harrison. "Pepe—Ybarra, that is—sprang it on me. In theory, if a man went back in time and killed his grandfather, he wouldn't be born to do it."

"But facts," said Carroll stubbornly, "are facts! If he did it, it would be done! If he killed his grandfather, his grandfather would have been killed, impossible or not!" Then he said wrily, "Anyhow, nobody else had the equipment to try my experiments. But the reputation of a young girl is a lot harder to hurt than the reputation of a researcher! I was denounced as a liar, a faker, a forger—practically a murderer of my own grandfather. Professionally, I was ruined!"

"I'm—sorry," said Harrison.

"So am I," said Carroll. "Because I got mad. I resolved to prove I was right. My trouble was having a short time-length to work with. I needed a metal casting that had solidified a long while ago and had never been moved. By pure chance I heard that this foundry shut up shop so fast it left its last cannon in the mould. So I had to have that cannon, undisturbed. That meant I had to have this cottage. And—the woman who is now Madame Carroll had just inherited it!"

Harrison said:

"And you married her for it?"

"No. I'm not *that* big a fool. I tried to buy it. She kept trying to get the last franc out of me. I must have acted rich. I offered twice its value and she asked three times. I agreed to three times and she demanded four. I fretted. I was taken ill. And she nursed me. Maybe she hoped to find out how far I'd go from hearing my delirium! Anyhow, one day the *maire* came to my room wearing his sash of office. And he married us! I must have been delirious at the time! But there it was! When I recovered, there was the devil of a row! She'd married me for money, and I wanted to spend it on scientific experiments! Harrison, you wouldn't believe such rows could end without homicides! But I made the time-tunnel, of nearly two centuries' reach. And it is stable! It can last forever! But—do you see the charming, ironic fact?"

"No-o-o. . . ."

"I found out that the past can be changed, and therefore the present, but there is no conceivable way to know what change will produce what result! I daren't use it, Harrison, not even to regain my reputation! It's too dangerous to be used by anybody but shopkeepers like my wife and M'sieur Dubois!"

Carroll grimaced.

"So I let them use it for a shop's supply of curios! I was a fool, but you can't say I wasn't practical, turning a means of time-travel into a shopkeeper's supply of back-number newspapers and similar oddments!"

He strode out of the room. Harrison looked after him. He felt singularly helpless. He was.

For the next three days he was acutely uncomfortable. He did not think it wise to write to Valerie because Madame Carroll would read the letter. He had to wait without being sure what he waited for. Once, half-heartedly, he tried to inform himself about the France he would presently visit. He learned that in 1804 handkerchiefs were not carried for the utilitarian purposes of more recent times. Smoking was practised, but snuff was more elegant. The reputations of many of the members of the Imperial court—including the Imperial family—were approximately those of domestic animals. And he learned that the sanitary arrangements in cities of the first decade of the 1800's were not primitive. They were non-existent.

He was waked on the third night after Dubois' departure. There was a terrific pounding on the home-made door to the time-tunnel. Carroll was there before him, unfastening the elaborate lock he'd installed the day after Albert's reappearance.

He opened the door. A sneeze came through it. Another sneeze. Strangling coughs. A moan.

M. Dubois came feebly into the cottage dining room from the year 1804. His eyes watered. His nose ran. He was half-starved and disreputably dirty, and he had a fever of thirty-eight degrees centigrade. Between coughs, sneezes, and moans of despair he confided to Carroll that he had been continually soaked to the skin for the past three days; that his horse had been stolen, and that his saddlebags with their precious contents of high-priced perfume were buried at the foot of a large tree a kilometer down-stream from a bridge beyond the village of St. Fiacre on the way to Paris.

Carroll gave him hot rum-and-water and got him into dry clothing. He put the plump little man to bed, where he moaned and wheezed and coughed himself into exhausted sleep.

Pepe Ybarra arrived next morning with the costumes and forged identity-papers and other documents to be filled in as the occasion demanded. He had a certain quantity of counterfeit *assignats*—authentic ones were too ancient to have a chance of passing unquestioned—and a note for Harrison from Valerie. The note was not remarkable at its beginning, but Harrison read the last page with enormous apprehension.

Valerie mentioned as a curious experience that she was in the shop, quite alone, when she felt oddly giddy for a moment. Then it seemed to her that the shop was strange. It was not the shop of Carroll, Dubois et Cie at all, but a place where pots and pans were on sale for housewives. And she was there to purchase something. She was not astonished. It seemed quite natural. Then she heard someone—perhaps the shop-keeper—moving in the back room as if to come and wait on her. She waited to be waited on. And then she felt the giddiness again and she was once more in her aunt's place of business and everything was as it should be. Then she was astounded. But she said that she had felt much *ennui* and undoubtedly had dozed for a moment and this peculiar dream was the result. It was the more singular because Harrison was not in it. She did not even think of him in it. He was, she confessed, present in most of her more ordinary dreams.

He went frantically to Carroll. Valerie had evidently had an experience like the one they'd shared, when he was convinced there'd never been a Maximilian, and Pepe had been sure there'd been four emperors of Mexico. The happening was pointless, and so was Valerie's, but there'd been a moment when she did not think of him! There'd been a temporary, substitute present in which she'd never met him! It could be a present in which he'd never been born! Something had to be done! This crazy de Bassompierre was trying to change past history! He was succeeding! At any moment another such thing might happen, and Carroll could talk all he pleased about history's modulus of elasticity and claim that events could be changed and of their own nature change back again. But there was also such a thing as an elastic limit! If the past were changed enough, it would stay changed! Something had to be done!

It was pure coincidence, of course, but while Harrison protested in a frenzy of apprehension, some eight thousand miles away the mainland Chinese exploded a second atomic bomb. It appeared that they intended a series of such explosions, by which they'd acquire the experience to make them equal to the other atom-armed nations in their ability to make earth uninhabitable.

Naturally, this was inconsistent with the theory that the cosmos was designed for people to live in, and therefore nothing would happen to stop them from doing it. This seemed to imply that humans didn't count; everything was chance; that the cosmos did not make sense, after all.

Which was deplorable.

6

Carroll made a definitely handsome figure in the costume of a well-to-do traveller in the France of an earlier time. He did not seem as ornamental as Harrison expected, but that was because he wore travelling-clothes. There were hessian-cloth breeches and high boots, and he wore an enormous cloak and a three-cornered hat. He didn't wear a periwig; such things went out of style during the 1790's. But he was impressive enough so that Harrison felt a little less foolish in his own get-up. He decided that nobody would look at him while Carroll was around.

Pepe, in a sports costume strictly of the present, regarded the two of them with uneasy eyes.

"I don't like this business of you going to Paris and me staying behind!" he said bitterly. "After all, it's my great-great-grandparents who're in Paris! And if anything happens—"

"Look!" said Harrison, fiercely. "Valerie went through a temporarily changed present—a time-shift—like we did. And in it there wasn't any shop of Carroll, Dubois et Cie! It was a pots-and-pans shop! And Valerie'd never met me! She didn't know I existed! Maybe I didn't! The normal past came back to her, as it did to us, but I can't have that sort of thing happening! We've got to get to Paris and find de Bassompierre! Fast!"

"But my great-great-"

"Dammit!" snapped Harrison. "If anything happened to your great-great-grandfather you'd never have existed and you wouldn't have spotted that shop and I'd never have seen Valerie again! I'll take better care of your great-great-grandfather than you would! But we can't waste time! We've lost enough waiting for these clothes!"

There came a knock on the outside door of the cottage. There should be no callers here. Pepe jumped. Carroll said irritably:

"My wife can't have gotten here this soon! Answer the door, Ybarra, and get rid of whoever's there."

Pepe went uneasily into the next room. Harrison drew a deep breath. He was feverishly anxious to start the search for de Bassompierre and the rival time-tunnel which obviously wasn't being used with proper regard to the elastic limits of history. It must be that de Bassompierre didn't realize the damage he was doing and the destruction he must cause, by passing out twentieth-century information in the early nineteenth. A reasoned explanation would certainly make him stop. Harrison was prepared to make any imaginable bargain as an inducement.

He heard the door open in the other room. There was a murmur of voices. Pepe tried to dismiss someone. That someone objected. Pepe was impatient. The someone else was firm. The door closed. Two sets of footsteps sounded inside. Pepe said, from the other room:

"Stay here! I will speak to M. Carroll—"

The voice of Albert the burglar said respectfully:

"Say that Albert needs most urgently to make a proposal of interest to him."

Carroll raised his eyebrows. He said angrily:

"Bring him in, Ybarra!"

Pepe came in, excessively uneasy. Behind him marched the reedy small burglar. He carried a parcel wrapped in newspaper and tied with string. His eyes widened as he saw Carroll's attire. He beamed when he saw Harrison similarly clad.

"What the devil do you want?" demanded Carroll.

"*M'sieur,*" said Albert politely, "I came to make a proposal. Beyond that door I had an experience which you know about. I made a splendid haul, of which you are aware. You, *m'sieur,* purchased some small things I brought back. *N'est-ce pas?*"

"I told you not to come back here again!" snapped Carroll.

"But *m'sieur,*" protested Albert. "It is a matter of business!

You cannot dream how primitive, how foolish are the locks of the citizens of—beyond that doorway! It would be ridiculous to abandon such an opportunity! So I have come, *m'sieur*, to propose a business arrangement. Let us say that I can acquire more such coins as you purchased for twelve hundred francs each. I will sell them to you for six hundred francs each! All I ask is the use of your doorway—did you call it a tunnel?—to pass through and after a suitable interval to return through! You evidently plan to make a journey yourselves. I am prepared for a journey also. Behold!"

He opened the newspaper-wrapped parcel. He spread out a costume of the very early eighteen hundreds. It was not the apparel of a rich man. It was not even the costume of a *bourgeois*. It was what a servant would wear. A lackey. Albert held it up with pride.

"There is no *costumier* in St. Jean-sur-Seine," he confided. "So I took a bus. Last night I examined the stock of a business supplying costumes to actors and persons attending fancy-dress balls. I chose this. Before, I could not move about freely at the other end of the tunnel. I was not clothed to pass unnoticed. But I observed from hiding. This is suitable. This is perfection! Now, *m'sieur*, I am prepared! It remains only to conclude an arrangement with you!"

There was silence. Carroll swore. Then Harrison spoke urgently, willing to make any sort of settlement that would get things in motion.

"We considered," he said impatiently, "that we ought to have a servant, but we couldn't imagine one. Maybe Albert would be willing to postpone his—professional activities to help us for a few days. He could—er—look over the ground. If he would play the part of a lackey for a few days—"

He made a hurried mental reservation, of course, that Albert would be rewarded for his efforts, but that his proposal for transportation to and from a life of crime in Napoleonic France would not actually be accepted. Harrison had fretted himself into a fever for haste, while waiting for the clothes he now wore. He wanted to get moving.

"Hm," said Carroll drily. "That's an idea! And he has his own wardrobe, too!" He said formidably to Albert: "Will you play the part of a lackey for M. Harrison and me and pledge your word not to steal from us for—say—three days? We will pay you, of course. But you will not rob us—"

"Not conceivably, *m'sieur!*" protested Albert.

"And at the end of three days we will decide whether or

not you can be trusted. Then we will make some arrangement, but I do not promise what it will be!"

"We begin at once?" asked Albert hopefully.

"At once," agreed Carroll.

Albert instantly stripped off baggy corduroy trousers, a blue sash, and a red-checked shirt. He put on the costume from the newspaper parcel. He began to transfer a series of small metal objects—like thin files turned into varied button-hooks—to his newly-donned clothing.

"Wait!" said Harrison. "Those are pick-locks, aren't they? You'd better leave them behind!"

"But *m'sieur!*" protested Albert, "I would feel unclothed without them!"

Carroll said tolerantly:

"Let them go, so long as he doesn't use them."

"*Alors!*" said Albert briskly. "I am ready!" He regarded the saddlebags lying on the floor. They were obviously Harrison's and Carroll's baggage for a trip into the past. He pointed to them and said, *"Messieurs?"*

Carroll nodded. He stood. Harrison shook his unfamiliar cloak to a more tidy arrangement. He felt absurd, clothed like this. But he wanted to make haste.

"Keep the door locked," said Carroll, "and don't let anybody through but us. I'm taking a chance on Albert, but nevertheless—"

Pepe looked extremely unhappy. Carroll opened the door. Albert festooned himself with saddlebags with a professional sort of air. Carroll went through the door first. Harrison followed, and after him came Albert with his burdens. There was the wrenching discomfort and giddiness of time-translation in the tunnel. They arrived in the resonant emptiness of the disused foundry. It was night. Very far away, a cock crowed. There was no other sound in the town of St. Jean-sur-Seine in the year 1804.

Albert said softly:

"Messieurs, I know the way to the door you established."

Carroll grunted for him to lead. They followed, stumbling. They went past the huge, cold brick furnaces which were but the vaguest of objects inside the building. Harrison heard the saddlebags brushing against what was probably a giant, man-handled bellows. A turn. Another turn. Albert said:

"Here, *messieurs!*"

A hinge squeaked. There was a slightly lesser darkness ahead. Albert went through. He waited for them. As Carroll came through last, Albert murmured admiringly:

"An excellent idea, that door! It cannot be detected from outside! Now—we go to Paris? You wish post-horses?"

"Naturally," said Carroll. He added: "We were landed from a boat, you understand."

"Mais non!" protested Albert. "I have listened to many conversations! You travelled by carriage, *messieurs,* and it broke down. So your driver departed to secure aid, and you reason naturally enough that he had gone to assemble brigands to rob and murder you. So when he had gone you came on to St. Jean-sur-Seine, and you proceed toward Paris. That is most probable!"

"Very well," agreed Carroll. "That's the story."

"Allons!" said Albert gaily.

They went along the unpaved street. Dark structures rose about them. Harrison continued to feel the need for haste. It did occur to him to wonder how Albert could take so calmly—after reflection—the utterly preposterous fact that there were two St. Jean-sur-Seines, remarkably similar in the streets and buildings that dated back for centuries, yet thoroughly different in all other respects. But he couldn't make any satisfying guess about Albert.

He stumbled. The street was not only unpaved, it was rough. He became aware of smells. They were noisome. They turned a corner. They went past a particularly redolent compost heap, doubtless prized by the man to whom it belonged. There was a small, flickering, yellowish glow some distance ahead.

"There is the inn," said Albert. "You may recognize it. The money is kept in a wooden shoe behind a cheese. Or it was."

They went on until they saw a whiskered man in an apron, dozing over what might be a counter. One candle vaguely illuminated the room in which he napped. The smell of wine was strong.

"Holloa!" said Albert briskly. "Up! Up! You have customers! We demand three horses, immediately!"

There followed confusion, beginning with the half-awake whiskered man, who was truculent until he saw the majestic appearance of Carroll and Harrison in their flowing cloaks. He shouted, and presently a hostler appeared, and then another, and another. There was argument. Debate. Bargaining. Harrison grew unbearably impatient. The innkeeper waved his arms. Albert spoke confidentially to him.

Horses appeared. There was more argument. Then the three of them were mounted. They trotted away through the narrow, abysmally dark streets. There were no lights anywhere. St. Jean-sur-Seine could have been a town of mausoleums for any sign of life it displayed except that twice, as the horses moved through the blackness, there were scurryings as of mice, only larger. They would be rats. There were smells. Incredible smells. It was a very great relief to get out of the town and to open country.

Harrison relaxed a little. He'd been impatient to get into the time where the destruction of all he knew was in process of arrangement. Now he wanted feverishly to get to work upon those eccentricities of the time-space continuum which nobody knew about or could be convinced of aside from himself and Carroll and Pepe and perhaps Albert the burglar. It had seemed urgently necessary to get into clothes that wouldn't draw attention and start to do something about the most appalling possibility the human race had ever faced. He had the clothing. He moved toward the action. Now he wanted to know what that action would be. Then he'd be impatient to start it.

He raised the question of how they could make de Bassompierre cooperate, even to the collapsing of the other tunnel. How—?

"I don't know!" said Carroll. "I've got a sort of *dossier* on him. Bourriene—Napoleon's secretary—mentioned him as a scoundrel who used perfume as lavishly as Napoleon himself, but added that he still stank in decent men's nostrils. Fouché—the secret police minister—used him but didn't trust him. Cambacières the consul despised him and even Savary would have nothing to do with him. Madame d'Epinay said he was a perfumed villain and Madame de Staël wouldn't let him in her house. And they were pretty tolerant people, too!"

"It looks," said Harrison, discouraged, "like he's a pretty low specimen!"

"You have a certain gift for understatement, Harrison," said Carroll. "But this whole thing is bad! My damned tunnel should never have been made! Before that, I shouldn't have lectured. When I contrived some interesting theories I should have kept them to myself instead of spouting them to young and eager minds, among which yours must be included, though you didn't make a time-tunnel and somebody else did. I made a fool of myself and I may have brought the ultimate disaster on the human race. And my only alibi is that I didn't mean to do it."

Harrison said in alarm:

"But you haven't given up hope?"

"The devil, no!" said Carroll. "I've been storing up information that might be useful. Now that we're starting out though, I have to figure out how to use it. I suggest that you let me!"

Harrison fell uneasily silent. The three horses went on through the night. The stars were few and very faint. A mistiness in the air made the Milky Way invisible. The ground on either side was abysmally dark. Where trees overhung the road—and France of this period had many more trees than it would have later—the blackness was absolute.

He racked his brains. He'd been doing little else for days, pending the arrival of suitable garments for a journey back in time. All his ideas were stale.

He tried to see things from a new viewpoint. After all, he'd been in normal time when he tried to think before, and there was inevitably a certain abstract quality in his estimate of what was practical. This period couldn't seem entirely real.

Now, though, he rode through darkness. It was real blackness. His horse was a real horse. It plodded on doggedly through the night. He breathed the air of early nineteenth-century France. There were thirty millions of people about him, of whom not one would ever see Valerie's next birthday. They were actual people. They had innumerable hopes and fears and aspirations. They loved each other, and lied to each other and betrayed each other and made magnificent sacrifices for each other. They cherished their country, and they dodged its taxes, and they died for it very valiantly—and they were fortunate not to know as much of its future history as Harrison did.

They were particularly fortunate not to realize that presently, truly and actually, other persons would take their places and they would not be remembered any more, and those who succeeded them in this nation and on this continent and on this world would make exactly the same mistakes they had.

To know this, genuinely, would be intolerable. Harrison almost came to realize it, and hastily thrust the thought away. He rode on, brooding, and presently thought of Valerie. He resolutely kept his mind on her and avoided even attempts to make plans for winning friends and influencing de Bassompierre.

Long, long hours later there was a grayness in the air, and presently the black shapes of trees were vaguely limned against it. Again presently they rode through a pre-dawn mistiness in which the trees and the roadway and all other objects appeared as ghostly, vaporous shapelessnesses, which took form and substance as they drew near, and when within yards were solid and real. But then as the horses plodded onward they became unsubstantial and ghostlike again, and vanished in the grayness left behind.

But Harrison's sense of frustration returned as the light grew brighter. He was tired, and he was impatient with himself because he felt commonplace fatigue upon the most desperately necessary enterprise in human history. It was also for Valerie, and therefore he should be superior to mere physical weariness. He remembered that he'd felt a certain scorn of Dubois when he returned wretched and wheezing from sad adventure in the rain now ended. Now he felt some scorn of himself.

Dubois had ridden his horse off a flooded-over bridge some distance beyond the village of St. Fiacre. He'd managed to get ashore while his horse went splashing down-stream. He'd followed it down the stream-bank, and managed to catch it as it came ashore, just in time to hide from some remarkably rough-looking characters who'd also seen it swimming and were hunting for it too. They began to search interestedly for it, and Dubois slipped off the saddlebags and drove the animal out to where they could find it without finding him as well. The horse satisfied them. They caught it and went off with it, doubtless to sell it. And Dubois hid the saddlebags and trudged back to the foundry, wheezing and developing a chest-cold on the way.

There were chickens cackling, off in the mist.

"That'll be a village. St. Fiacre, most likely," said Harrison restlessly. "I suppose we'll stop to eat."

"Naturally," said Carroll. He yawned. "I've been thinking of my sins. Thinking of breakfast will be a welcome change."

An angular shape appeared at the side of the road. It was a house. Another. And another. They were suddenly in a village, whose houses were characterless and dismal. It was a small place; there could hardly be a hundred houses altogether. But there were more than a hundred smells.

Harrison suddenly thought of another frustration that was possible. He said:

"I just thought of a complication. Albert has no papers. Maybe they'll be asked for. The police of this time are inquisitive."

Carroll grunted. He turned in his saddle and looked at Albert. Albert was unalarmed. He turned back.

"We'll worry about it after breakfast."

They drew rein at the village inn. The fact that it was an inn was made evident by the combined smell of wine, cooking, smoke, and of the stable attached to it. Albert leaped to the ground. He took charge with a fine assurance. He bustled here and there, commanding this service and that for Harrison and Carroll. Once, as he passed close by Harrison, he observed zestfully:

"C'est comme les films!"

They breakfasted, which in this area was more than rolls and coffee. They had eggs, fresh. Meat, not fresh. The bread was coarse. There was no coffee at all, which was a result of the subsisting war with England. Obviously coffee and sugar and colonial products generally were in short supply.

Albert's voice raised in a fine, infuriated tone. This inn, like the one in St. Jean-sur-Seine, was a post-house. Horses were to be had. There was a document that travellers by post should carry, but Albert quarrelled so shrilly over the animals offered that the question did not come up.

Presently, fed, they rode on. The morning mist dissolved away and sunshine played upon the trees and roadway. To someone acquainted with France of a later date, the amount of uncultivated land was astonishing. Presently Carroll said drily:

"Albert, you saw me about to pay for my breakfast with a gold napoleon. You slipped smaller coins into my hand."

"The innkeeper could not have made change, *m'sieur*," said Albert discreetly. "I thought you would not wish a long discussion, and I—happened to have coins such as he would expect. You can repay me at your leisure, *m'sieur*."

Harrison frowned. Carroll grunted. After a hundred yards or so he asked:

"Do you happen to have identity papers now, Albert?"

"But yes, *m'sieur*."

Harrison said hotly:

"Look here, Carroll! Albert will be making changes in the course of future events all along our route! He's stolen identity-papers and he undoubtedly robbed the inn-keeper! I know you say history isn't easily upset, and we're going after somebody working at it deliberately! But if this keeps up—"

"It is not important," said Carroll, "that every small detail in a given time be left undisturbed by travellers from another period, like ourselves. The important thing is that nothing inconsistent with the time takes place. And to travel in France of this year with a completely honest servant . . . It could smash the Empire!"

Harrison found the statement irritating. He was filled with anxiety about Valerie and his own future and the existence of everything he'd ever known. He was bound rather splendidly upon the rescue of Valerie from danger. Most men imagine deeds of derring-do to be performed for the girls they happen at that time to adore. But Harrison could not satisfy himself with dreams. He really did have to perform the most remarkable feat that history would never record. He had to change the past so the time he considered the present would return to a proper stability. Such a feat seemed highly abstract, but it had to be accomplished in a world of plodding post-horses and malodorous towns, and upstart scheming emperors and grandiose proclamations and—in short—in a world of very unsatisfactory reality.

They rode, and rode. Presently Carroll said:

"There's supposed to be a bridge somewhere near here."

Almost as he spoke the unpaved highway turned, and there was the bridge. It was not an impressive one. It was made of roughly squared timbers with pit-sawed planks for a road. Some of the planks had floated away in an obviously recent flooding. With a foot of water over it, any horse could be expected to get into trouble when crossing it.

"To the left, downstream, and perhaps a kilometer," said Carroll, "there ought to be a large tree beside the stream with a lightning-gash down its trunk."

They picked their way off the highway beside the stream. The water had been higher. The stream meandered. Some distance down it there was a drowned pig, already swollen, caught in the brushwood near the water. Beyond that place a man of distinctly unprepossessing appearance gazed at them from the stream's other side. He pushed bushes away and vanished when he saw that he was observed.

There appeared a huge tree, taller than its fellows. It almost leaned over the stream and there was a long slash down its trunk, where lightning had run downward under the bark and turned the sap to steam.

"This should be it," observed Carroll. He reined in.

Albert said helpfully:

"*M'sieur,* would it be that something is hidden here?"

"It would," agreed Carroll.

Albert dismounted. He delicately plucked a leaf from the ground. He held it up.

"There is mud on the top side of this," he pointed out. "The *m'sieur* who hid something here does not know how to strew leaves over a hidden thing. The mud should always be underneath."

He scratched away at dirt under a layer of dropped leaves. The dirt was soft. He plunged his hand down into the loose stuff. He tugged. He brought out two saddlebags and brushed them off. He offered them to Carroll.

"You can carry them," said Carroll.

Albert re-mounted. He listened suddenly.

"I trust," he observed, "that the *messieurs* have pistols. It seems that persons approach with stealth."

Carroll grunted. He took out two over-sized flint-lock pistols and examined them carefully.

"Do you know how to check a priming, Harrison?" he asked. "If not, lift the frizzen and squint to see if the priming powder's still there."

He demonstrated. Harrison looked at his own two weapons. He felt some indignation about this irrelevant emergency. It was absurd to be in danger from brigands when the future of all the world was in danger and only he and Carroll were doing anything practical about it. It was ridiculous!

"I," said Albert, "have no pistols. So I will depart now."

He rode toward the highway, looking behind him. Carroll grunted:

"There's one of them!"

He swung his horse about and spurred it. It bounded forward, toward a figure which had believed itself creeping unnoticed toward him. Harrison dashed in his wake. A man leaped up and fled to one side, howling in terror. Harrison saw another to the left in the act of lifting a heavy musket to bear upon Carroll. Harrison plunged at him, shouting angrily:

"Watch out, Carroll!"

"Coming!" said Carroll.

On the instant the musket boomed thunderously. The man who'd fired it raised it frantically for use as a club when Harrison bore down on him. Harrison leaned far forward and thrust his pistol-muzzle forward like a stabbing weapon. He pulled trigger and was deafened by the roar. He heard Carroll fire.

Then the two horses, made uncontrollable by terror, plunged madly through the underbrush toward the road from which they'd come. There was a mighty thrashing ahead of them. They overtook Albert and Harrison struggled to get his mount in hand. He succeeded just as they broke out of the brush at the roadside.

Strangely, there was little comment when they had rejoined each other. Harrison was unhappy. He rode beside Carroll without speaking until after they'd crossed the bridge with due care for the missing planks. Then Carroll said:

"We may as well trot our horses for a while."

And as the animals moved more swiftly, Harrison said:

"I poked my pistol at that character until it almost touched him. I wanted to be sure he wasn't killed. He might be somebody's great-great-grandfather."

Then he was suddenly sick. A man of modern times is not accustomed to death and destruction on a small scale. He thinks with composure of atomic war, and he is not disturbed by the statistic of so many tens of thousands of persons killed each year by automobiles. But it is unnerving to think of having used a pistol on a brigand to keep from being murdered by him. That is not part of the pattern of existence in the latter part of the twentieth century.

They rode on, and on. Presently they let their horses drop back to a steady, purposeful walk. Harrison said painfully:

"We'd better reload our pistols."

He managed his own, clumsily, more by theory than any actual knowledge of the art. From somewhere in the depths of his mind he recalled that the charge for a muzzleloader was enough powder to cover the ball held ready in the palm of one's hand. They had powder and ball and coarse paper patches, carried as part of the authentic cos-

tume of the time. They reloaded as they rode. They overtook an ox-car heading as they were headed.

"How far to Paris?" asked Harrison when it had been left
behind.

"Dubois makes it in a day and a night," said Carroll.

Harrison went on gloomily. What savor of adventure this
journey might have possessed was gone now. Men had
matter-of-factly intended to kill him for what possessions he
carried with him. It was not a glamorous affair. From now
on, Harrison would regard this enterprise as something to be
accomplished for the benefit of two people who would presently be Mr. and Mrs. Harrison. It was no longer splendid and
romantic. It was something that had to be done. Grimly.

It was very late when Paris appeared before them. Its
buildings made a jagged edge to the horizon on ahead. Harrison said:

"I've thought of a possible way to find de Bassompierre."

Carroll turned his head. Harrison explained. M. Dubois
might have thought of it, if he'd needed to discover somebody
from the world of Madame Carroll who'd been translated back to the time of the Empress Josephine. It was quite
commonplace.

"Try it, by all means," said Carroll. "I've got another
approach. You try your way and I'll try mine."

Albert, riding subduedly in the rear, said:

"Pardon, *messieurs*. If I am informed of the purpose of your
journey, it might be well . . . Perhaps I can find information
which will serve you."

Carroll said:

"We want to find a man called de Bassompierre. We want
to talk to him. If you should hear of such a person, it will
be well worth your while."

"We will see, *m'sieur*," said Albert. "Have you a choice
of an inn in the city yonder, and do you know where it is to
be found?"

Carroll named the inn used by Dubois on his journeys to
this extraordinary metropolis which gradually spread out
to either side as they approached it.

Albert settled back in his saddle. Again Harrison wondered how Albert accounted to himself for the totally unimaginable world the time-tunnel had opened to him. But
again he dismissed the question. The three horsemen rode
forward into the Paris of 1804. Night fell before they quite
reached it and they rode into a blackness more dense and

more abysmal than anywhere outside the city. There was smoke, to dim the stars. There were tall buildings, to channel movement within narrow, malodorous, winding canyons. Only occasionally did a candle burn in a lantern—more often glazed with horn than with glass—and there were only rare and widely separated moving lights carried by lackeys or burning faintly in lurching coaches to break the look of gloom and desolation.

It was coincidence, of course, but in a peculiarly simultaneous fashion, at just that moment in the latter part of the twentieth century, a supersonic passenger plane crossing the Arctic had its radio equipment go dead. Therefore it did not give the usual continuous advance notice of its identity, course, and speed. This would have caused no more than a precautionary alert, but—this was where the danger lay—a second plane's radio went out at the same instant. Radar immediately reported the suspicious fact of two supersonic objects without identification moving across the North Pole. The immediate consequence was a yellow alert. Then there came a third unfortunate report, of a possible contact with a surfacing submarine off the Atlantic coast of the United States.

Automatically, the situation developed in gravity. Strategic air-force planes, aloft with the weapons they were meant to carry, swerved from their rendezvous patterns and moved toward their assigned positions of maximum availability for counter-bombardment. If the unidentified objects over the Pole and the possible rocket-firing submarine were not completely explained within five minutes, there would be a condition red alert over all the Western Hemisphere. Counter-measures would begin. Warning was already transmitted to Europe. All the world was ready for that Armageddon which all the world wearily expected almost any day.

But in the inn in Paris, Harrison followed a candle-bearing inn servant to the rooms assigned to him and to Carroll. Albert followed with the saddlebags. It was Albert who suspiciously examined the beds. It was he who pointed out by the feeble candle-light that the beds were already inhabited. The candle-bearer was astonished that anybody would expect the beds of an inn to be free of insects.

Wearily, Harrison prepared to go to sleep on the floor.

The tense situation in the latter half of the twentieth century could provide, of course, conclusive evidence about whether the universe made sense or not. Obviously, if the cosmos was designed for human beings to live in, it would have built-in safeguards so that human beings could continue to live in it. They would not be destroyed by an atomic war set off by accident—not if the universe was designed with meaning.

But on the other hand, if it didn't make sense; if all was chance and random happen-chance—

7

Next morning Harrison waked and breakfasted—badly, because there was no coffee—and presently set out upon a business errand. Paris of 1804 was a city of half a million people. It had no railroads. It had no police in any modern sense of the word. Save for certain particular avenues, its streets were unpaved. It had no street-lights; not electric, not gas, not oil, not even publicly provided candles. It was supplied with food by creaking, oilless farm-wagons, except for such foodstuff as came down the Seine by barge and was distributed in unbelievably clumsy carts. It had no potable water-supply. There were wells and cisterns and buckets, to be sure, but nobody who could help it ever drank water. The reason was that there was then no known objection to the use of wells for drowning puppies and the like, and most well-water was unwholesome in the extreme.

There were not even horse-drawn omnibusses in Paris. The city had no sewers. Its streets had no street-signs, because only a small part of the population could read or write, and signs would have been useless. In all its sprawling noisomeness there was not one water-tap, nor any way more convenient than flint and steel to make a fire. There was not one postage-stamp in all of France, and cotton cloth was practically unknown. All fabric was linen or wool or, rarely, silk. In all the world nobody had conceived of power which was not water-power or animal-power, save in

Holland where some folk got motion from the winds by wind mills. In all of France, though, every horse power of usable energy save water mills was provided by a horse, and only three people then alive had ever conceived of a steamship, and all of them were across the ocean in America.

It did not seem that such a city could exist in a cosmos in which human beings were intended to survive. Humans had invented cities, apparently, with something of the invincible wrong-headedness that in Harrison's own era had made them construct atomic bombs. It appeared that throughout all the ages mankind had tried zestfully to arrange for its own extinction. It was difficult to think of Paris as anything but a vast device for the development and propagation of diseases. The death-rate was unbelievable. Ignorance of sanitation was unimaginable. And in a city whose most aristocratic quarters swarmed with flies, the idea of filth-borne disease did not exist and the washing of one's face and body was done for cosmetic reasons only. Nobody —not even surgeons—dreamed of washing for any abstruse idea of cleanliness. The slums were like the dens of beasts, and their inhabitants took on much of the quality of their environment.

But even so, matters were better than in older times. There had been a time when it was said that Paris could be smelled down-wind for thirty leagues. Now it could hardly be detected for more than fifteen. But to Harrison the improvement was not noticeable.

He left the inn with Albert in his wake, carrying Dubois' saddlebags over his shoulder. Harrison saw the citizens of Paris going about their business. Some were sturdy and well-fed and complacent. Some looked hawklike and tense, which was a reasonable response to the state of things at that time. There were beggars. There were children performing the office of scavengers. Judging by their starveling look, it was not profitable occupation.

The two of them—Harrison and Albert—went almost wordlessly from the middle-middle-class quarter in which the inn operated, to an upper-middle-class section where no inns were to be seen. Here the people were better dressed. There were fewer beggars. Begging is not a paying proposition where people are well-to-do. There were stepping-stones at some of the corners. Presently they came to a wider street than usual. It had a cobblestone surface, which was remarkable.

"This," said Harrison over his shoulder—Albert followed respectfully behind him, as a servant should—"this is probably the street we are looking for."

"But yes, *m'sieur*," said Albert cheerfully. "Paris has changed much since I saw it last week, but I think this is the Boulevard des Italiens. The perfumer you look for should have his shop in that direction."

He waved his hand. Harrison accepted the direction. He turned, Albert following as before. A vast and stately coach, drawn by four horses, rolled and lumbered down the street. It was accompanied by outriders, servants in livery prepared to defend it against brigands in the rude environment outside the metropolis, or to force aside any traffic that got in the coach's way. There were other horsemen on the street. Hoofs clattered on the cobblestones. There was a sedan chair, occupied by a bearded man with lace at his collar. There was—

Harrison said suddenly:

"Albert, you just said that Paris has changed."

"Yes, *m'sieur,* it is very different indeed."

Harrison said with a sort of grim curiosity:

"How do you account for it? St. Jean-sur-Seine, on this side of M. Carroll's tunnel, is very different too. You must have some explanation for yourself!"

Albert was behind him, but somehow he knew that Albert shrugged.

"*M'sieur,* you know that I was a burglar by profession. I did not say that I had retired, save for strictly amateur moments. But I am professionally retired, *m'sieur,* and since I do not need to struggle for a competence any longer, I have adopted a hobby. The strangeness you speak of fits in admirably with it. If you think of explaining matters to me, I beg you not to do so."

Harrison blinked. He went on. Albert followed. A knot of perhaps a dozen cavalrymen came down the street, their horses' hoofs clattering loudly. The uniforms of the cavalrymen were ornate, but untidy and soiled. Evidently elaborate equipment was worn as service dress.

"When I retired, *m'sieur,*" said Albert comfortably, "I resolved that I would change all I did not like about my life as a burglar. For success, you will comprehend, I had constantly to plan, to anticipate, to foresee. Nothing is more fatal to a burglar than to be surprised! One must anticipate everything!"

"I can see that," said Harrison. A bugle blew somewhere. No one paid any attention.

"So for my hobby in retirement," said Albert, "instead of avoiding surprises, I sought them! I became an *amateur*—a connoisseur of surprises! I began to live a life of adventure, such as the demands of my profession had forbidden. Each morning I would say to myself, 'Albert, at any instant absolutely anything is more than likely to happen!' And the thought was pleasing, but it was unfortunately not quite true. It is terribly difficult to arrange surprises for oneself! But when M. Carroll had once taken me through his tunnel—ah, I was terrified! But I forced myself to go through again. Whatever happened was bound to be a surprise! And so it was! I was surprised at the strange St. Jean-sur-Seine that I encountered. I was surprised at the costumes, at the inhabitants, when I could not return, when you called to me, when M. Carroll bought the gold-pieces I had acquired! Everything was astonishing! So long as I have no explanation for this *milieu, m'sieur*, I shall find surprises. I may say that it was surprising to find what is practically paradise for a competent burglar! I revel in all this, *M'sieur Harrison!* I would regret infinitely if I became able to anticipate events here, as one cannot help doing in St. Jean-sur-Seine the other side of M. Carroll's tunnel!"

Fifty yards ahead, a footman in livery held the heads of two horses. The livery was distinctive. Harrison had noted other uniformed servants, but all were distinctively French. This was different. Harrison was somehow reminded of the paintings of Goya. He guessed at a Spanish origin for the costume of this lackey.

"*M'sieur*," said Albert behind him, "there is the perfumer's."

The held horses were in front of the perfumer's shop. Harrison nodded and walked ahead. He turned into the shop.

It was not an ordinary place of business. It looked like a drawing-room for the reception of persons of rank. There were carpets. There were paintings. There was statuary and there were silken hangings. But it was a shop, because a man in the costume of a well-to-do *bourgeois* listened patiently while a dark-haired man in riding clothes rated him icily for having failed to fill some order. The dark-haired man haughtily refrained from anger, but in Spanish-accented French he gave the perfumer the devil.

"But, *M'sieur* Ybarra," said the perfumer politely, "Madame the Empress herself sent a lady-in-waiting to secure all of that special perfume that I possessed! She wishes to have it exclusively for herself! I could not refuse to obey her command! But when more arrives—"

"It is not often," said the dark man coldly, "that I dispute with a merchant. But this I say, the *Señora* Ybarra ordered you to furnish her this special perfume! And you will do it or my lackeys will make you regret your failure!"

Harrison had started slightly at the name Ybarra when the perfumer spoke it. Its second use made him stare. But there was a certain family resemblance between this man and Pepe.

"Pardon," he said politely, "but perhaps my errand will solve the difficulty."

The dark man stared haughtily at him. Harrison told himself that this arrogant young man was Pepe's great-great-grandfather-to-be. It was an odd sensation. He said pleasantly:

"I travel in France for pleasure—" It was not true, but he could hardly tell his real purpose—"and some few days back I stopped at an inn . . ."

He told the story he'd made ready before. He said that he'd found a poor devil of a merchant in the inn, sneezing his head off and in sad estate after an encounter with brigands. He'd had to hide in a stream from them, and he'd gotten back to the inn with his precious stock-in-trade, but he was still fearful that the robbers would come to the inn itself to plunder him. So he had begged Harrison, as a gentleman whom brigands might hesitate to rob, to carry his treasure to Paris where it would be safe.

"His treasure, he said," added Harrison amiably, "was perfume. It may be—"

The perfumer stared at the saddlebags. Albert handed them over and stood respectfully against the wall.

"*M'sieur*, was the merchant's name Dubois?"

"Probably," said Harrison. "I think so. He was short and plump and miserable."

"Ah, *M'sieur* Ybarra!" said the perfumer, "This is providential! Let me make sure." He opened the saddlebags and sniffed rapidly at one bottle after another. "But yes! The perfume that Madame the Empress has chosen to have exclusively for herself! *M'sieur*,"—this to Harrison—"my obligation to you has no limit! Now I can serve *M'sieur* Ybarra to the limit of his desires! I beg you to name any way in which I can discharge my gratitude for your condescension to this Dubois!"

Harrison said mildly:

"I will be happy if you supply M. Ybarra with whatever he wishes. But, to be truthful, I am most anxious to make the acquaintance of a M. de Bassompierre. If among your patrons—"

The dark-haired man—Pepe's great-great-grandfather—said with dignity:

"I have his acquaintance. He has been in Paris. He is not here now. I expect to see him within a week."

Harrison's pulse had leaped at the beginning of the statement. Then he was bitterly disappointed. The perfumer regarded him shrewdly before he tactfully offered Ybarra whatever he chose of the saddlebags' contents. It occurred to Harrison, despite his disappointment, that his willingness to sell the Empress' special perfume to someone else came from the fact that Josephine would buy anything from anybody, but paying for it was another matter.

Ybarra, with vast dignity, ordered the entire shipment of the Empress' perfume delivered to his wife. Madame— *Señora*—Ybarra would be pleased. He added negligently that his major-domo would have orders to pay the price in gold on its delivery. Which was grandeur. Gold was at a premium in Paris because of the English war.

Before he left, he assured Harrison profoundly that he would inform M. de Bassompierre that M. Harrison of *les États-Unis* wished urgently to speak to him.

He left, but before Harrison could leave the perfumer made a gesture asking him to stay.

"M'sieur," he said warmly, "I am deeply in your debt."

"Then you can give me a receipt," said Harrison amiably.

"But of course!" The perfumer wrote out a receipt with a quill pen. "And I should pay for the merchandise—"

"When Dubois comes to you for the money," said Harrison. He did not want to have to account to Madame Carroll for any business transaction. "I am not in business."

The perfumer reflected. Then he said very carefully:

"You said you wished to meet M. de Bassompierre. Have you paid your respects to the American ambassador as yet?"

When Harrison shook his head, the perfumer said with even greater care:

"I suggest it, *m'sieur*. He may give you valuable advice."

"About M. de Bassompierre's reputation?"

The perfumer shrugged.

"I am in your debt," he said. "I simply urge you to visit the American ambassador. I say no more."

He bowed. Harrison went out. In the street he said to Albert:

"The man we want to find has so foul a reputation that even a tradesman tells me I'd better ask questions about him before I make his acquaintance. The devil!"

He made the same comment to Carroll when Carroll returned to the inn near sundown. By that time he was depressed. He was desperately impatient to do something about de Bassompierre. He felt that within a week almost any change in the state of things in this period might have produced catastrophes in his own—and Valerie's—era.

"In a week," said Carroll comfortably, "we'll move to a more respectable address and bribe Ybarra's footman to tip us when de Bassompierre turns up. I enjoyed myself today, Harrison!"

Harrison spoke restlessly, not paying attention.

"A week . . . Anything could happen in a week, back where we came from! History's changing between now and the time we were born! It's changed at least twice and each time it changed back but—"

"I'm arranging that," said Carroll blandly. "I begin to think I can handle de Bassompierre! But I still want to find out about that other time-tunnel! You see, Harrison, I went to see Cuvier, the naturalist, today. What name do you think I sent in to him?" He grinned. "I sent in my name as de Bassompierre! Do you see the point?"

Harrison gazed at him, appalled. Carroll grinned more widely.

"Think it over! Cuvier received me, a splendid, stout, gray-bearded character with a magnificent sense of his own importance! And my name was de Bassompierre! I congratulated him upon his eminence. I said that I'd been travelling for some years, but on my return to France I'd heard of nothing but his fame. I implied that nobody considered Napoleon especially important, compared to Cuvier! He thawed. He warmed up. We began to talk natural history. We discussed the recapitulation of primitive forms in the developing embryo. We discussed the metamorphosis of insects. We had the devil of a good time, Harrison! In spite of my disillusionment and disgrace, I was born to be a college professor, and we talked shop. I made a definite impression on Cuvier! He won't forget me! I said that I planned to go to the United States to study the Red Indians. He almost begged me to stay here and meet his *confrères* . . ."

Harrison said stridently:

"But look here! That—that—"

"That," said Carroll amiably "means that the real de Bassompierre will be indignantly shown the door if he ever attempts to meet Cuvier! Cuvier knows M. de Bassompierre! Me! He will have no use for anybody else using that name! Tomorrow I visit the Marquis de La Place. We call him La-place. I'll dredge up some astronomy and flattery to deliver. When I'm through, anything de Bassompierre attempts to say to any learned man will be indignantly ignored! You see?"

Harrison hesitated. He didn't feel at ease in scheming. He couldn't estimate the effectiveness of devious behavior. But his own efforts had produced nothing, so far. At least Carroll was getting something done. He was discrediting de Bassompierre in advance. Maybe this was why he, Harrison, had found the intellectual dynamite in the Bibliothèque Nationale completely disregarded. Maybe this trick of Carroll's had prevented de Bassompierre's letters from having any effect!

But still there was the other time-tunnel to be discovered, through which de Bassompierre had gotten the information he'd tried to disseminate before its proper time.

He yielded. He knew frustration and the need for patience. He was excessively worried about Valerie. She'd be imagining all sorts of dangers for him. She'd imagine bandits and diseases and hardships and infections. Maybe she knew that in this period it was considered certain that everyone would have smallpox as, at a later date, everybody was sure to catch the measles. She'd be worried.

It is typical of the romantic human male that he believes the girl he cherishes worries only about him. The girls, in turn, are convinced that romantic young men worry only about them. And they are right. Harrison, for example, was not disturbed about the possibility of atomic war in the time he'd come from. That prospect was so familiar that he didn't worry about it at all. Anyhow he knew nothing of a yellow alert brought about by failure of radios on two supersonic passenger planes at once. He hadn't heard of counter-attacks almost ordered because of an amorous sperm whale leaping out of the water to impress a coy lady whale off the Atlantic Coast of North America. Radar had reported the whale as a possible rocket-launching submarine, and it was a very close call indeed.

Actually, if the situation had gone unresolved for just about five minutes more, unlimited catastrophe could have resulted. But Harrison did not think about such things. He worried about Valerie worrying about him, and he sweated in anguish whenever it occurred to him that Valerie might feel a slight dizziness, and find herself in a changed present in which she was married to somebody else. And that that present wouldn't change back.

In accomplished fact, of course, a sea patrol plane had dropped a flare where the possible submarine contact was reported by radar. It photographed the sperm-whale courtship in progress. It so reported. And an Arctic patrol plane intercepted one of the two muted but properly lighted passenger planes over the Arctic, and made passes at it when it did not reply to radio signals. That patrol plane herded it back to its airport of departure. And the co-pilot of the other muted plane found a loose wire in his plane's equipment, and fixed it, and there was no longer a condition of yellow alert.

That whole matter ended with ponderous praise from high military officers on the splendid efficiency of response to a supposed emergency by the men and planes under their command. Et cetera and et cet. And that was the end of the incident.

Valerie knew nothing about it. Her aunt was in St. Jean-sur-Seine, tending M. Dubois and Valerie was in complete charge of the shop. She knew of nothing to worry about except a discrepancy of twenty-two francs in the cash drawer. There was that much too much on hand. Valerie really worried only about Harrison.

The rest of the affair of the time-tunnel continued in typically irrational fashion. Only commonplace things happened to the people involved, but they happened for preposterous reasons. There was also something of the inevitable about the various incidents, as if the cosmos had really been designed for people to live in and it would remain possible to survive despite their most earnest efforts to the contrary.

Naturally, then, Harrison's life remained a mixture of the unpredictable and the tedious. He remained in 1804. In Paris. He was seen in suitable public places and was casually accepted as a travelling American who must be rich to travel from so remote and savage a place as *les États-Unis*. He kept his ears feverishly open for any clue however faint to the spread of information from the twentieth century into the nineteenth. If such leakage could be discovered, it would indicate another time-tunnel in operation.

The only thing suspicious was that jokes told in the United States after nearly two hundred years were essentially the jokes told in the France of Napoleon. But they would probably be told centuries later still, and still be laughed at.

Carroll had a better time. He visited prominent scientists. He presented himself as M. de Bassompierre, returned to France after long travel, and filled with reverence for the learned men of the time. He discussed mathematics with Lagrange, and the fact that he'd specialized in statistical analysis made him a discerning and marvelously welcome visitor. He talked electricity with Ampère, and they got along so splendidly that Ampère made him stay to dinner and they talked garrulously of the recent discoveries made by M. Faraday in England.

"I've been careful," he told Harrison satisfiedly on the fifth night of their stay in Paris. "I haven't told them anything they don't know already. But I can understand what they're driving at. When they say something, I know what they mean. And it's pathetic how grateful they are to be admired by somebody who realizes what they should be admired for!"

"I'm going to send Albert to make a deal with Ybarra's footman," said Harrison restlessly. "De Bassompierre should be back in town in a day or so." He added. "I can't help worrying about Valerie. There's always the chance that another time slip will happen. I know! There's a modulus of elasticity in historic events. They can be stretched, in fact as well as by historians, and they can snap back. But there must be an elastic limit, too, and if they're stretched just so far they won't go back to normal! They'll stay stretched! I'm thinking that we could go back and find—"

He made a helpless gesture. Everything that had happened or that he'd done had been drudgery or common sense, and there was no feeling of achievement. Right now it was a painful business, simply sitting and waiting for the fate of all the world he knew to be decided by something it wasn't time for him to do yet.

Albert, however, seemed to enjoy life. Upon occasion he attended Carroll or Harrison when they went somewhere that an attending lackey was called for. Once Harrison went to the theater and saw Thalma playing a translation—and revision—of the *School for Scandal*. Nobody mentioned its English origin. Harrison thought it intolerably over-acted.

Once he saw the Emperor, in an open carriage with a cavalry guard, driving like mad for somewhere or other. Doubtless he saw other historic figures, but nobody identified them and he didn't know. Which was the sort of thing that will happen to any stranger in any city. But it was not amusing. Only Albert wore the air of someone who loves the life he lives.

Once Harrison asked him almost enviously if Paris-this-side-of-the-tunnel was still as diverting as at the beginning. Albert said zestfully:

"Ah, *m'sieur*, you would have to be a retired burglar to realize what it is like! The locks are of an age of barbarism! The strong-boxes, one could make better ones of cheese! Had I a farm-wagon, and if I were not retired, I could load it to capacity without an atom of risk!"

"Look here, Albert," said Harrison firmly, "you can't go burgling here! We can't risk anything like that! Our mission—"

Albert said reproachfully:

"But did I not tell you that I am retired? Of course on my first visit to St. Jean-sur-Seine this side of the tunnel, —you comprehend, *m'sieur!* There was an emergency! As was the need for identity papers. But I have acted truly only as an amateur here! It would be undignified to take advantage! These childish locks, these prehistoric strong-boxes . . . I would be ashamed! I have had but one real temptation since we arrived, *M'sieur* Harrison!"

Harrison regarded him suspiciously:

"Resist it!" he warned. "You could ruin everything! And the task M. Carroll and I have set ourselves is so important that I do not know how to tell you of its necessity! You mustn't risk burglaries here, Albert!"

"The danger is over," said Albert. "I yielded to the temptation at two hours after midnight last night. Strictly as an amateur, *m'sieur!* It is ended. Do not reproach me! I achieved what no man of my former profession has ever achieved in all of history! There was once a Colonel Blood who attempted it in England, but—"

Harrison's blood tended to run cold.

"What did you do?" he demanded.

"*M'sieur*," said Albert, grinning, "I ventured into the establishment of the jeweller who had made the crown for the Emperor's coronation. And I, *m'sieur*, took the crown in my hands, and I sat upon the throne made ready for the coronation ceremony, and—I crowned myself, m'sieur! No other burglar in all of history, retired or active, has ever had an Emperor's crown in his hands with a way to carry it away quite open, but who instead has simply crowned himself with it. But I did!"

Harrison tried to swallow.

"The crown," confided Albert, "was a trifle small. It would have had to be altered to fit me. But in any case my action was purely that of an amateur. I pursued a hobby, only. So I put it back in its place and only you and I know of the event. But consider, *m'sieur!* Where but beyond M. Carroll's tunnel could such a thing occur? Here it is true that anything at all—even that I did not take such trumpery—anything at all is much more than likely to happen!"

Albert went proudly away and Harrison held his head.

He already had a nightmarish suspicion that at any instant he might do something, without even knowing it, which would cause something else to happen, and that something else would cause something other, and so on and so on until by the late twentieth century all of Europe would be totally unlike the Europe he'd known. And—this was especially nightmarish—if the future from here, which was the present as he knew it, if the future from here was changed, when he went back to it he would never meet Valerie. Or, he might not have been born.

Curiously, though, he only worried about possible disasters in the line of danger he'd discovered. He didn't think of the longer-established perils the twentieth century tried not to think about. For example, he didn't worry at all about atomic war. He didn't think of it.

But it was danger enough. Harrison had known without interest of the explosion of an atomic bomb by China. He was in his own time then, and absorbed in his romance with Valerie. He had not noticed that the Chinese atomic potentiality was said to be the work of a Frenchman who'd decided that the Russians were political reactionaries. He'd been unaware of a near escape from nuclear war when a sperm whale and two plane radios conking out nearly touched off a red alert. He'd missed the explosion of the second Chinese bomb, which emphasized the message of the first. But now, when he was separated from Valerie by nearly two centuries, the real danger, the deadly danger, the certain catastrophe which meant the end of the world took place.

The Chinese exploded a fifty megaton bomb. In less than

three calendar weeks the celestial kingdom had changed from a seemingly sleeping giant to a modern atomic-armed Great Power. But it was different from the other great powers. Its rulers were calmly prepared to lose half or more than half of their population in war. So they could—and would—start a war if they were crossed.

They said so, frankly. To begin with, they demanded the surrender of Formosa, with no guarantees for its population. They observed that China was now the greatest of great powers, and it expected to exercise much influence in the world from this time on. And it wanted Formosa surrendered as the first exercise of that influence.

There was the dubious possibility that it bluffed; that it didn't have the atomic weapons needed to smash the rest of the world while being blasted from without. If it bluffed, it might be destroyed. If it didn't bluff, history would simply come to an end. So the rest of the world drearily prepared to act as if it were a bluff, and call it. There wasn't anything else to do except surrender. Which wasn't worth while.

Harrison was in the Inn when Pepe Ybarra arrived from St. Jean-sur-Seine with the news. Pepe had been prepared to travel with the others. Now he arrived dusty and exhausted and pale, and gave them the news. Madame Carroll tended her brother, still sneezing and still coughing but likely to survive until the bombs began to fall. Valerie was anxious about Harrison. But Pepe was beside himself.

The Chinese could start atomic war. They would. Some damned renegade Frenchman, defecting from Russia, had given the Chinese the bomb. One crazy, fanatic Frenchman. And the world was doomed. Even the atmosphere of Earth would become poisonous when enough bombs had been detonated in it. Not one animal or plant or moss or lichen would survive. Perhaps no fish or crustacean in all the world's seas would continue to live. It might be that not even single-celled creatures would go on abstractedly feeding upon organic debris, with pauses to multiply by division, in the deepest trenches of the ocean's depths. It was at least probable that Earth would die to the last least quasi-living virus particle under its skies. And history would end.

From one viewpoint this would appear to settle permanently the abstract question of whether or not the universe made sense. If war came and Earth died, it didn't make sense. The cosmos would not have been designed with any special solicitude for the human race. If humanity could destroy itself, it was merely an unedifying random happening on an unimportant planet.

But—there were still the time-tunnels. There was strong reason to believe that through the time-tunnels the past could be changed. If the past changed, the present must also change. If the present changed, the future must be modified. And since it appeared in the early nineteenth century that history would end in the late twentieth—why—if the present in the nineteenth century could be changed sufficiently, it might change the state of things in the twentieth so that history might stagger along for a few more chapters.

Pepe was a tragic figure, explaining the situation to Harrison and Carroll.

"But we can do something!" he said savagely. "Even if we can't guess what the result will be, it can't be worse than is getting ready to happen now! We start things! We do things! It's a gamble, but to hell with that! We can't lose and we might win!"

He turned to Carroll.

"Look!" he said fiercely. "You know science! Give Napoleon something—smokeless powder, percussion caps, dynamite! Start new industries! Give them steam-engines! Let 'em have dynamos. Show them how to prevent diseases and then they can get to work on how to cure them! Do something—*anything*—to change the future, whatever the future may turn out to be! Anything's better than what will happen otherwise!"

Harrison was deathly pale.

"Right!" he said evenly. "You attend to that, Carroll. I've got something else that has to be done first. I'm going back—"

"Are you crazy?" demanded Pepe. "We've got to do things here!"

Harrison began to change to clothing in which a man travelling by post-horse would seem merely to be a man in a hurry.

"Surely," he said grimly. "We do have to do things back here! But Valerie's not in this time. There'll be bombs and devastation and fall out where she is! I'm getting Valerie!"

"But—"

"Dammit!" said Harrison violently. "If I were with her when bombs began to fall, don't you think I'd try to get her into a bomb shelter or a fall-out shelter where she'd be safe?"

"But there'll be no place—"

"No?" Harrison jerked on his riding-boots. "Can you think of a better shelter against atom bombs or fall out than the year eighteen hundred and four?"

He snatched up the clumsy flint-lock pistols that were essential parts of a gentleman's travelling costume. With a peculiarly practised gesture, he made sure of their priming.

8

But all four of them started back to St. Jean-sur-Seine, instead of one. Harrison and Carroll and Pepe Ybarra and Albert set out together and at once. Pepe was a pathetic figure. He was exhausted when he arrived, and once he'd told his story he seemed to sink into bitter despair. But he would not stay in Paris while they went back to St. Jean-sur-Seine. He seemed to think that continual urging would make them take the actions which would be the wildest and most reckless of gambles, but still might give the world he remembered at least a faint chance of surviving. Otherwise there could be no hope.

His reasoning was emotional, and therefore simple. They alone were able to treat two widely separated historical moments as separate present times. But one of those presents followed the other. Therefore events in the later were at least partly determined by what happened in the earlier. They could change what happened in that earlier. They could then find out what resulted in the later. They couldn't predetermine the result of what they did, because the cosmos is much too complex to be manipulated for one's individual ends. But by changes, and if necessary changes of those changes, they should ultimately arrive at a tolerable—at least non-lethal—latter part of the twentieth century. It was by no means sure. But they should try it.

Carroll soothingly agreed with him. But nevertheless they

made their way out of the city. Once they had to stop, at the barriers where the *octroi* was due. All persons entering and leaving the city had to pay this tax, but the collectors were sleepy and bored, even when three gentlemen and one man-servant seemed in such haste at such an unseemly hour. Carroll paid the toll for all of them by the light of a flaring torch. When they rode on he said annoyedly:

"Damnation! It's lucky you came when you did, Ybarra! I didn't realize how low my funds were getting! Did you bring any currency of this period?"

Pepe said dully:

"There were some coins. I used them. Madame Carroll sold them to me. She is indignant because you haven't gotten back with new stock for the shop."

Carroll grunted.

"And we didn't collect for the perfume, either! I'll catch the devil when we get back!" They went on through the darkness. Carroll said, "Harrison, you're planning to bring Valerie back to 1804 for safety. I'm sure your intentions are honorable. But I have a question. I didn't bring enough money here to live on indefinitely. You'll need to. How are you going to do it?"

Harrison had been absorbed in the frantic necessity to get back to St. Jean-sur-Seine, and from there to Paris, and then to explain to Valerie the desperate need for her to go through the time-tunnel with him to reside in the period of Napoleon. She'd need to stay there until either atomic war destroyed the world they were born in, or his and Carroll's actions made that war unlikely. He'd been worried for fear she'd hesitate to take so drastic a step. Now he had a new worry. They'd need money on which to live, even in 1804. He set a corner of his mind to work on that problem. It was a part of the commonplaceness of all the preposterous angles of this whole business of travel in time. But mostly he tried feverishly to calculate whether the war would have begun before he could get to St. Jean-sur-Seine, and from there to Paris, and back through the tunnel with Valerie.

Carroll spoke again in the darkness, with the horses' hoofs making muffled sounds on the roadway.

"Yes . . . Money's something we've got to think about. Hm . . . Albert, have you any to speak of? Money that's good here?"

"But yes, *m'sieur*," said Albert apologetically. "I do not anticipate events, as I told *M'sieur* Harrison. I prefer surprises. But the kind of surprises I prefer are more likely when one has money. I will be happy to share with you."

To Harrison this sounded nightmarish. To worry about money when all the world of his generation seemed certain to commit suicide very shortly, seemed insane. But it no longer seemed peculiar to him to be clothed in the costume and to be riding on this highway of a hundred years before his grandfather was born.

"Better think it over," said Carroll, very seriously. "I suspect Harrison will emigrate to this period, with Valerie. If you're wise, you'll probably do the same. In that case you'll need all the money you've got."

"I can always get more, *m'sieur,*" said Albert. "I have retired, but for emergencies . . ."

"Another problem," said Carroll, reflectively. "For you, Harrison. Valerie will need clothes of this period, at the beginning, anyhow. And we can't risk waiting for them to be made for her."

Pepe said fiercely:

"The thing to do is to prevent the need of it! To do things! Now! What can you do after the bombs fall?"

"That's the odd part," said Carroll. "In your experience you've known that things that had happened changed, and hadn't. Maximilian and the four emperors of Mexico, for example. If we change things so bombs didn't fall, even after they did, it'll be all the same, apparently . . . But somehow I don't think they'll fall."

"Why?"

"It wouldn't be sensible!" said Carroll vexedly. "It would mean that there was no point in existence! Coincidences would be only coincidences! There'd be no meaning in meaning. Nothing would mean anything, but we humans have been designed to see meanings! Patterns wouldn't exist, and design wouldn't exist, but we're designed to see design and discover patterns, and it makes no more sense for us to be equipped to discover what isn't there, than it would make sense for an animal to exist with needs that the universe didn't supply. We've got to do something, yes! But there's something for us to do! There apparently always has been. I suppose there always will be."

Pepe was silent. But it was a scornful silence. Harrison worried. Albert seemed to be puzzling quietly in the darkness as the horses went on. Carroll did not object when Harrison pressed the pace.

"To be practical, again," said Carroll, "if you don't decide to keep them for yourself, which would be wise if you decide to stay here, we'll buy your gold pieces, Albert. Certainly M. Harrison has decided to emigrate to this time, because he and *Ma'mselle* Valerie will be married and he wishes safety for her. He'll need gold pieces, but I could not honorably advise you to sell them. They're always worth something and paper need not be. You may need them."

"But *m'sieur*" said Albert politely, "I can always get more! I am retired, but for emergencies—"

"We've got to get more perfume, too," said Carroll, to Harrison. "Dammit, we need capital! We need working capital! There's no way to know how long we'll be here! But of course we can tell through the tunnel when we've succeeded. You've got to think of clothes for Valerie! She can't go around in modern dress. Not here! And we can't wait for clothes to be made!"

Harrison's mind dwelt harassedly on that problem for a moment. He thought of the *costumier* from whom Albert had secured his lackey's outfit. That might or might not be a possibility. But he wanted Valerie safely on this side of the tunnel at the earliest possible instant. She'd pass through the tunnel practically only over Madame Carroll's dead body, of course . . ."

Pepe said bitterly:

"You haven't said a word, yet, about doing something to keep the Chinese from starting a war! Damn people who won't let other people live the way they want!"

Harrison heard Albert speak solicitously, and realized for the first time that out of habit they'd talked in French and that he could catch every word.

"*M'sieur* Carroll, will you tell me who attempts to change my way of life? I am a Frenchman, and I resist such things!"

The four post-horses went on through the night. Harrison heard Carroll explaining the consequences of time-travel as practised through his time-tunnel. It was not information to to spread abroad, yet there was no particular need to refuse to tell it, because nobody who hadn't passed through the tunnel would believe either that it existed or that anybody who claimed to have passed through it was sane. It was a secret which would keep itself. Nobody who told it would be believed. Albert had even insisted that he did not want to understand the strangeness beyond the tunnel. But as Carroll explained, now he asked questions.

"Ah!" he said profoundly, "it is as if it were a way to walk through a tunnel into a motion picture, and the only way out were that same tunnel. Eh?"

Carroll agreed. He went on. Presently Albert was asking:

"But *m'sieur*, how did you make the tunnel in the wall act as a tunnel into the past?"

Here Carroll was less than explicit. Harrison only half-way listened. He had learned, said Carroll, of a cannon left in the mould in which it was cast. It therefore provided a fixed point in time. So it was possible to use it to produce an opening, a passage way, a tunnel between two eras. The statement was less than a complete explanation to Harrison. He could follow the statement that if one went through it on a Wednesday and remained a day, that one would come back into Thursday. But Harrison was not clear in his mind why every time one passed through it from the twentieth century one arrived at a later date in the nineteenth. It seemed, however, somehow to be tied in with the fact that if the time-tunnel ever collapsed it could never be reconstituted. It would be gone forever. A fresh item of once-melted metal which hadn't been disturbed since its solidification would have to be found, and the new time-tunnel would only be of the length—duration, time-interval—between the time of the freezing of the metal and the formation of the tunnel.

Albert said respectfully:

"But suppose, *m'sieur*, that one went through a tunnel and then it collapsed?"

Carroll observed that tunnels of short period were unstable. If only of days or weeks they did collapse. But a tunnel a century in extent should last indefinitely. The tunnel in St. Jean-sur-Seine had almost two centuries between its ends. It could be broken and then would be gone forever, but it was inherently stable.

They covered the first distance between post-houses in little more than an hour. They changed horses and got fresh ones. They went on again through the night. Pepe was utterly weary. He'd ridden from St. Jean-sur-Seine to Paris without rest, and now was headed back to St. Jean-sur-Seine with no time out for repose.

The third post-house was an inn, and there was a coach in its courtyard. There were four liveried outriders, heavily armed, and they had stirred the inn awake and torches burned smokily and hostlers scurried about trying to supply horses while cooks supplied some sort of midnight refreshment for a scowling man in a black velvet cloak.

Pepe sagged in his saddle while Albert arranged for fresh horses. Carroll dismounted and went into the inn. Harrison paced back and forth, to loosen up his muscles after unaccustomed riding. Someone came out of the inn with a tray. He approached the coach with it. Harrison saw two heads at the coach windows. One was a girl of about Valerie's age, with Valerie's coloring. Her expression was infinitely sad. The other was an older woman, possibly in her middle thirties wearing the headdress of a Spanish widow. She had a plump figure and a cheerful expression. She looked like someone it would be pleasant to have around. She opened the door, received the tray, and drew it into the coach. The door closed again.

Carroll came out of the inn. Albert had disappeared. There came a sudden uproar. The inn servants rushed. The liveried outriders went to see. When a single bellowing voice could be picked out, howling curses, the scowling man in the black velvet cloak went authoritatively to end the tumult.

He returned, followed by his coachman, dripping and enraged. Some person unknown had up-ended a wooden bucket of water on the coachman's head and left the bucket sticking there. The bucket had had to be broken to get it off. Now the man in the black velvet cloak was icily angry with the coachman and savage with the outriders.

In minutes, the coach's horses were back in place and it went rolling and rumbling toward Paris. The horses of the outriders made a steady mutter on the highway.

The four from the twentieth century rode away from Paris, on the way to St. Jean-sur-Seine. Pepe was utterly exhausted. It would be literally impossible for him to continue for another day and night of top-speed travel. Two post-houses beyond the inn, Harrison said anxiously:

"Carroll, we're going to lose time with Pepe! He'd better stop for a few hours! You stay here with him! I'll ride on ahead!"

Carroll said:

"Better not. I've got things to do, too! Albert, will you stay here to take care of M. Ybarra and get him to the tunnel at the earliest practical instant? M. Harrison and I should ride on. It's urgent."

"But certainly, *m'sieur*," said Albert. "I myself would relish rest. I have moved about a great deal, by night."

Carroll arranged with the post-master for Pepe to have accommodations at the post-house. Albert would sleep on the floor of the same room. Harrison verified that the door opened inward. It couldn't be opened without waking Albert. Pepe stumbled up the stairs and collapsed, worn out.

Carroll and Harrison went on. They rode at a headlong pace, and walked their horses for a time, and went on again at top speed. It was the way to make the best time without exhausting their mounts. They arrived at post-houses, and changed horses, and continued their race against time and fate and the zestful efforts of the human race to destroy itself. Their rate of travel was unprecedented, in the France of 1804, except for couriers bearing military messages. The sky was just beginning to gray at the east when St. Jean-sur-Seine appeared.

They took a considerable risk. They unsaddled their horses and turned them loose. They hid their saddles. The horses being from the last post-house would eventually turn up at this one. And Harrison and Carroll made their way into the town on foot. But they reached the foundry and got into it unseen by any of the local citizenry.

There was tumult when Madame Carroll unlocked the door of the time-tunnel and let them into the cottage of their own era. Even M. Dubois came stumbling down the stairs in his nightshirt. He was evidently still treated as an invalid by Madame Carroll. She demanded fiercely to see the articles Carroll should have purchased and brought back with him for her new and profitable art-dealer customer. Ominously she began to open the saddlebags Carroll and Harrison had brought. Her face crimsoned with fury as she found no fresh stock for the business of Carroll, Dubois et Cie. She did not even find currency to pay for the perfume M. Dubois had risked his life to deliver! Then she tore open a bag which was not a saddlebag, and which Harrison didn't recognize, though he'd probably carried it. She flung out its contents and displayed truly impressive rage. Because the contents of this bag—of all imaginable objects—was female garments.

Harrison was very weary, but he came back to full wakefulness at sight of a woman's costume among their possessions. Then he remembered, vividly, the travelling coach in the inn-yard which was the third post-station out of Paris. There had been tumult, out of sight, and then the disclosure of a wooden bucket jammed down on the head of the coachman who drove that carriage. Everyone had gone to see what the uproar meant.

"That was Albert," he said to Carroll, while Madame Carroll rose to unprecedented speed and fury in her denunciation. "Albert made the uproar so he could get this out of the coach's trunk. Probably because he was bound to be surprised when he opened it!"

Carroll nodded. He looked at his red-faced, vociferating wife. He picked her up and carried her, kicking and yelping, into the kitchen. Harrison heard him ascend the stairs. He heard a door slam. A lock clicked. Carroll came downstairs again.

"Georges," he said to the trembling Dubois, "can you tell me the time?" He looked out the window. "Clock time is different," he commented to Harrison. "I tend to forget it. It was dawn at the other end of the tunnel. Get changed, Harrison! We've got to catch the bus to Paris!"

He began to strip off his costume of the early nineteenth century. M. Dubois, trembling, helped him find his garments of the late twentieth. He produced Harrison's clothes. Carroll said detachedly:

"Georges, what are the Chinese doing? Have they bombed Formosa yet?"

M. Dubois' mouth dropped open. He could imagine nothing more irrelevant—with his sister kicking her heels and screaming on the floor above—than a question about international politics or Far Eastern Affairs.

"My—my sister," he said, trembling, "I fear for her health! She is in—such extreme distress! She has waited so anxiously to receive the shipment from—where I purchased the stock for the shop! She is beside herself! I fear—"

"We're leaving for Paris," Carroll told him. "Listen to me, Georges! I'll be back perhaps tonight, if anybody is left alive. Then I'll return to my wife every centime that's left of my money. Listen! I—will—return—to—my—wife—what—money—is—left! Tell her that. Tell her I've spent only a fraction of it! I'll give her back nearly all the money I drew out of the bank! She'll rage, but she'll still be a rich woman and she knows it! And without me she would not have been rich! I'm going back through the tunnel and perhaps—just possibly!—everything will go on as it has, except that I will live in Paris of 1804 and send you the goods you want in the shop and you will not ever have to go through the tunnel again—and she'll be more prosperous than ever before!"

M. Dubois seized upon the faintest possible hope of calming his sister.

"That—that would be admirable," he said, still trembling, "But, until it occurs—"

"She'll raise hell. Of course!" Carroll fished in the pockets of his contemporary costume. "Damnation! She cleaned out my pockets! Lucky I put my money in another bank! Harrison, have you any modern currency to pay the bus fare to Paris?"

A little later they left the cottage. Harrison remembered to give warning that Pepe and Albert were still to arrive, probably twelve hours or so from now. The town of St. Jean-sur-Seine looked remarkably familiar, because it looked like parts of Paris of 1804. There were minor modifications—such as street-lights—but it was very similar, quaint and unspoiled and unattractive.

The bus waited, wheezing. Harrison bought a newspaper. The mainland Chinese had consented to delay the bombing of Formosa. They said blandly that they would not consider a change in their demand for its surrender, but if the people of Formosa chose to rise against their criminal *bourgeois* rulers, the mainland government would give them a reasonable time in which to do it. In effect, they offered to regard the people of the island more kindly if before surrendering they killed everybody the mainlanders disliked. They would give five days' grace for the suggested murders if the murderers-to-be asked nicely.

The rest of the news story dealt with negotiations, with profound statements by the President of France, the debates in the United Nations, the remarkable refusal of some African countries to join in the United Nations protest, and so on. But it was not the exclusive news story on the first page. There had been a fire, and much editorial eloquence described the destruction of that ancient wooden building on the Rue Colbert which was precious to the hearts of all Frenchmen because in it had lived Julie d'Arnaud, mistress of Charles VII of France. It was considered the most ancient wooden structure still standing in Paris, and its leaden roof had resisted the rains and storms of six hundred years. There was also, on an inside page, an editorial about the tragedy, to France, that the Chinese threat to the rest of the world had come about through a French scientist, defected first to Russia and then to China. But Carroll did not read that editorial. It was unfortunate. It named the Frenchman.

Carroll read only the nuclear news. He put the paper aside.

"Better cash in your letter of credit," he observed as the bus rolled on. "If we have to spend possibly months working on the future, from back where we'll be, we don't want to be having to try to find employment back there! I don't know whether I told you about calling on Gay-Lussac, the chemist. He envisions great things for the science of chemistry. Of course he doesn't believe that organic compounds can ever be synthesized, but he has an idea that precious stones may some day be synthesized. He's very hopeful about artificial diamonds."

Harrison was thinking anxiously about Valerie. He said absently:

"I think it's been done."

"Not gem stones," said Carroll regretfully. "If we could take some of them back . . ."

Something clicked in Harrison's mind. The part of it that he'd set to worry about money made a clamor against the rest. But he stared out the bus window. If the universe was not especially designed for humans to live in, then presently these fields would be thin dust or mud, with stark, bare trees in frozen gestures above a world on which there was nothing green anywhere. Houses that men had built would be abraded by desert winds blowing foolishly here and there. Eventually they would fall, but they would not decay because there would be no decay-bacteria alive to feed on them. There would be sunrises and sunsets with no eyes to see them, and there would be sounds of wind and rain and thunder, but no ears to hear.

He turned suddenly from the window.

"Synthetic rubies," he said. "Synthetic sapphires. That's the answer! At cents per carat. They're real rubies and sapphires. They're genuine. They simply aren't natural ones. And there are cultured opals, too. They're genuine. They just aren't wild. They're cultivated."

Carroll said wrily:

"I suspect my wife never happened to think of that! Yes. We'll get some. But not for trade. In case of emergency only. I don't mind Albert stealing. It's his nature. But I've a quaint objection to acting like a tradesman."

Harrison made no comment. His thoughts went back to Valerie.

The bus reached Paris. Harrison went to the Express office. He acquired flat packets of currency for his letter of credit. He got a cab to the shop of Carroll, Dubois et Cie. The streets were the same. There was a blockade across the front of a scene of much destruction by a recent fire. It was that very, very old wooden house once occupied by the mistress of a forgotten king. From one gaunt blackened timber there dangled a peculiar glittering shape of metal. It was like an icicle, except that solidified lead from the roof had formed it.

Harrison saw posters on the kiosks where newspapers were sold. Russia offered alliance with the West. India considered a non-aggression pact with China. *Les États-Unis* announced that the bombardment of Formosa would be considered an act of war. England attempted to negotiate a compromise. France warned the world that it would use the atom in its own defense. The Scandinavian countries joined Switzerland in proclaiming their unalterable policy of neutrality. West Germany demanded atom bombs for its own defense. But there were no gatherings of people to buy newspapers. The public was accustomed to crises.

Harrison's cab stopped before the shop. There was an elderly customer inside. He chatted amiably and interminably before he purchased a copy of the *Moniteur* of March 20th, 1804. It contained a mention of his great-grandfather. He confided gleefully that he would yellow it with coffee and antique its texture with a flat-iron, and frame it for his descendants to consider an original.

He went out, chuckling to himself. And Harrison acted as an engaged man is likely to, when he has not seen his particular girl for well over a week.

Presently he explained the situation. Valerie smiled at him and objected that the shop had to be kept open. She could not leave Paris. Harrison spread out the newspaper and pointed out that Paris was not likely to exist for more than a limited number of days. Valerie permitted him to kiss her and said regretfully that her aunt would be frantic if she lost money by the closing of the shop for a single day.

When Carroll appeared at dusk Harrison was in a highly unstable condition. Valerie wanted to do as he asked, but she was alarmed. She tried to change the subject. She told him that she had witnessed part of the conflagration when the most ancient wooden building in Paris burned. He wouldn't listen. She had to come to St. Jean-sur-Seine and go through the tunnel.

But Carroll's arrival solved the problem. Carroll explained that though Harrison had not been present at the time, her aunt wished Valerie to come at once to St. Jean-sur-Seine to receive instructions about the shop. It was, of course, a whopping lie. Harrison couldn't lie to Valerie—at least, not yet—but he didn't feel that he had to contradict so useful a prevarication.

They took the seven o'clock bus out of Paris. They

reached St. Jean-sur-Seine. Valerie dutifully delivered to her aunt the contents of the shop's cash drawer. Madame Carroll retired with her, immediately, to count the money and demand precise and particular accounts of every transaction and sale.

Pepe and Albert arrived later, from 1804. Pepe was again in a passion of desperate anxiety, and the newspapers Carroll had brought from Paris were not in the least reassuring. The tone of all the news accounts was that this was another crisis; a grave and indeed an appalling crisis. But every one found room on its front page for a news item about the destruction of the residence of the mistress of a long-ago king. Not one made the statement that history could be about to end, the human race to become extinct, and that it would thereby be demonstrated that the universe was not designed for humans to live in, because they were going to stop living in it. Pepe read, and reached the verge of tears. He had a grandmother who was in Tegucigalpa, but that would be no safer than anywhere else on earth.

"I saw your great-great-grandfather," Harrison told him. "I provided him with perfume for your great-great-grandmother."

He hadn't thought to tell Pepe about it before. But Albert interposed as Pepe would have asked morbid questions.

"*M'sieur*, my clothing of this period—"

"Ask Dubois," said Harrison. "Hold it! Are you going to stay in this time? This side of the tunnel?"

"*M'sieur*," said Albert in a subdued tone, "I think I shall do so. I could not possibly do anything more magnificent than I achieved in the jewellers' you know of. I wore Napoleon's crown before he did! I shall remain here and contemplate that achievement. I shall retire contentedly even from my hobby! I shall make a hobby of my recollections!"

"Read these newspapers," commanded Harrison, "and if you don't change your mind I've a pocketful of paper currency with which to buy any gold pieces you may have accumulated."

Albert waved the papers aside. He shook his head.

"*M'sieur*," he said firmly, "*M'sieur* Carroll explained to me the France behind the tunnel. I now understand it. Unhappily I can now anticipate events in it. I even understand your and M. Carroll's intention to change the past so the present will become other than as it is. But that cannot be predicted! It is impossible to guess what it may be! And it will no longer be my hobby, but it will give me pleasure to observe. So as a former connoisseur of surprises I shall remain at this end of the tunnel to see what comes next. I shall be surprised at anything that happens, and most of all if nothing happens. So I will be happy to exchange my napoleons for the paper money of modern France!"

He dumped out the contents of his individual saddlebags. Gold coins seemed to cover the floor. He stacked them matter-of-factly while Harrison counted his paper money. Albert named a sum. Harrison paid it. There was paper money left over. Harrison said:

"You may as well take this too."

"No, *m'sieur*," said Albert proudly. "We are friends. If you will arrange to get my proper costume for the present time, I will leave you and return to my retirement."

Dubois came down the stairs. He looked precariously relieved. His sister seemed to be talking almost tranquilly with Valerie. She had even determined that Valerie should wear the female costume of 1804 in the shop. It would make the shop distinctive. And if Carroll would take up his residence in the era of Napoleon, and if he would supply from that period the stock she required, M. Dubois need never again risk pneumonia by travelling in the past. And M. Dubois was almost cheerful, because his sister was less agitated than he'd seen her for months.

He gave Albert his corduroy trousers and sash and the red-checked shirt. Albert put them on and stuffed his pockets with paper money. He swaggered to the door. Then he stopped. He returned to shake hands emotionally with Carroll and Pepe and Harrison. Then, from apparently nowhere, he produced a much-folded scrap of paper. He pressed it into Harrison's hand.

"Do not read this," he said unhappily, "until I have gone."

He went swiftly to the door, gazed back at them as if through brimming eyes, and went out. They heard his footsteps hastening away.

Harrison unfolded the paper. Crudely written with a strictly improvised pen, he read:

"Monsieur; I have to confess. It was after I had put the bucket on the coachman's head and taken the parcel from the coach that I learned from the innkeeper that the gentleman in the black cloak was M. de Bassompierre. Then I dared not reveal it. I weep that I disarranged your plans. I beg your forgiveness,

Albert."

Carroll said:

"The devil! We missed a possibly lucky break! But it's too late to repair it now! We're starting back, anyhow. Get into your 1804 clothes, Harrison. Ybarra, you don't have to change. Pack these books with that newspaper. The paper should convince de Bassompierre when we find him again! You've got a good lot of cash, Harrison!"

Harrison looked up. He was startled by what he'd just found out.

"Albert told me how much I owed him, and I paid him. But he figured the napoleons at six hundred francs each, instead of twelve!"

"That was the bargain he offered," said Carroll dryly. "A most admirable character! But get changed. We want to get moving!"

Harrison changed. And he was thinking morbidly that he hadn't yet gotten Valerie to consent to move into the past as an atom-bomb-proof shelter when he heard her come down the stairs from the upper floor. He looked yearningly at the door of the kitchen, to which the stairs descended.

She came through that door, smiling. She looked to Harrison for approval. She wore the costume looted from the coach at the post-house.

"*Ma tante*," she said demurely, "told me to try on the costume I am to wear in the shop. Does it become me?"

Harrison could only babble. Anguish filled him. Valerie mustn't share the disaster due to come upon the earth! He remembered the fields and towns and highways on the way to Paris. He'd imagined them as they seemed certain to become if the events of 1804 were not changed so definitely that reality could not cover them up by making them never to have been. He'd pictured all living things as alive no longer. Trees no longer in leaf. Grass no longer green. Cities no longer inhabited. All solid ground mere lifeless dust or else thick mud; all the seas empty of life; the air never echoing the sounds of birds or insects or anything but thunder and rain and wind and surf with no ears anywhere to hear. . . .

"Listen!" he said thickly, "Come through the tunnel with me, Valerie. I want to talk to you!"

She followed him unquestioningly. He warned her of the symptoms she'd feel during the passage through the tunnel. Then they were together in the resonant, echoing emptiness of the foundry building which did not exist in the same century as the cottage.

He tried to explain. She looked about her. She was astonished. There was brand new daylight filtering through the cracks in boarded-up windows of the foundry. But it was deep night outside the cottage! Here it was day! He explained that oddity, desperately aware that what he told her was no less preposterous than what she saw.

Carroll appeared behind them. He carried saddlebags. He put them down, nodded, and said:

"There is going to be an argument with your aunt, Valerie. For some unknown reason I feel responsibility for her. I shall try to persuade her to join us. Heaven knows why!"

He went back through the tunnel and therefore nearly two centuries into what was here the future. Valerie said uneasily, "But is this the arrangement my uncle uses to get the merchandise for the shop?"

"He came through here, yes," said Harrison. "You see—"

He tried again to explain. She put her hand tremblingly upon his arm. He ceased to explain. There were matters much more urgent than explanations. Carroll returned with more saddlebags. He deposited them and said dryly, "I'm only Valerie's uncle by marriage, Harrison, but I think I should ask your intentions!"

Harrison swore at him and then hastily apologized to Valerie.

"The war has begun," said Carroll. At Harrison's violent reaction he explained. "No, not the world war. Not atomic war. But my wife is in action. I've told her I want her to come through the tunnel because I intend for Valerie to stay there until the war scare's over. She can't imagine such a thing. She hasn't bothered to refuse. She's just working up to a completed description, in detail, of my criminal insanity."

He went back. Valerie said shakily, "Should—should I try to calm her?"

"Have you ever managed it?" asked Harrison. "Look! There's going to be atomic war! But Carroll and Pepe and I have some faint chance of preventing it! We don't know what will take its place, but I won't let anything happen to you! I won't do it!"

Pepe came out of the tunnel, carrying bags. He put them down. He said distressedly:

"*Dios mio!* If Carroll does persuade her to come—"

He made an appalled gesture. He went back. Valerie said:

"I *am* frightened. Of my aunt. Not—of anything else."

Perhaps ten minutes later Carroll came through again. M. Dubois came with him. Dubois said agitatedly:

"Valerie, your aunt commands that you return! At once!

She is agitated! She is angry! I have never seen her so angry! Come!"

Valerie stirred in Harrison's arms. He tightened them about her. She said faintly:

"I—I cannot!"

"But your aunt demands it! She threatens—she threatens—"

Pepe came out of the tunnel with a last parcel. He said with some grimness:

"She swears that if *Ma'mselle* Valerie does not return at once that she will disown her forever! She will endure this state of things no longer! She will abandon her and—"

Carroll said kindly:

"Maybe you can calm her down, Georges. This thing is more important than her getting her way again. Better try to make her see it."

Dubois went shakily back to the world of the future. Almost instantly thereafter Madame Carroll's voice reached them. It was thin and muted by its passage through time, just a muttering. Madame Carroll cried out fiercely in the totally uncontrolled fury of a bad-tempered woman. Her voice sounded far away but shrieking. Then things came flying out into the foundry. They were the twentieth-century garments Valerie had removed to put on the costume for the shop. Madame Carroll's voice shrieked like the ghost of an outcry of rage.

Then there came a peculiar, echoing, musical sound. It was like the string of some incredible harp, plucked once and then very gradually dying away. It seemed to make all the ground hereabouts vibrate. Their bodies vibrated with it. It ended.

Carroll jumped, startled and angry.

"Damnation! She saw me throw a switch on to make the tunnel! To make a threat, she's thrown it off! And the tunnel's collapsed and can't be made again! We're stuck here!"

9

Four days later they arrived at an inn still a few hours' journey from Paris. As inns go, it was distinctly an improvement on most such stopping places in the France of the period. Harrison felt that their appearance was improved, too. Carroll and Valerie rode grandly in the lumbering coach they'd acquired. He was the uncle by marriage and he wore the air of an uncle-in-fact. He'd mentioned that she ought to have a maid along as a travelling companion, but an extra pair of listening ears would have been a nuisance. Harrison and Pepe rode beside the coach, armed as a matter of course. Pepe's regard for Harrison's priority with Valerie made him act with the perfect, amiable disinterest of a cousin. Harrison had the role of fiancé. He could not have played any other. He tended to bristle when anybody tried to look into the coach where Valerie was. There were two mounted lackeys trailing behind. They resembled Albert solely in being wholly without conscience.

All these semblances of respectability had been secured by the use of gold napoleons and a swaggering air, plus complete disregard of the literal truth. Carroll seemed to take pleasure in inventing grotesque but convincing lies to make whatever they did seem perfectly natural.

The coach turned into the inn courtyard and there was another coach already there. A liveried servant held the horses of the other vehicle. There were yet other horses, saddled and tied to hitching posts. There was a cheerful, comfortable bustle round about. There was smoke from a badly drawing chimney. There was the smell of strongly-odored cooking. The courtyard was mostly mud, though straw had been spread here and there for better footing.

"Ybarra," said Carroll amiably, "see if we can get suitable quarters here."

Pepe beckoned to one of their two lackeys, rode to where the ground was not wholly mud, and dismounted. He tossed his reins to the lackey and went inside.

"I think," said Carroll reflectively, "that I'll call myself de Bassompierre from now on. I'm anxious to find that character! I shall expect to make a deal with him for the use of his time-tunnel. But that's in addition to reforming him so he won't write to learned men."

Harrison bent over to look inside the coach.

"Are you all right, Valerie? Comfortable?"

She smiled at him. He felt a desperate pride in her. But she felt safe, and she felt approved of, and a girl can face most things with such assurances.

The time and place and atmosphere were totally common-place, for Napoleonic France. There was nothing remarkable in view. Some two or three post-stages to the south-east lay Paris. In it candles and torches prepared to substitute, feebly, for the light by which people saw during the day. Travelling coaches like theirs would be hastening to arrive at stopping places for the night. In an hour all of France would be in-doors. Nothing out of the ordinary appeared to be in prospect. But actually the ordinary is remarkable. Nothing ever happens unless the odds against it are astronomical. Nobody in all of history has ever anticipated an event and had it come out in all its details as it was foreseen.

Certainly nobody could have guessed at any imaginable actual linkage between the pause of a particular travelling coach in the France of 1804 and the events on the island of Formosa nine thousand miles away and nearly two centuries later. But the events were intimately connected.

The island of Formosa lay in bright sunshine under threat of destruction by atomic bombs from the mainland. One would have anticipated swarming panic and flight, especially by foreigners. One would have looked to see its harbors empty and its cities seething masses of humanity, frenziedly killing other humans, in the hope that through murder they could avoid being murdered from the sky.

But it wasn't that way at all. There were ships steaming

away from it at topmost speed, to be sure. But there were other ships rushing toward it at full speed ahead. Its harbors were crowded with vessels, taking on refugees to the limit of sitting-down space on their decks. As they were loaded, they headed away to the nearest unthreatened harbor to discharge them and go back for more. There was an incredible stream of planes flying to and from the island. Every air field was devoted exclusively to the landing, loading, and dispatch of a most motley assortment of flying machines, which descended to take in passengers and immediately flew away again.

There were no men in uniform among the refugees. Women, yes. Children, in multitudes. Ships of the sea and air swarmed to carry away as many of its helpless population as could be removed. But among the men left behind there was no resignation. There was no despair. There was fury and resolve, instead. When a flying transport landed and brought a ground-to-air missile and a crew to launch it, there was grim rejoicing. Formosa was going to attempt a defense against atomic attack. The military of a hundred nations wanted passionately to know whether defense was possible. All the world had defenses of which much was hoped, but too little known, just as all the world had bombs for attack. If Formosa could be defended, then war need not mean despair. But if Formosa could be bombed against all-out defense, then there was not much point to anything. Already it was understood that if war came all the West would act as one. It was more than suspected, though, that some nations had made private bargains to send their rockets at Chinese-chosen targets, in return for a promise of more-than-slave-status when the Chinese ruled the earth. But Formosa would be defended. If there was no longer any real hope of avoiding nuclear war, there was at least some sort of hope for humanity's survival.

This was the situation nine thousand miles, a hundred-odd years, some weeks and days and a few hours from the inn courtyard where Harrison assured himself that Valerie was comfortable. There was another coach in the yard. Pepe was inside the inn, asking questions. It seemed that nothing could conceivably be more unconnected than the situation in this inn yard in Napoleon's time and the situation on Formosa nearly two hundred years later.

In the later time and far-away place, a broadcast was received. It was from the mainland government, and it was bland and confident. It announced that planes carrying atomic bombs would shortly appear over Formosa. If they were fired on, they would drop their bombs and a full-scale bombardment by all the mainland air force would follow. If they were not fired on, the granted time for revolt and surrender would still be allowed. The broadcast seemed incredible, but the local military rejoiced by anticipation. No planes would ever reach Formosa to drop bombs! An air umbrella already existed above the island. Ground-to-air missile crews were already on twenty-four-hour alert. When and as the radar screen notified approaching planes, they would be blasted to atoms!

Then the Chinese bombers came. The radars detected them at once. But they could not locate them. The Chinese had a radar jamming device, as effective as the radio jamming device used within the iron curtain. The radar showed something in the sky. But they said it existed at all altitudes up to eighty thousand feet, and at every spot along an eighty-mile front. It was a target worse than useless to shoot at.

Presently the clumsy Chinese bombers circled placidly over Formosa. They stayed an infuriating six thousand feet up. They were vulnerable to anti-aircraft fire. To anti-missile missiles. They were sitting ducks! But they couldn't be detected on the way to Formosa, and when they arrived defense was useless.

They were not fired on, and they circled placidly until night fell. Then they climbed up and up and up until they couldn't be spotted by telescopes, and then they went away. It was not possible to trail them. The radar jamming radiation dimmed and dimmed. Presently it stopped. It had been demonstrated that Formosa could be bombed whenever the mainland Chinese felt like bombing it.

So could any other city in the world.

In the inn yard in France, somebody in the other, waiting coach summoned a servant to the coach window. That servant turned to look at the coach with Harrison close by it and Carroll and Valerie still within.

Pepe came out of the inn; hastily, almost running. It was dusk, now, though the sky was still a lucent blue overhead. Pepe came hastily across the mud and straw. He reached the coach-side.

"He's in there," panted Pepe. "I saw him! De Bassompierre! To make sure, I asked the innkeeper! He's sitting there with food and wine before him! The man whose coach Albert robbed!"

Carroll was instantly outside the coach.

"Ah! And this is a good place to talk to him!"

"But Valerie—"

"Stay with her," commanded Carroll. "This is going to take time, anyhow. There'll be argument. You can bring her in later."

He went swiftly after Pepe. Harrison looked irresolutely after them. But, servants or no servants, he wasn't going to leave Valerie alone in the coach in an inn yard of this period!

"This is bad!" he said restlessly. "We've got to talk to him, but—"

A voice said obsequiously:

"Your Excellency's pardon! Madame de Cespedes begs that she may speak to you!"

Harrison swung about. A liveried servant from the other coach stood hat in hand beside him. He bowed.

"Madame de Cespedes, Excellency, begs your Excellency's aid in a matter of life and death! She is in the coach yonder."

The lackey's French was thick with a Spanish accent. Harrison recognized his livery. He'd seen it outside the door of a perfumer's shop in Paris. Ybarra.

He gestured to his own lackey to bring the coach after him. He rode to the other coach. He started. Peering appealingly at him from the coach window, he saw the woman who with a dark-haired girl had been in the travelling coach six days previously, when Albert abstracted a travelling case from the coach's trunk. She had looked plump and good-natured then. Now, as then, she wore the headdress of a Spanish widow. Then, but not now, she looked amiable and contented. Now she was composed but fiercely in earnest.

"M'sieur," she said desperately, "I am in most great need of the aid of a gentleman. I am the *Comtesse* de Cespedes. I am the sister-in-law of *Don* Ignacio Ybarra. His wife and I —we have been robbed of our jewels by *M'sieur* de Bassompierre, who is in the inn yonder. My servants do not dare lay hands upon a gentleman. I beg your aid!"

Valerie in the coach had followed closely enough to hear every word. Now she said warmly:

"But of course, Madame! *M'sieur* Harrison and his friends will be happy to serve you!"

Harrison closed his mouth; opened it, and suddenly saw the possibilities. De Bassompierre had the very worst of all possible reputations. They had need to stop him from changing the past to bring about who-knew-what—but certainly atomic war—to the time they'd come from. If they could prove him a common thief, he must meet any terms they chose to set, including the revelation of the other time-tunnel Carroll at once could not believe in and could not fully deny. In short, Madame Cespedes' predicament might be the solution to their problem.

He gave crisp orders to the lackeys, who led the two coaches to where it was possible for a woman to alight without spoiling her foot-gear. He helped Valerie to the ground, and then the slightly chubby occupant of the other coach. Grandly, he escorted them into the inn.

They entered a large, smoke-stained, odorous room in which a huge fire burned. There were some rough tables. Some travelers, by their attire merchants or the like, ate rather noisily by one wall. At the choicest table, because nearest the fire, sat the scowling, becapped individual Albert and this innkeeper had identified as M. de Bassompierre. Carroll loomed over him, stiffly polite but not to be put off. Pepe stood nearby, in a state of inexplicable agitation. The scowling man waved Carroll aside, as one too insignificant to be listened to.

Then Madame de Cespedes said in a clear, indignant voice:

"That is he! *Messieurs,* I ask you to request him to return my and my sister-in-law's jewels!"

De Bassompierre jerked his head around. His face went blank. Then he ground his teeth. Madame de Cespedes, despite her plumpness, was a perfect picture of dignity and contempt.

"*M'sieur* de Bassompierre," she said icily, "you greeted me in my brother-in-law's coach on the Avenue des Italiens today, as I waited for my sister-in-law. You dismounted and spoke to me at the coach door. And *m'sieur,* I smelled perfume upon you. And it was a very special perfume, possessed only by my sister-in-law and Her Majesty the Empress herself! You went on. I sent a servant to call my sister-in-law. I told her of the event. We went immediately and my sister-in-law found her perfume disturbed and her jewels gone. Mine were gone, also. My sister-in-law instantly sent servants in search of her husband, *Don* Ignacio Ybarra. I ordered the coachman to drive me in the direction you had taken, to keep watch for you. I have overtaken you. Now, in the presence of these gentlemen I request that you return my jewels and those of my sister-in-law!"

Madame de Cespedes was a small woman, but her manner was dignity itself. She held her head high.

De Bassompierre said roughly:

"I have never seen this woman before. I know nothing of her jewels!"

He stood up, arrogantly.

"I do not care to know you or her!"

He flung his cloak about himself. His hidden hand took an odd position, if as threatening the use of a weapon. Carroll made an exactly similar gesture. The innkeeper came waddling anxiously:

"Messieurs! Messieurs! I beg you—"

Pepe said imploringly, and Harrison wondered even then why he was so disturbed, "Let's talk this over! M. de Bassompierre, we mean no harm! To the contrary, we've been looking for you very urgently—"

He stammered suddenly. To recite, in public, the facts of time-travel to a man just accused of robbery is not the most convincing way to argue with him. Pepe realized the fact.

"Messieurs!" protested the innkeeper "I beg you not to quarrel in my inn! There is all outdoors to quarrel in! I beg—"

"Give us a room where we can be alone," snapped Carroll, not taking his eyes from the arrogant dark man. "I agree that there is no need to quarrel! I prove it! *M'sieur*—" Then he said, very distinctly: "United Nations! Communist Russia! Electronics! Railroads! Airplanes! Those words will tell you where we come from!"

The dark man sneered. Pepe was trembling, deathly white. Harrison found that he bitterly regretted that he had left his pistols in their saddle holsters. Then the dark man said, again arrogantly:

"If they are code words for recognition, I do not know them. But I take it you think you have business with me?"

"Very much so," said Carroll coldly. Over his shoulder he said, in English: "Harrison, what the devil's this robbery business?"

"It seems the truth," said Harrison. "And if he's de Bassompierre we've got him where we want him."

"Then we negotiate," said Carroll, again in English, "for the use of his time-tunnel and other assurances." He switched back to French to command the landlord to show them to a private room. "There is no need for violence."

"Mais non!" chattered the landlord. "This way, *messieurs!* this way!"

He backed before them. He came to a door. He opened it. He bowed them through it, babbling. A candle burned on a table. The dark man noted the position of the windows.

"You may speak," he said harshly. "Of what?"

Pepe edged close to Harrison. He whispered in English:

"Harrison, what's this? Who's the woman? What's she got to do with our affairs?"

"She's Madame de Cespedes," said Harrison in the same language. "She says he robbed her and Ybarra's wife. Your great-great-grandmother. She's Ybarra's sister-in-law."

"Dios mio!" panted Pepe. *"Dios mio!"*

The dark man said scornfully:

"I hear words which may be *l'Anglais*. Are you English spies who hope to bribe me to aid you?"

Pepe chattered hoarsely in Harrison's ear:

"This is awful! I told you I had a great-great-grandfather in Paris! You met him! But I've got two! M-madame de Cespedes is going to marry de Bassompierre! They'll have a daughter who'll marry Ignacio Ybarra's son, who'll be born next year or the year after! So she's to be my great-great-grandmother too! And-and de-de Bassompierre's another great-great-grandfather of mine! So if anything happens . . . I won't be born!"

Harrison blinked. There was the sound of another arrival in the inn yard. There were the creakings of a heavy coach, and very, very many horses made hoof sounds on the ground. Then Carroll said suavely:

"M'sieur, I believe we share a secret with you, but you cannot believe we share it! I mention more words. Métro! Underground! Eiffel Tower! World War Two! Those names have meanings to us. Will you deny that they have meanings to you?"

The dark man stared.

"I'll give you proof you can't deny!" said Carroll coldly. "I'll—"

Harrison said:

"Look! What we want is important, but Madame de Cespedes has been robbed. If he'll give back her jewels we'll get along better."

"No!" snapped Carroll. "We'll take up the jewels later. First, hold this!"

He thrust a small and very elegant flint-lock pistol into Harrison's hand. It was probably from the stock of the shop. It was grotesque to be holding it, and embarrassing to wonder what exactly he should do with it. There was no present excuse to hold it aimed at de Bassompierre. It was an awkward situation to be in. Carroll went out. Long seconds passed.

Then a voice outside the building boomed:

"De Bassompierre! De Bassompierre! Holà!"

The face of the dark man filled with astonishment. The voice that called "De Bassompierre" was not an authoritative voice. It was a friendly one, calling recognition in a tone of pleased surprise. But the greeting was for someone outside the inn, not inside. The same voice boomed on in a lower, confidential tone. Harrison's scalp crawled. He knew what was going on in the other man's mind. Somebody else had been called by his name. That somebody else was now in conversation with the person who'd called him. It would be a nightmarish sensation to anybody. But—

The door opened. A short, stout, beaming man marched in, saying over his shoulder:

"Nonsense, de Bassompierre! It was the most pleasant of surprises to see you, but an even greater pleasure—"

He saw Valerie and the plump Madame de Cespedes. He stopped and removed his hat with something of a flourish.

"Pardon."

A thin man in a long gray cloak followed him into the room. This man limped slightly. Carroll, his face singularly set and grim, followed the second individual. Madame de Cespedes gave a cry of satisfaction.

"M. de Talleyrand! Ah, you can attend to everything! This scoundrel has robbed my sister-in-law and myself! These gentlemen were trying to make him yield his booty. These two and that gentleman also."

The thin man in the gray cloak smiled pleasantly. He looked at the man in the black velvet cloak, and de Bassompierre sweated suddenly. Charles Maurice Talleyrand de Périgord, once Bishop of Autun, now Grand Chamberlain of the Empire, and eventually to be Prince of Benevento, was not a welcome sight to a man accused of robbery despite his supposed status as a gentleman. When Talleyrand smiled gently and benignly upon de Bassompierre, and Valerie and Madame de Cespedes and Harrison and Pepe, all but de Bassompierre felt comforted. De Bassompierre sweated and went starkly white.

"Ah!" said Talleyrand, in a mild tone but in a voice which even his enemies admitted was strong and deep, "but Madame, we will have to look into this! Pray tell me—"

Madame de Cespedes told with dignity the story she'd told before, as an accusation of de Bassompierre. That he'd stopped at her coach door and she smelled the perfume only her sister and the Empress possessed. The quick suspicion and investigation. The valiant, angry pursuit by coach of de Bassompierre on horseback.

"M. de Bassompierre?" asked Talleyrand mildly. "You are sure it was he?"

"Yes! He!" said Madame with superb indignation, pointing to the dark man, now very pale indeed.

The short stout man who'd first entered the room now said indignantly:

"But Madame! You are mistaken! He may be a robber, but he is not M. de Bassompierre! I have the honor to be acquainted with M. de Bassompierre! We have talked often together! He is my friend! Not five men in France have the knowledge of the sciences that he possesses! Madame, you are mistaken! *He* is not M. de Bassompierre! M. de Bassompierre stands there!"

He extended a fat hand dramatically toward Carroll.

Harrison's scalp crawled again. Carroll, his features still peculiarly set, bowed politely. Valerie drew in her breath sharply. Pepe uttered an inarticulate sound. Madame de Cespedes gasped.

"As surely," pronounced the stout man firmly, "as surely as my name is Georges Léopold Cretièn Frédéric Dagobert Cuvier, the name of this gentleman is de Bassompierre, and of that—that robber and imposter—I do not know!"

The tall man with the slight limp spread out his hands.

"So it would appear," he said as mildly as before. "But let us make quite certain. *M'sieur*," he bowed with infinite politeness to the dark man, "Madame de Cespedes accuses you of the robbery of her jewels. Where are they?"

De Bassompierre could have been half-mad of bewilderment. Perhaps he was half-mad with despair. Tracked down —when it should have been impossible—after a robbery of which he should not have been suspected, he was denied his own name and found someone else credited with his identity. And this before the second or third most powerful man in France!

Talleyrand's smile faded. His face in repose was not benign. It was utterly, terrifyingly cold. He repeated:

"M'sieur?"

The man in the black cloak reacted in a fashion which in a woman would have been called hysterical. He cried out in a terrible voice. His hand darted inside his cloak, and Harrison instinctively leaped before Valerie. The hand came out with a pistol in it. Harrison shouted fiercely. He was not really aware of what he did. But the heavy pistol roared, and the smaller weapon in Harrison's hand made a lighter sound in the same fraction of an instant.

Then the room was full of stinging powder-smoke. The figure in the dark cloak seemed to stagger toward a window, as if to carry out his purpose and leap out to flee. But he did not reach it. He went somehow bonelessly down to the floor. The candle, after wild leapings and gyrations of its flame, steadied and gave light again. Harrison, numbed with sudden horror, realized that Carroll was in front of Madame de Cespedes as he was where he would shield Valerie.

"*Dios mio!*" said Pepe in a thin voice, "Ah, *Dios mio!*"

Then Talleyrand's voice said with perfect mildness:

"But we should be quite certain! M. Cuvier, you are certainly impartial, and as a naturalist you may feel less of repugnance. Will you see if Madame de Cespedes' and Madame Ybarra's jewels have been recovered?"

The stout man knelt on the floor. Harrison swallowed. Cuvier looked up.

"A necklace, at least," he said professionally. "And—ah! Yes. Rings. Bracelets. He had stuffed his garments with jewels!"

Talleyrand said inexorably:

"But one more question. He has been proved a thief, and has paid for it. *M'sieur*, you are called de Bassompierre. Have you proof that that is correct?"

Harrison felt Valerie grow tense. His own scalp crawled yet again. Carroll stood quite still for a moment, except that one hand dabbled a handkerchief at his temple. Blood flowed where a bullet had just barely grazed the skin. Half an inch to the right and he would have been a dead man. A quarter-inch and he'd have had a serious wound. But now there was only a small, steady welling of red stuff which tried to run down his cheek.

"Can you," repeated Talleyrand politely, "prove that you are M. de Bassompierre?"

Carroll dabbed at his temple again. Then he said carefully:

"I have been travelling for some years, M. de Talleyrand. I have the usual papers, but they could be forged. But since Madame de Cespedes' jewels are found, perhaps these . . ."

His hand disappeared. It came out with a small cloth bag in it. He unknotted the string and poured out a dazzling array of cut stones. There were rubies and sapphires, all of them large. None was under two carats and most were nearer five. Harrison said to himself, "Synthetics!" He was not surprised when a pearl necklace slithered snakily out on top of the rest.

"They are cut," said Talleyrand, "in a strange fashion. I would guess the Orient."

Carroll brought out a second bag. He displayed its contents.

"There are more," he said, "but these—"

"They prove," said Talleyrand in gentle cynicism, "that you cannot be other than a gentleman of rank. It is modesty not to claim a dukedom, M. de Bassompierre!"

Then there was confusion. Valerie whispered warmly to Harrison:

"Oh, my dear! You made a shield of your body for me, when he drew that dreadful pistol!"

Harrison felt numb. He'd killed someone. Perhaps he'd saved Carroll's life, but it had been completely automatic. He was numbed by the shock of what had happened.

"I have an escort," said Talleyrand benignly. "M. Cuvier and myself planned to dine here and then drive on to Paris. On a metalled road one may doze while travelling. If you will join us we will make a grand cavalcade that bandits would not dream of hailing."

Talleyrand went out the door, limping slightly. Cuvier followed him. Carroll said in a queer voice:

"Harrison, he didn't know about a time-tunnel! He didn't know at all! Do you suppose there is one? What the devil has happened?"

Harrison shook his head. Then his eyes fell upon Pepe's face. Pepe looked like a desperately ill man. And Harrison suddenly realized what was the matter.

Pepe had confided to him that besides his great-great-grandfather Ybarra, in Paris, he'd had another great-great-grandfather, who was de Bassompierre. And his great-great-grandfather had been killed, without arranging for Pepe to possess a mere great-grandfather. Pepe had apparently never been born, and the fact would have to appear. One would expect him to vanish instantly.

Nearly two hundred years later, plus some weeks and days and hours, and nine thousand miles away, some millions of people were vaguely aware of a fugitive sort of dizziness. It was very slight. Not one of all the innumerable people who experienced it was really sure that he or she had actually felt giddy. In any case there seemed to be no consequences. None at all. The world rolled on its axis and the sun shone and rain fell and everything proceeded—well—it seemed to proceed exactly as usual. Nobody noticed any change.

But there were changes in the time of Napoleon. M. Georges Léopold Cretièn Frédéric Dagobert Cuvier, perpetual secretary of the Institut Nationale in the natural and physical sciences, made sure that all the jewelry belonging to Madame de Cespedes and the *Doña* Mercedes Ybarra was removed from the cadaver of someone who insolently and for years had posed as M. de Bassompierre. Before that task was complete, the *Señor Don* Ignacio Ybarra came pounding up to the inn on horseback, with an accompanying dozen troopers borrowed from the military governor of Paris.

He was infinitely relieved and grateful to find his widowed sister-in-law quite safe and again in possession of the jewels which were her and his wife's treasures. He was admiring of Carroll and Harrison—but Pepe's stricken pallor did not attract him—for their services to his sister-in-law and himself. He recognized Harrison as having been kind to a poor devil of a merchant named Dubois, and that his kindliness at that time had secured a full shipment of the Empress' exclusive perfume for his wife. He mentioned that the perfume was the cause of the pseudo de Bassompierre's immediate detection as a thief. He was polite—but with vast dignity—to M. Talleyrand de Périgord, who happened to be Grand Chamberlain of France, but naturally would not awe the head of a great family in the Spanish colony of Mexico.

They dined; Carroll with some appetite, Harrison with very little, and Pepe with none at all. He was convinced that he had never been born, because his great-great-grandfather had been killed before his eyes, without having begotten a great-grandmother who was necessary for Pepe's existence. Valerie regarded Harrison with shining eyes because he'd put his body between her and danger. Madame de Cespedes ate composedly and with careful moderation because of a slight plumpness which to a widow of thirty-and-something was undesirable.

M. Talleyrand asked questions. They were searching questions. Toward the end of the meal Carroll gave him the newspaper he'd left the candle-lit room to get, when he'd met the newly-alighted Cuvier and Talleyrand. The newspaper was of the late twentieth century. It developed that the cavalry escort had not been provided with a meal. M. Talleyrand ordered a delay while he read the newspaper and they were fed. He set up six candles for good light and perused the newspaper carefully and with an enigmatic expression. When he had finished, he took Carroll aside for a conference.

Therefore it was very late when the three coaches set out for Paris with their escort augmented by the troopers who'd come with Ybarra. They would arrive in Paris not long before sunrise. But on a metalled highway—and the rest of their journey would be on cobblestones—one might doze.

Valerie rode with Madame de Cespedes, and the *Señor Don* Ignacio Ybarra rode with Cuvier and Talleyrand for the conversation. With plenty of escort outside, Carroll and Harrison and Pepe rode and tried to relax in a heavy coach swaying on an uneven cobblestone highway. The interior of the coach was abysmally dark. Harrison still felt numb and shocked. Pepe was practically wordless because he considered that he should not be alive. Carroll was partly disturbed and partly satisfied.

"De Bassompierre," said Carroll, frowning, "didn't recognize words a time-traveller to our era would certainly have recognized. So I have to revise my opinion. There was no second time-tunnel. But the identity of the de Bassompierre who wrote those letters you learned of, Harrison, is still in doubt. For the moment the name is mine. But Talleyrand is too shrewd a man to attempt to deceive. That's why I loaned him the newspaper. He suspects that I may—just possibly— have told him the truth. He is resolved to find out. I could be of great value to him, if I'm not a liar."

Harrison numbly did not comment. Pepe remained speechless. He swayed and stirred with the motion of the coach in the darkness. From time to time he moistened his lips.

"He wants to be sure I really know French history before it happens," said Carroll meditatively. "He set me a test. Napoleon has twelve hundred flat-bottomed boats ready to land a hundred and twenty thousand men and ten thousand horses on the English coast. Talleyrand asked me when the invasion will take place. I've told him never, because Napoleon will make a fool of himself and send an insulting note to Russia, and Russia will get ready to declare war, and that will be no time to invade England! It'll never be time for it."

"But—"

"Historically," said Carroll, "those are the facts. I've simply stated them before they become factual. Talleyrand has probably guessed what's in the cards, anyhow. He knows Napoleon. But he was interested that I could tell him. He read every word in that newspaper. He's a brilliant man, Talleyrand!"

The coach swayed and lurched and rolled and rumbled. If one were weary enough, it might be possible to sleep. But one would have to be very weary! Harrison said helplessly:

"I can't understand it! De Bassompierre was supposed to be Pepe's great-great-grandfather! And he's dead. And there's Pepe."

Carroll sat up sharply.

"What's that?"

"It's Pepe's family tree," said Harrison. "Madame de Cespedes is the widow of *Doña* Mercedes Ybarra's brother. That's where the sister-in-law business comes in. Pepe's family tree says that de Bassompierre married her, and they had a daughter who married Ignacio Ybarra's son—whom he hasn't got yet—some time in the 1820's when Ybarra's back as ambassador from Mexico. And they'll be Pepe's great-grandparents. But de Bassompierre is dead. So he can't marry Madame de Cespedes. So Ignacio Ybarra's son can't marry his daughter, so he can't be Pepe's great-great-grandfather. Therefore Pepe's great-grandfather won't exist, naturally his grandfather can't beget his father, and if none of them ever exists, why, Pepe couldn't be born!"

Caroll said skeptically:

"How do you feel, Ybarra? Do you feel anything missing since you lost a great-great-grandfather?"

"I feel horrible," said Pepe in a thin voice. "I'm waiting to just vanish. It's not pleasant."

There were hoofbeats on the cobbled highway over which the coach rolled toward Paris. There were three coaches in train, with cavalrymen to escort the Grand Chamberlain, troopers brought to help Pepe's great-great-grandfather—the living one—to seize de Bassompierre, and the liveried lackeys belonging to each coach separately. There was a very considerable clatter as they made their way through the night.

Harrison spoke suddenly, in an astonished voice:

"Look here! We're going at this thing the wrong way! Look at it in a new fashion! Our whole point—the basis of everything we've been trying to do—is that the past can be changed! We want to change it because the consequences of the things that formerly had happened were appalling. The consequences! You see?"

Carroll shook his head in the blackness.

"I agree with what you say, but I don't know where you go from there."

"Why—why—if a thing has consequences, it is real! It is actual! It hasn't been changed from something that happened into something that didn't! It hasn't—unhappened! It's really a part of the actual past and its consequences are really a part of the present. But an event that has no consequences wasn't a real event and didn't happen. That's clear, isn't it?"

"Clear," admitted Carroll, "but not lucid. What follows?"

"Look at Pepe," said Harrison, almost stridently. "He considers that he's lost an essential ancestor and must silently fade away. But if he didn't have a full set of ancestors he wouldn't have been born! If de Bassompierre was his great-great-grandfather and died before marrying Madame de Cespedes, Pepe wouldn't have had one great-grand-mother, one grand-father, one father—or himself. He wouldn't be! But there he sits! So he must be the consequences of marriages—call them events—which had consequences! That were actual! That didn't unhappen! And therefore nothing which would make him impossible can have taken place— such as the premature killing of his great-great-grandfather!"

"I admit the logic," said Carroll. "But de Bassompierre—"

"Ask Cuvier," said Harrison triumphantly, "if de Bassompierre was killed! Ask Talleyrand! Ask Gay-Lussac and Lagrange and Champollion. No. Not Champollion. He's a prig. But ask Laplace! You ask! They'll think you're crazy! Because you're de Bassompierre, now! You can write letters about science. Who else could? You've the beginning of a friendship with Talleyrand. Who else can advise him about French history in advance, so he'll call the turn for the rest of his life without one blunder? There isn't any other time-tunnel! You'll—"

Harrison found himself tripping over his own words. He stopped, for the breath he'd lost in his haste to get the thing said.

Carroll said surprisedly:

"Well, I'll be damned! Maybe you've something there! Ybarra! Ybarra! How'd you like to be my great-great-grand-son?"

Pepe said in a thin voice:

"What's this? A joke?"

Carroll stirred. Harrison knew, despite the darkness in the coach, that he'd run one hand through his hair and left it standing on end, which had been a familiar gesture in his classroom in Brevard University a couple of centuries from now.

"When you think of it," said Carroll thoughtfully, "it is perfectly reasonable! After all, this is 1804 and I certainly haven't gotten married in 1804! Or 1803 or 1802 or any year before that! So that as of the first of August in 1804, I have never been married! Quaint, eh? And if I'm the Bassompierre who'll write the letters you'll discover, Harrison, nearly a score of decades in the future, I will die in 1858 at the age of ninety-one. And that will be almost a safe century before Valerie's aunt comes into the world! So I obviously can't marry her!" he added. "Somehow I am not moved to tears."

Harrison said, with the beginning of doubt:

"But you did marry her . . . If you hadn't married her there'd have been no Carroll, Dubois et Cie, I wouldn't have met Valerie, I wouldn't have found you, and you wouldn't have come back here. None of this would have happened!"

"True," agreed Carroll, with a vast calm. "But you're on no rational foundation either, Harrison! This is eighteen-four, and you were born at least a century and a half in the future. If you stay here you'll die of old age some decades before you're born! What are you going to do about that?"

The clatter of horses' hoofs outside was suddenly muffled, as if they trotted over earth washed by rain upon the cobblestone military highway. Carroll said reflectively:

"Anyhow, she looks good-natured . . ." He stirred. Then his tone changed. "Do you know, Ybarra wasn't a very good student at Brevard. But I didn't flunk him. Perhaps it was unconscious great-great-grandparental favoritism! Eh?"

Harrison did not like Paris. Pepe liked it less. Valerie liked it least of all. There were the smells. There were the shocking differences in social status which had been destroyed, in theory, by the Revolution of the 1790's, but had now been reëstablished by the Emperor Napoleon. He was already Emperor of the French and would shortly be crowned by the Pope. These things offended Valerie. And there were others.

They had taken lodgings—the four of them—in the same building in which Ignacio Ybarra and his wife lodged in considerable grandeur. To that house there came a coach, one day, bringing a dark-haired girl with an expression of habitual sadness. She was the girl they'd seen in the post house yard when Albert unwittingly stole female garments from the coach's boot. She was an orphaned female connection of the Ybarra family. Pepe's great-great-grandfather—he was actually a year or so younger than Pepe—had generously provided her with a dowry and arranged a marriage for her. He'd sent de Bassompierre to bring her to Paris, duly chaperoned by Madame de Cespedes. She now came to pay her respects. Her expression of sadness was now heart-breaking. Valerie did not like this period of time. Pepe restlessly explored the city. Carroll spend much time with Talleyrand.

They'd been in Paris for two weeks, and Harrison was about to make depressed inquiries for an estate to which he and Valerie could retire after their marriage, when Carroll came zestfully to him. He spread out one of the newspapers of the twentieth century, now creased and beginning to be tattered. It had seemed to fascinate Talleyrand. He'd read even the advertisements over and over again, and cynically decided that he preferred the period in which he had been born.

"Harrison! Look at this!"

Harrison read where Carroll pointed. He'd bought the paper in Paris of the twentieth century when they went back for Valerie before the bombs should fall. It was an item in a grieved editorial, speaking of the tragedy it was for France that one of her sons, a renegade of renegades, had given the atom bomb to China. Disgracefully, it was a French nuclear scientist who'd first defected to Russia and then, dissatisfied by the reactionary policies of that nation, defected again to China. The editorial named him. The name was de Bassompierre.

"Talleyrand pointed it out," said Carroll. "I guessed that this de Bassompierre could be my great-great-grandson, but more probably would be the great-great-grandson of the man who'd been impersonating me. Talleyrand looked very cynical, but he politely accepted my statement. Do you see?"

Harrison felt what might be called tentative relief.

"Maybe it's all right, and if so I'm certainly glad. But—"

"The newspaper," said Carroll, "is a remarkable invention. It enlightens, it informs, and sometimes it solves problems. I have two problems, Harrison. One is that Ybarra's great-great-grandfather has hinted that he would consider the arrangement of a marriage between Madame Cespedes and myself. She is moderately dowered, and with my wealth in rubies and sapphires it would be an admirable match. And she seems to be an amiable woman."

Harrison said restlessly:

"I suppose it's all right . . ."

"But," said Carroll, "there is Valerie. I suspect she'd consider me a bigamist. Which is my second problem. Our time-tunnel was destroyed. But I would like to know that in causing the death of this de Bassompierre who stole jewels and perfumery together, we prevented him from having a renegade great-great-grandson who would defect to the Russians and then the Chinese with very practical knowledge of how to make atomic bombs. If we prevented him from existing, and thereby avoided an atomic war, I would be pleased. But without a time-tunnel to our own era there is no way to be sure. I would like, Harrison, to feel that I helped avoid the extermination of the human race!"

"But there's no way to make a time-tunnel—"

"Unless you know of metal," said Carroll, "which has not been disturbed since it solidified from a melted state. But that's why I eulogize the press."

He turned back to the first page of the newspaper. He put down his finger on the news account of the conflagration that had destroyed the oldest wooden house in Paris. That very ancient dwelling in the Rue Colbert had belonged to Julie d'Arnaud, mistress of Charles VII in ages past. It had still been covered with the quarter-inch-thick leaden roof originally placed upon it. The roof had melted, of course, from the fire.

"I saw the ruin," said Harrison. "On the way to the shop to try to persuade Valerie—" He stopped. "I saw what looked like an icicle, only it was lead from the melted-down roof, freezing to solidity as it dripped down. Do you mean—?"

"Talleyrand," said Carroll, "has agreed that it would be interesting to find out. There may be pools of solidified lead among the ruins. He's arranged to borrow the house, which isn't burned down here. I'm to make the necessary technical devices. Perfectly simple!"

Harrison said yearningly:

"If only everything's all right and the war is cancelled! Valerie would like so much to leave here."

"So would Ybarra," said Carroll benignly. "I've no reason to leave and plenty of reason to stay. For one thing, I have some letters to write during the next few years. And for a reason affecting Ybarra." He said vexedly, "Dammit, if I'm to be Ybarra's great-great-grandfather, it seems I should be able to call him by his first name! But I can't seem to do it! Anyhow, I think I can make a new time-tunnel. If there hasn't been war, rather, if the war-scare is over, you and Valerie and Ybarra can go back to your own time, which won't be mine any longer."

"Is there anything I can do to help?" asked Harrison feverishly.

The house was empty and even in the early nineteenth century smelled musty and ancient. Harrison and Valerie and Pepe rode to it in Carroll's coach. Carroll had set up the technical part of the performance. It was irritatingly simple, but Harrison could make nothing of the circuit. Talleyrand, inscrutably smiling, looked on.

"It looks like everything's all right," said Carroll. "Nothing seems to have happened to Paris, but it's been daylight. I've been waiting for dark, when somebody can appear from nowhere with a chance of not being seen. Change your clothes, Harrison, and you can make a trip through to get a newspaper. If all's well—Valerie's clothes are ready for her too. And—ah—those of my great-great-grandson-to-be."

It happened that the time-tunnel existed at a spot closely corresponding to a doorway in the ancient house. Harrison went through. Giddiness. A spasm of nausea. Then he smelled charred wooden beams and wetness and ashes. He heard taxicabs. He heard the sounds of up-to-date Paris. It was night. There was a newspaper kiosk not far away. He went to it and bought newspapers. He scanned the headlines by the light of street lamps as he hurried back to the barricaded, blackened ruin of an old, old, heavy-beamed house.

"It happened!" he said exultantly, back in the First Empire. "The headlines are about a *monte pietá* scandal in Boulogne! There's been a row in the Chamber of Deputies about a political appointment! There was an explosion in a coal mine in the Ruhr! Nothing about China! Nothing about Formosa! Nothing about atomic war! Not on the front pages, anyhow. We did it!"

So, very shortly, three figures in perfectly ordinary twentieth-century costume emerged inconspicuously from the scorched ruins and ashes of the very ancient residence of the mistress of a forgotten king. Immediately afterward there was a peculiar musical noise, like the string of a gigantic harp plucked once and then allowed to die away.

The sun shone placidly upon Formosa. People moved without haste through its cities' crowded streets. There were steamships in its harbors, some of them languidly loading cargo, or unloading it, or laying at anchor. Nobody thought of killing anybody else except for strictly personal reasons. There was no haste. There was no tumult. There was no war or rumor of war. It was as placid and commonplace and tranquil a picture as, say, the great wide flight of steps before the principal entrance to the Louvre. Above and upon those steps pigeons fluttered. In the wide street before it, taxicabs trundled and on the sidewalks children walked sedately with grown-ups. Harrison was on those steps, and Valerie was with him, and they had come to see a picture Pepe had urged them to look at. Pepe seemed somewhat embarrassed about it.

They entered the splendid building. They consulted the memorandum Pepe had given them. They consulted a guard, who gave them directions. They wandered vaguely through the vast corridors. Presently they found what they were looking for.

It was a portrait by Antoine Jean Gros, though not of his best period. It was a bit late for that. It had been painted in the 1830's, when Gros had passed his peak, but it was still a highly satisfactory piece of work. They stared at it, and Valerie shrank a little closer to Harrison. The portrait stared back at them. Humorously.

"It—it is he!" said Valerie breathlessly.

Harrison nodded. He read the identification plate. It read, "*Portait of M. de Bassompierre as an Alchemist.*" There was other data, but Harrison did not need it. The portrait was of Carroll. He was older than when they'd left him a few days since. Naturally! He wore over his alchemists' robe a cordon and the badge of one of the highest Bourbon decorations. Behind him, for background, there were various cryptic symbols and bits of alchemical apparatus. And there was a glowing design which didn't belong in a picture painted in the 1830's. It was a perfectly modern symbol for an atom of something or other, but it didn't belong so far back. Yet it belonged in a picture of Carroll, if he'd had it painted expressly to tell somebody in the remote future that he'd made out all right.

They didn't comment. They looked, and looked, and then they went quietly away. And as they went down the wide, long steps to the street again, Harrison said:

"He handled it just right. De Bassompierre didn't have a son, which he would have had but for our appearance on the scene. But Carroll, marrying Madame de Cespedes as he, had a daughter—so there wasn't a renegade to give China the bomb. So Carroll wrote those letters to Cuvier and Ampère and Lagrange and all the rest. If he hadn't written them, there might have been other changes. When, our present de Bassompierre didn't have a son, no other changes were needed—"

He felt slightly giddy. He stopped. It was not a marked

giddiness. It was not easy to be sure he felt it. Still, Valerie pressed closer to him again, and for an instant it seemed that all the world blurred just a little. Buildings became indistinct and clarified again not exactly as they'd been. The taxicabs were longer and lower. The noises of the city became confused, and then cleared again. Harrison blinked.

A cannon boomed somewhere, and the humming of innumerable saucer-shaped aircraft overhead wavered in a peculiarly flute-like fashion. The cannon boomed again. Of course! The guns were firing a salute to the brand-new son and heir of Napoleon the Fifth, born that morning and already King of Rome.

Harrison watched the ground-cars, floating swiftly through the streets of Paris, not on wheels, like the coaches of ancient days, but on sustaining columns of rushing air. The costumes were familiar, too; men wearing furs and women garbed in those modern, brilliant, and practical fabrics of metal foil.

"Nothing's changed!" said Harrison, in satisfaction. "Nothing!"

He and Valerie continued down the steps. Halfway to the bottom, there was the feeling of giddiness again. It was very slight, and the fresh blurring of all outlines and their re-solidification happened so quietly and quickly that one could ignore it. A chuffing taxicab with badly-worn tires came to a halt at the curb in response to Harrison's gesture. He helped Valerie in. He felt slightly puzzled; just slightly. But then he didn't remember what he'd been puzzled about.

"Yes," said Harrison. "Nothing's changed at all. Just there's no more threat of immediate atomic war."

And he was quite right. Nothing had changed. Not so one would notice. It couldn't. Because Paris was part of the cosmos and the cosmos was made for people to live in. And since it happens that humans will always try industriously to destroy themselves there have to be safety devices built into the scheme of things. So they go into operation if atomic war becomes really inevitable, for one example. They may turn up as time-tunnels, or somebody going back in time and accidentally killing their grandfathers, or—or.

But it could be anything. For example, a man needn't kill his own grandfather. If somebody else, however accidentally, killed somebody who was somebody else's great-great-grandfather, and this happened before his great-grandfather was fathered, then obviously his great-grandfather could not have existed to carry on the family name, nor his father, nor he himself. And a radical nuclear scientist would never be born to defect to Russia and afterward to China. Somebody else might be born instead. For instance, Pepe.

It was perfectly simple. The mainland Chinese didn't have an atom bomb. They'd never had one. They'd never fired off even low-yield ones, and certainly no fifty-megaton ones. They hadn't exploded any atomic bombs at all. So there'd never been a threat to Formosa or the rest of the world, and therefore no time-tunnel, and therefore no Carroll, Dubois et Cie, and therefore . . . .

Harrison thrust things out of his mind. They would only be confusing. They were useless.

"Nothing's changed!" said Harrison doggedly. "Facts are facts! And if they're impossible, they're still facts!"

It was true. Harrison was pleased that it was true.

He and his wife went back to their hotel.

At the Sign of the Green Door

the greatest mysteries in paperback 50¢ PER COPY

THE GREEN ACE by Stuart Palmer	R-995
FIRST COME, FIRST KILL by The Lockridges	R-996
THE RED BOX by Rex Stout	R-983
FER-DE-LANCE by Rex Stout	R-970
GIDEON'S WEEK by J. J. Marric	R-947
DEATH AT DEEP END by Patricia Wentworth	R-932
THE LEAGUE OF FRIGHTENED MEN by Rex Stout	R-919
MING YELLOW by John P. Marquand	R-873
GIDEON'S NIGHT by J. J. Marric	R-872
MADAME MAIGRET'S OWN CASE by George Simenon	R-825

10 Books For $5.00; 4 Books For $2.00 (Postage Paid)

Note: Pyramid pays postage on orders for 4 books or more. On orders for less than 4 books, add 10¢ per book for postage and handling.

——— WHEREVER PAPERBACKS ARE SOLD OR USE THIS COUPON. ———

PYRAMID BOOKS
Dep't K-106; 444 Madison Avenue, New York, N. Y. 10022

Please send me the Green Door Mysteries circled below.

I enclosed $_____.
R-995 R-996 R-983 R-970 R-947 R-932 R-919 R-873 R-872 R-825

Name_____

Street Address_____

City_____State_____

**PYRAMID
BOOKS**

PENGUIN BOOKS

PUT YOUR MOTHER ON THE CEILING

Richard d_____or,
a scienc_____
psycholog_____k
at the U_____
he taug_____
California, _____. Author of science,
educational, and popular articles, he is
currently a research consultant specializing
in free-response surveys. He is also the author
of *Two Qualms & a Quirk: Three Stories*.

PUT YOUR MOTHER ON THE CEILING

Children's Imagination Games

Richard de Mille

Penguin Books

Penguin Books Ltd, Harmondsworth,
Middlesex, England
Penguin Books, 625 Madison Avenue,
New York, New York 10022, U.S.A.
Penguin Books Australia Ltd, Ringwood,
Victoria, Australia
Penguin Books Canada Limited, 2801 John Street,
Markham, Ontario, Canada L3R 1B4
Penguin Books (N.Z.) Ltd, 182–190 Wairau Road,
Auckland 10, New Zealand

First published in the United States of America
by Walker & Company 1967
Viking Compass Edition published 1973
Reprinted 1973, 1974 (twice), 1976
Published in Penguin Books 1976
Reprinted 1977, 1979, 1981, 1982

LIBRARY OF CONGRESS CATALOGING
IN PUBLICATION DATA
De Mille, Richard, 1922–
Put your mother on the ceiling.
Includes bibliographical references.
1. Play. 2. Imagination. I. Title
[LB1062.D4 1976]   155.4'13   76-29638
ISBN 0 14 00.4379 9

Printed in the United States of America by
Offset Paperback Mfrs., Inc., Dallas, Pennsylvania
Set in Linotype Caledonia

*This edition reprinted by
arrangement with Walker & Company*

To
Tony
who started off with
a levitation machine
and Cecil
who said, "That's crazy!
You can't walk through
a tree trunk."

Contents

Preface to the Penguin Edition

Imagination exists to be used, but many neglect it. About halfway through World War One, Carl Gustav Jung wrote: "Imagination...has a poor reputation among psychologists, and [up to now] psychoanalytic theories have treated it accordingly."[1] Jung valued imagination as an agent of spiritual growth, which it announced through dreams and daydreams. He urged people to discover themselves by heeding the products of imagination. In contrast, both Freud and the behaviorists depreciated imagination.

The behaviorists liked to deal exclusively with stimuli and responses or (after Skinner) with acts and consequences (which they called "operants" and "reinforcements"). An operant was what a person or an animal did —if relevant to an experiment. A reinforcement was any closely following event that made a particular act more likely (positive reinforcement) or less likely (negative reinforcement) to be repeated. Some of us common-sense people might prefer to talk about "rewards" and "punishments," but the true behaviorist was repelled by words that connoted desires, fears, or other mental processes. In his view, operants (like pigeon pecks) and reinforcements (like food pellets) were real; subjective experiences (like imagination) existed only in the imagination.

[1]Carl G. Jung. The structure of the unconscious. In *Two essays on analytical psychology*. New York: Meridian, 1956. P. 298.

By training countless caged animals to do a variety of unnatural tricks, the behaviorists discovered how best to schedule reinforcements to speed learning. Concentrating on this one aspect of learning, they developed an educational method called contingency management, which directs teachers to: describe each task as concretely as possible; penalize failure seldom; reward success promptly and often, but not predictably; ignore misbehavior when possible; meet the child where he is; and find out what is rewarding to him. Quite sensible—but one thing that is very rewarding to a child is using his imagination. Behaviorism tells us nothing about imagination or how to use it.

Freud, on the other hand, thought he knew all about imagination and what to do with it. Happy people, he said, never made up fantasies; only unsatisfied people did that. Imagination was not creative but reactive. The most inventive dreams and daydreams, correctly understood, told the same disguised story of frustration, over and over, in case after case. One purpose of psychoanalysis was to banish such troublesome fantasies, along with the other signs of neurosis.

Oddly enough, what the psychoanalysts and their patients have been doing in all seriousness for seventy-five years looks like a complicated imagination game to me. First we set out the pieces (id, ego, superego, defense mechanisms), which are visible in the beginning only to the doctor. Then we establish the rules (free association, resistance, transference), and the game begins:

Let us pretend you are a bottle of joy juice./Let us pretend the only part of you that knows what's what is the cork./Let us pretend there is a strong wire hat on the cork to keep you from popping your cork./Now imagine your joy juice surging up against the cork, while the cork hangs on grimly./Have the cork intoning a magic spell—"Day by day in every way I am sticking tighter and tighter." / Have the cork make excuses and blame others. / Have it refuse to look reality in the eye. / Have it forget how to say "Cork."

Notice that a lot of sediment is settling in the bottom of your bottle. / Have the sediment turn into a cranky temper. / Begin snapping at your family. / Refuse to lend money to your friends. / Try to control what everybody does. / See yourself arriving at the psychoanalyst's office. / Discover that a psychoanalyst is an amorphous significant person who sits behind you where you can't see him and don't know what he is up to.

Have the psychoanalyst tell you to say whatever comes into your cork. / Try to do it. / Discover that there is a homuncusexual little priss in your cork who won't let you say anything naughty. / Have a hard time producing the daily quota of entertainment for the retrosedentary amorphous significant person.

Imagine that over the years the r. a. s. p. is transmogrified into the supersignificant person—Rudolph Valentino, Elizabeth Regina, or your Little Old Winemaker or Woomother. / Have the pressure build up in your joy juice. / Have your wire hat snap and your cork blow out. / Have your vicious secrets spray all over the room and run down the walls.

What an imbroglio! And yet a stranger thing remains to be told. The first formally reported, intensive use of explicit imagination exercises in psychotherapy came not from the psychoanalysis game but from the animal laboratory. Having conditioned some unfortunate cats into an "experimental neurosis," psychiatrist Joseph Wolpe then deconditioned them right back to normal by closer and closer approximations to the original unhappy experience. Applying the same principle of systematic desensitization to human beings, Wolpe found he could quickly relieve irrational fears (of snakes or dogs or what have you) by getting the patient to *imagine* successively closer approaches to the frightening object. Later research confirmed the effectiveness of Wolpe's procedure.[2]

This clinical triumph using an imagination technique once more raises the old philosophical question whether the mind of man can cause anything to happen in the world or must remain only a passive mirror reflecting external or bodily events. The behaviorists characteristically wrote as though they believed conscious experience to be no more than froth floating on a mighty ocean of behavior. Even Wolpe calls his imagination technique "behavior therapy"—but we are entitled to doubt Wolpe's behaviorist explanation of his success. His procedure seems to contradict every major premise of behaviorism and to rest instead on a hidden assumption that the conscious mind is an active, causal agent.[3]

Several years before Wolpe, Frederick Perls had described some less systematic uses of purposive fantasy.[4] Perls made it quite clear he thought imagining could change personality. Jung, however, had already staked out the extreme position, teaching that man inherits—in his very brain function—a hunger for certain kinds of symbols, which arise into consciousness as needed to guide him through life, often against environmental pressures.

In writing this book, I assumed that conscious and unconscious mental processes were just as real as overt behavior and that they could cause important changes in behavior. I also assumed that imagining could change be-

[2]Wolpe's method includes other elements, notably systematic relaxation (S. Rachman. Systematic desensitization. *Psychological Bulletin*, 1967, 67, 93-103), but instructed imagination has been called the only necessary element (Wallace Wilkins. Desensitization. *Psychological Bulletin*, 1971, 76, 311-317). For a general discussion of directed imagery, see: Jerome L. Singer. Imagery and daydream techniques employed in psychotherapy. *Current Topics in Clinical and Community Psychology*, 1971, 3, 1-51.

[3]Edwin A. Locke. Is "behavior therapy" behavioristic? *Psychological Bulletin*, 1971, 76, 318-327.

[4]F. S. Perls, R. F. Hefferline, and P. Goodman. *Gestalt therapy*. New York: Julian Press, 1951.

havior as effectively as reasoning, willing, or remembering. Nothing I have seen or read since has caused me to doubt these two assumptions.

A more technical question weighs the relative merits of spontaneity and instruction. Should we wait for images and ideas to emerge spontaneously, as they do in dreams, daydreams, and other mental play, or should we impose outside direction on the imaginer, as Wolpe and this book do? The answer depends on what we are trying to accomplish —whether to discover the inner world of one person, to remedy a thinking disorder, or to give practice in a mental skill.

The games in this book require only limited self-expression, though a parent or a teacher can easily modify them to invite more. They will remedy specific faults, such as fear or deprecation of the inner world, magical beliefs in the physical power of ideas, or a disinclination to be aware of bodily sensations. And they will give practice in visualizing or in distinguishing fantasy from reality. The didactic structure of the games serves these ends well.

Inspired by Jung, some contemporary psychotherapists have described a middle ground between spontaneous and imposed fantasy. In the directed daydream technique,[5] the therapist suggests the key features of a visual fantasy, while the patient fills in the details. The patient may be allowed more or less control of the daydream accordingly as the therapist judges his imaginative productions to be more or less beneficial. Some frequently suggested fantasies involve: confronting frightening figures, feeding powerful giants, and making friends with hostile beings. Imaginary locations include: meadow, house, mountain, cave, forest, and ocean bottom. The reader will find similar elements in this book, as well as opportunities for the imaginer to take control of his own fantasy.

[5]Max Hammer. The directed daydream technique. *Psychotherapy*, 1967, 4, 173-181. Keith W. Johnsgard. Symbol confrontation in a recurrent nightmare. *Psychotherapy*, 1969, 6, 177-182.

Because people are sometimes afraid that imagination will run away with them, or with someone, I wrote a set of instructions for banishing persistent images. One rationale for this procedure goes back forty years to Dunlap's principle of negative practice: A person can gain discriminative control of a habit by practicing both the desired and the undesired form of it.[6]

The theory of imagination is growing rapidly today. Fantasy has been vindicated from charges that it is useless or neurotic and has been recognized as an indispensable resource for normal living.[7] The day has passed when a psychoanalyst could solemnly ask whether children were not being damaged by all that cruelty, destruction, and annihilation in *Alice in Wonderland*.[8] Creative persons are said to need full access to their own private imagery.[9] Vivid imagery is found in the same persons that perceive the real world accurately.[10] Persons who are willing to fantasize are thought to understand themselves better, to live more imaginatively, to have more fun, to discriminate fantasy from reality better, and to be less disconcerted by unexpected thoughts and images.[11]

We are now ready, it seems, to do something for the little boy who told his teacher he could not concentrate on

[6]Knight Dunlap. *Habits: Their making and remaking*. New York: Liveright, 1932. The same principle is implied in discussions of rubricizing (A. H. Maslow. *Motivation and personality*. New York: Harper, 1954) and subsidiary awareness (Michael Polanyi. *Personal knowledge*. New York: Harper & Row, 1964).

[7]Eric Klinger. *Structure and functions of fantasy*. New York: Wiley, 1971. P. W. Sheehan (Ed.). *The function and nature of imagery*. New York: Academic Press, 1972.

[8]Paul Schilder. Psychoanalytic remarks on *Alice in Wonderland* and Lewis Carroll. In Lauretta Bender, *A dynamic psychopathology of childhood*. Springfield: C. C. Thomas, 1954. Pp. 210-218.

[9]Marie Dellas and E. M. Gaier. Identification of creativity. *Psychological Bulletin*, 1970, 73, 55-73.

[10]P. W. Sheehan. Functional similarity of imaging to perceiving. *Perceptual and Motor Skills*, 1966, 23, 1011-1013.

[11]Jerome L. Singer. *Daydreaming*. New York: Random House, 1966.

his school work because his imagination kept getting into fights with his mind.[12] Curriculum developer Gloria Castillo has reported an eight-month classroom test of *Put Your Mother on the Ceiling*. The games were a new experience for her first-graders and brought out unsuspected feelings, which could then be integrated into better understanding. The children gained confidence in their own minds by learning that the rules of reality do not apply to imagining. They discovered, for example, that they did not need imaginary scuba gear to imagine walking on the bottom of the sea, though they would need real scuba gear to really walk there.[13]

Some children feel they have little control over what happens to them.[14] This usually false notion blocks self-assertion and lowers self-esteem. As a remedy, educational psychologist Mary Meeker recommends imagination games to increase children's belief in their own effectiveness.[15] First-grade teacher Helen Hammer finds the games useful for turning reticent pupils into spontaneous participants.[16]

In a letter to me, quoted below, Gloria Castillo gives a more detailed picture of how a teacher can use imagination games:

When I was teaching first grade, I read the games in order, as opportunities arose. That took three months. "Boys and Girls" demands a rather long attention span from first-graders; so I think a first-grade teacher might well omit the last repetition of each idea in that game [I concur—R. de M.]. The later games get so interesting that there is no problem with attention.

[12]George I. Brown. *Human teaching for human learning*. New York: Viking-Compass, 1972. P. 274.

[13]Gloria Castillo. Eight months in the first grade. In *Human teaching for human learning*, pp. 131-193. (See footnote 12.)

[14]J. B. Rotter. External and internal control. *Psychology Today*, 1971, 5, 37-42, 58-59.

[15]Mary N. Meeker, director of training school psychology, Loyola University of Los Angeles, personal communication.

[16]Helen Hammer, Santa Barbara, personal communication.

Many of the children responded to your style of "story telling" by making up their own games. Later, they even wrote in that style. They loved using the slashes.

During discussions after games, some children would bring up fears or difficulties that were bothering them. This helped me to understand, and sometimes alleviate, personal problems that were interfering with learning.

Often a child would ask to repeat a game. Whenever we did that, the child who had asked seemed calmer and less anxious afterwards. Later, if I noticed that a child was edgy or out of sorts, I would hand him the book and ask if he wanted to play one of the games. Usually, he would choose one, and we would all play it. Because of the simple titles and the built-in drill and repetition, almost all of the children could find their way around in the book without any help.

In summary, I used the book in the first grade as a story to develop listening skills, as a stimulus to imagination, as a language developer, as a story model, as a way to write, and as a tool for dealing with the concerns of the children. No wonder I kept it so handy and suggested it to so many teachers!

Looking back over nineteen years of directed imagery, I find certain people did things great or small that formed a fragile but sufficient chain of events leading me finally to this preface. In chronological order, I take this opportunity to thank: Tom Esterbrook, L. O. Anderson, Laeta and Wayne Dunbar, Laura Archera Huxley, Aldous Huxley, Richard Farson, Lyn Tornabene, Miriam Chaikin, George Brown, and Gloria Castillo.

Readers who enjoyed Aldous Huxley's novel *Island* may feel a *déjà vu* when playing "Animals," which Huxley adapted for his Palinese school children, transforming my mice into one-legged myna birds.[17]

Richard de Mille

Santa Barbara, September 1972

[17]Aldous Huxley. *Island.* New York: Harper & Row, 1962. P. 262. (*Or*: Bantam, 1963. Pp. 230-231.)

WHY WE SHOULD PUT MOTHER ON THE CEILING

There seems to be a permanent war going on between reality and imagination. The battleground is childhood. On the side of imagination we have the child, eyes great with wonder, mouth issuing fantasies, misconceptions, and unreliable reports. Parents, teachers, the peer group, and the police are on the side of reality. They keep insisting on truth, accuracy, conformity, and obedience.

Sometimes the fight is fierce. *Make up another story like that and I'll tell your father.* But at other times it is just a holding action. *Don't sit there dreaming — get your clothes on.* Occasionally we negotiate. *Never mind the pillow fairy. Give me the tooth and take the quarter.*

Stop the War

This is not a war to take sides in, because there is much to be said on either side. The main purpose of putting Mother on the ceiling is to stop the war, so that reality and imagination can live in harmony.

The demands of growing up put a premium on realism. The world is a complicated, difficult, often dangerous place. Parents want children — especially their own children, whom they love very much — to be able to understand it, cope with it, and survive in it. They know that a realistic attitude can be a great help, and they work hard teaching children to recognize what is fact and what is fiction.

There is no need (Mother points out) to exaggerate. *Daddy didn't chase the burglar. He just called the police.* Imaginary playmates do not rate full privileges. *I'm not setting any place for Charlie Brown — or for Snoopy either.* Stories are just stories. *It's too hot at the center of the earth. No one can go there.* The dark won't hurt you. *See? It's not a bear, it's a chair. When I turn the light off again, it will still be a chair.*

Wouldn't it be fun if stories were true, Daddy were a hero, and we could know comic-strip people! On the other hand, it is a good thing the furniture remains harmless while we are sleeping.

Distinctions between reality and imagination are necessary, and it is important that they be learned. But it is also important to teach the distinctions in a way that does not turn off the imagination.

Stale Freshmen

In a state that boasts one of the nation's best supported and most advanced educational systems, a recent survey encountered the repeated complaint that college freshmen lack imagination and independence of thought. The complainers were college and university professors, who said the typical freshman believes there is one right answer to every question and just hopes it will be given to him. When he is asked to develop a theme, his thoughts run through channels well worn by his predecessors. He is, in short, a conformist bore. How did he get that way?

I am convinced that two kinds of training experienced by children have turned the once entertaining and inventive child into the stultified freshman. At home, it is the wrong kind of reality training. At school, it is spoon-feeding, indoctrination, or child programming.

A human being may be taught to give exactly right answers to thousands of questions, as a computer may be programmed to give the location of any item in a warehouse or to compute interest on savings for any day in the year. The recall of facts and the calculation of right answers are indispensable in the conduct of daily life, and the schools would be negligent if they did not urge youngsters to master them. But such skills are only part of what a child should learn.

Learning by Thinking

For years, educators have been talking about learning through problem solving, inquiry, or discovery. John Dewey himself brought the subject up, in 1896, but even today what goes on in the typical classroom does not live up to Dewey's ideas. We have failed in all that time to correct the overemphasis on teaching by telling, giving the facts, and accepting right answers only. Our teaching practices have not caught up with what we know about human thinking and problem solving. Very little time is devoted in our schools to the learning of productive and evaluative mental skills.

Good judgment, originality, fluency and flexibility of thought, the ability to redefine situations or see their implications — such qualities are prized in human society. In everyday life, they reap rewards of wealth, responsibility, or prestige. In times of peril, they may determine who will survive and who will not. Teaching these abilities should be a major purpose of education.

Contemporary research has shed new light on these neglected mental skills, and this better theoretical understanding is helping educators to place an appropriate emphasis on productive and evaluative thinking when developing innovative curricula for the schools. A psychological theory called the Structure of Intellect subsumes most of the neglected skills we have been talking about under two formal headings: *divergent production* and *evaluation*.

Divergent Production

The main difference between divergent production and other kinds of thinking is that it involves the production by the thinker of a *quantity* or *variety* of ideas. The detective who asks himself, "Where did Phil Pickpurse hide those jewels?" must come up with some likely hiding places. All of his ideas must be appropriate. If his ideas are arbitrary or ridiculous, he will waste a lot of time looking where the jewels could not possibly be. But only one of his ideas is likely to be *right*. Rightness is not important in the kind of thinking we call divergent production. Appropriateness, quantity, and variety are important.

Divergent production results when the doctor asks himself, "What are the diseases that show this particular symptom?" It results when the furrier wonders how many ways there are to skin a cat. The law student, taking his examination, needs it to list all the laws that could apply to a particular dispute.

At the factory, the engineer says, "What can we make automobiles out of now?" Across town the junk dealer is thinking, "Now what can we make out of automobiles?"

The mystery writer asks himself, "What are the fifty tight spots Mike Rake will get himself into in my next book?" And the politician sharpens his pencil to list the many disasters that will surely befall his fair and sovereign state if a certain obviously unqualified candidate of the other party is elected.

Mother herself is familiar with two recurring questions of this kind. One is the child's question: "What can I play now?" The other is her own question: "What can we have for dinner?"

The menu planner has great need for divergent production. When she sits down, pencil in hand, numerous animal and vegetable thoughts should flow through her mind. Only with a variety of good possibilities will she be able to plan for each day, not *the* good dinner, but *a* good dinner that has not been served recently. Menu planning is creative work. All creative work depends in part on divergent production.

Perry at West Point

Divergent production can be taught at school. To

take an example from the field of history or social studies, Matthew Perry's visits to Japan in the 1850's are said to have brought Japan into the modern world. In less than a century, Japan changed from a predominantly feudal agricultural society into an industrial power that could challenge the most powerful nation on earth, both in commercial trade and in land, sea, and air warfare. The student may be aware of the events of World War II and may understand that Japan was not one of the very first industrial nations, but will he grasp the significance of Perry's mission?

The teacher has a choice. He can, on the one hand, tell his students that Perry's insistence on negotiating a treaty changed the histories of Japan and the United States. The students may remember that or they may forget it, but either way they will not have had much practice in thinking. On the other hand, suppose the teacher says: "What would have happened if, in 1808, Perry had joined the Army instead of the Navy?"

A panorama of historical possibilities opens up. Each student can now imagine a new history for Japan or the United States. Perhaps President Fillmore would have sent another man who would have done the same things Perry did. But if not,

Japan might still be feudal today. Or Japan might now be part of the Soviet Union. Since there would have been no Pearl Harbor attack, the United States would have stayed out of World War II. On the contrary, we would have entered the war sooner because there would have been no worries about what Japan was going to do. And so on.

This is the inquiry, or problem-solving, method of teaching. Instead of presenting the student with the facts and nothing but the facts (Perry visited Japan. A treaty resulted), or with conventional interpretations (Perry brought Japan into the modern world), it poses a problem for the student and lets him do his own thinking.

At least three advantages are inherent in this method. First, the student has more fun participating in an imagination game than passively soaking up facts from the teacher or the textbook. Fun makes learning more effective.

Second, he has a chance to compare real events with hypothetical events. The comparison improves his grasp of the real events and makes their implications clearer to him.

Third, he has practice in productive thinking. Since the student will not always be in school, where someone knows all the right answers or seems to know them, he should learn to produce answers for himself as early in his career as possible.

Evaluation

In the solution of practical problems as well as in creative work, it is not enough to have a variety of good ideas or to see a number of possible actions that can be taken. The thinker must usually choose one or a few alternatives and reject the others. In order to choose well, he must know which possibilities are most correct, suitable, adequate, or desirable. He must, in other words, exercise his judgment. In the Structure of Intellect theory, the judgmental process is called evaluation.

Judgment, or evaluation, occurs in all human activities. It occurs when you amuse yourself by trying to answer a question like "What's wrong with this picture?" A student practices evaluation when he decides whether a statement is logical, whether a sentence is complete, or which of two words sounds better in a sentence.

The businessman dictating a letter judges whether it is best to end it with *sincerely, cordially,* or *respectfully*. The voter evaluates the candidates before complying with the instruction, *Vote for one*.

A husband needs all his powers of evaluation to respond to feminine queries like "Which looks better on me?" The impoverished suitor must face the evaluation dilemma hidden in the question, "Do you want to take me to Romanoff's or Chick's Dip?" The teen-age boyfriend must choose wisely between the cautious request and the impulsive first kiss.

The engineer selects the best material for the bridge. The menu planner has the good sense to avoid combinations like ravioli, fried rice, and baked potatoes. The employee knows whether to call his new boss Alf, A.E., or Mister Neuman.

Some evaluative decisions are made under pressure. A husband calls to his wife, "The smoke's getting thicker! What shall we save now?" The startled driver wonders, "Shall I try to squeeze between those trucks or run off the road?" The defense lawyer asks his client, "Do you want to plead guilty and throw yourself on the mercy of the court, or not guilty by reason of insanity?"

Except in a very rudimentary form, human judgment is not something we are born with. The ability to make correct decisions about problems of living and work must be learned.

A prominent obstacle in the path of evaluation in the classroom is the usual overemphasis on telling, giving facts, and accepting right answers only. Another obstacle is the teacher whose very word is law. But evaluation can be taught in school, if time is devoted to the exercise of judgment, and if the teacher encourages students to reach their own decisions.

Naturally, there should be little ultimate disagreement on the facts of history, the laws of physics, or the rules of mathematics or grammar. But during the process of learning there should be plenty of room for considering alternatives, expressing preferences, and arriving at conclusions independently. The student cannot become a thinker by swallowing the facts whole. He can become a thinker only by working with information. Where he fails to deal with information adequately, the teacher can supply direction or further information that will help him.

The purpose of such instruction is to prepare the student for responsible decision-making by teaching him the dignity as well as the mechanics of choice and allowing him to be a judge of information among his peers in the classroom. The teacher has a dual role, partly a peer, partly a referee and guide.

In the hypothetical problem in which Matthew Perry becomes an army officer, the students imagine many possible historical outcomes. Not all of the imagined outcomes are plausible. Some are more desirable than others. Each student's idea is evaluated by members of the class, who give their reasons for rating it high or low in plausibility or desirability. The teacher helps the class to see the implications that may be missed.

In the end, the students not only know what happened in history, but they care about it; and they have learned something about using independent judgment. Such interest and judgmental skills will be indispensable in the later exercise of adult responsibility, when there will be no teacher to give the facts or to act as referee and guide.

In the years to come, education is going to include more instruction by inquiry or problem solving, and students are going to become more productive, creative, and self-reliant. In order to prepare children to make the most of improved instruction in the schools, I believe a better kind of reality training is needed in the home.

Household reality training often puts an exclusive emphasis on learning the rules and remembering the facts. It effectively discourages creative or inventive thinking and the practice of judgment.

The world is round, and children are not supposed to think it is flat, but how many parents listen all the way through the terrifying tale of the ships that fell off the edge before presenting the conventional view? Good manners are a subject of daily instruction in many families, but how many parents have asked a child to explain, from his own understanding, why people try to treat each other with consideration? Not many. The consequent short-circuiting of productive and evaluative thinking by the immediate parental presentation of facts and rules is not good preparation for later learning through active inquiry at school.

As the child goes through reality training at home, he learns to recognize what is real and what is not. That is good. "We presume," psychologist George Kelly wrote, "that the universe is really existing and that man is gradually coming to understand it." Unfortunately, many children also learn during reality training that imagination is neither admired nor accepted by adults — that what is real is always better than what is only imaginary. "People's thoughts," George Kelly went on to say, "also really exist, though the correspondence between what people really think exists and what really does exist is a continually changing one."

Most psychologists would agree that prominent among the essentials of human thinking is the ability to discriminate: *A* is not *B*, dog is not cat, boy is not girl, and real is not imaginary. In reality training, mastery of what is real requires a corresponding mastery of what is not real. The first fact one must know in order to understand a dream is that it *was* a dream. Without comprehending the fact of its unreality, one cannot comprehend anything else about it. A philosopher might say that our grasp of reality improves as a function of the visibility of the spectrum of ontological probability. In ordinary language, the more you know about what isn't, the more you know about what is.

How can the parent help the child to master both the real and the imaginary? An important step is to allow the child full expression of the fantasy before introducing the reality with which it should be compared. In interpersonal communication, full expression depends partly on a show of appreciation by the listener. The appreciation should be genuine, and it should be shown. After the parent has listened, with enjoyment, all the way through the child's version of what is, he can offer his own version — presumed to be a more realistic one.

The games in this book are directed visual fantasies that a parent can read to a child or a group of children. Playing them constitutes a kind of reality training that does not discourage imagination. While reading the games to the child, the parent can learn more about how to allow and reward the expression of imagination. The child can learn that there are times for fantasy and times for realism, and that each is good in its own time.

My Son, the Spectator

We should not make the mistake of believing that when a child is exposed to the products of other people's imagination he is necessarily encouraged or taught to use his own imagination. The average unimaginative high school graduate is reported to have completed 10,800 hours of schooling — and to have watched 15,000 hours of television. Only sleeping has taken up more of his time. A great many of those television hours, especially during the preschool and early school years, have been spent watching animated cartoons and live-action fantasies.

Television and comic-book fantasy can hardly be expected to cultivate the imagination, because it is already completely formed, on the screen or on the page. Nothing is left for the child to do but absorb it. The experience of the child is passive. It is not *his* imagination that is being exercised, but that of some middle-aged writer in Hollywood, New York, or Chicago.

Even when the child carries the commercial formula fantasy over into his own play, he is accepting a ready-made product. His use of the product may be purely imitative. To follow the rules of Wondermom or Mouseman is scarcely more imaginative than observing the rules of social etiquette — and it is a lot less useful.

At the risk of being called an extremist, I should like to point out that even when the child is reading *Alice in Wonderland* or *The Hobbit* it is Carroll's and Tolkien's imaginations that are doing most of the work. Of course, great books provide great models — which Wondermom and Mouseman do not. And when the child is reading a book, he must supply the visual content himself — which is a great improvement over pure spectatorship.

Despite what may seem to be the trend of this argument, I am not pleading for any reduction of television spectatorship, and I am certainly not advocating less reading. My recommendation is that we help the child to become active with the raw materials offered him by our frantically productive entertainment industry and our marvelously varied literary fraternity, so that he can go beyond those materials into his own creativity.

A New Track

Thus far I have been emphasizing the positive side of my subject, discussing imagination as an intellectual ability that can be improved by practice. In the past, many writers have emphasized the interference with imagination or the reduction of creativity by "preconscious" or "subconscious" mental blocks. The Freudian theory of the mental defense mechanism has a direct bearing on the degree to which imagination may be available for productive or creative use.

Briefly defined, defense mechanisms are mental tricks we have learned that protect us from thinking thoughts which would provoke anxiety if fully formed in consciousness. These tricks are learned and used unwittingly. When they are used, ideas that would be uncomfortable are replaced by other, comfortable ideas. Thoughts of next Sunday in the country help us to forget that this Friday we must visit the dentist. What we did to get a certain job is easily recalled, but not what we did to lose it. The lovely evening with the Joneses is brighter in memory than the awful night the Smiths left before dessert. In each case, the defense mechanism selects the pleasant thought for us, without letting us know that an unpleasant alternative also exists. In action, it may be compared to an automatic switch for a metaphorical train. Just before a dark and spooky tunnel comes into view around the bend, a switch is thrown, and the train (of thought) is deflected down a new track where sunnier prospects lie. The passenger does not realize what has happened. For most people, it works very well, most of the time.

Defense mechanisms are part of the normal mental equipment, but many people maintain more of this kind of equipment than they actually need for day-to-day comfort and effectiveness. There is a tendency never to throw any of this equipment away, no matter how outdated or superfluous it becomes. Overdependence on defense mechanisms can result in constriction or even impoverishment of mental activity. Excess defensive switches protect us not just from uncomfortable thoughts, but also from thoughts that are merely unfamiliar. The fact that imagination could be frightening, as in a nightmare, results in the general interdiction of imagination. Only a few much-used mental tracks are open for travel.

One purpose of imagination games is to open up closed territory in the mind — to run the train of thought down some of the important common tracks and get rid of unnecessary defensive switches. The player learns to think thoughts and visualize events that at first may seem forbidding. He learns that the domain of his imagination is larger and safer than he thought it was.

A contemporary psychologist talking about defense mechanisms would probably avoid mechanical analogies — trains, tracks, tunnels, territory, switches — and use the language of learning theory, albeit with a slight bend toward mentalism. He might say that repeated avoidance of certain implicit responses (in this case, mental events, or ideas) has resulted in a low probability that those responses (ideas) will occur. The games, then, could be said to provide practice of the avoided responses (ideas) to make them more probable (available). Or, in plain English: practice makes perfect.

The wrong kind of reality training and the accretion of defense mechanisms can inhibit imagination so that an entertaining four-year-old could — within a mere decade — become a pedant or a dunce. Imagination games are intended to render the imaginative faculty enduring, by substituting discrimination and mastery for inhibition. Do the games work? I wish I could report that fifteen years of research at Galton University's Thurstone Institute had proved that children who put their mothers on the ceiling end up on top. Unfortunately, this research has yet to begin. At present, the only evidence I can offer is that numerous parents and some teachers have used the games in an informal way and have been impressed by what they took to be learning — and pleased by what they took to be laughter.

Visualization

One thing that can be said with some confidence is that the games provide practice in visualization. During the eighteenth and nineteenth centuries, visual and nonvisual mental imagery was a subject of much interest to philosophers and psychologists. When the conceptions of the mentalists were swept away by the irresistible tide of behaviorism in the early twentieth century, questions of inner experience were left largely to the psychoanalysts. Neither the Freudians nor even the Jungians were concerned with the study or cultivation of mental imagery as an ability. They wanted images all right, usually dream images, but they wanted them as symbols of complex motivations, which they then interpreted to their patients.

Along with other mental abilities, visualization is being studied by some modern psychologists. Several different kinds of visualization are now recognized as factors of intellect that contribute to creative effort in many fields involving the understanding and manipulation of form and space. Visualization enters into such disparate activities as painting, sculpture, choreography, architecture, astronautics, engineering, and photography. It is also helpful in playing baseball, moving furniture, and driving a car. An extreme example of the use of visualization may be found in the mental life of the formerly sighted person who is now blind; but most of us rely on visualization and other kinds of mental imagery more than we realize.

It comes as a surprise to many people that the ability to visualize is not uniformly distributed throughout the populace. Some people report having dreams or waking mental images that are sharp, bright, enduring, and full of color. Other people's visualizations are limited to gray tones, with occasional impressions of color. Still others have only hazy or intermittent impressions. A few swear that they cannot visualize anything at all

These individual differences in the ability to visualize may occasionally be noted in playing imagination games, but they do not constitute an obstacle, and they can generally be ignored. Despite the wide range of differences, visualization is a common human ability. Furthermore, it is very unusual for anyone, especially a child, to say that he cannot *imagine* anything. A person who can *imagine*, or *pretend*, can play imagination games. In a group of children playing the games, we may be sure that some are experiencing more vivid, exact, and constant images than others. But each is imagining in his own way. That is all that is necessary.

The Wise Child

Part of the so-called cultural revolution among the younger members of our society is an increased valuation of nonverbal inner experience, involving mental images. Various chemical compounds have been used to "expand" the mind. One of the more powerful chemical agents, LSD, seems to expand the mind rather as a firecracker expands a tin can, leaving it battered and full of holes.

As a corrective to this unfortunate playing with fire in the brain, some serious persons are evincing a renewed interest in purely mental methods of expanding consciousness. The purposive use of imagery, for example, is an ancient means of mental development. Modern psychological conceptions can render it relevant to and useful in the twentieth century.

Many of our young cultural revolutionists believe that they are breaking out of a mold of over-intellectualization and inhibition into a new freedom for perceptivity, intuition, creativity, and emotional expressiveness. In these aspirations, they have my support. I see no reason why adults in our society should not be intuitive, flexible, and expressive; I don't know why they should be doomed to clumping around their offices, bedrooms, and supermarkets like moderately hostile blocks of concrete. But not all ways of escaping the mold are good ways.

Risking disorganization of the personality and damage to the brain by the ingestion of LSD and other alien substances is not a good way.

Though there has been widespread experimentation, formal and informal, with a number of chemical agents, some relatively harmless, others subtly or even grossly injurious, we have so far discovered nothing beyond ordinary health measures that can be relied upon to optimize brain function. Our best hope for more fully functioning or self-actualizing human beings is still to have them use whatever brains they possess — dull, average, bright, or brilliant — to improve their living through learning.

People can learn to be intuitive and expressive, flexible and perceptive, and they can do it without giving up reason, communication, purpose, or emotional control. They can learn to distinguish the season for each thing, and to discriminate the inner from the outer world without destroying either.

It helps to start this learning as a child.

HOW
TO
PUT
MOTHER
ON
THE
CEILING

It takes at least two people to play imagination games. One person is the child. The other may be a parent, a teacher, an adult friend, or a teenager. The older player holds the book and reads it to the younger.

Each game has a short introduction that gives some idea of what the game is about and establishes a reference point in reality for that game. Remember that while these are imagination games, they are also a kind of reality training.

The name of each game is given at the beginning of the game and requested from the child at the end. If the child does not remember the name, you can remind him. The name serves as a signal that the game is ending and that the rules of reality are in effect again, until the next game begins.

At the end of each period of play, it is a good idea to play either HERE or TOUCH, games whose purpose is to bring the child's attention back to reality.

In general, earlier games are easier than later games. For best results, play the games in the order given in the book. Of course, it is always all right to go back and repeat an earlier game, but do not jump ahead to games you think might be more interesting. Work your way up to them.

That way, the child should get the most out of each game.

Allow the child to repeat any game or part of a game whenever he wishes.

At the end of each game you will find open-ended questions: "What would you like to do now? / What now? / What now?" These are important. They allow the child to complete the game in a way that satisfies him. If the child wishes to make up an imagination game of his own, encourage him to go on with it as long as time permits and fun continues. Such spontaneous flights of fancy should take precedence over the games as written You can always come back to the book, but the child's creative act of imagination must be caught when it happens.

The Right Time and Place

The sure test of the right time and place is enjoyment. Whenever both players enjoy the game, the time and place are right. Two conditions will help make it happen.

The first condition is the *absence of distraction*. It takes concentration to put Mother on the ceiling — at first, anyway. The television set should be turned off. Household pets and children who do not want to play should not be chasing each other around the players.

An even more important condition is the *desire to play*. Completely voluntary participation may not always be necessary for reading stories or playing checkers, but it is indispensable for imagination games. A nagged parent, for example, is likely to try to hurry the child through the game — which will spoil the game altogether. If either player is at all reluctant, put off playing until later.

Before beginning, it is a good idea to set a time limit or agree on how many games are to be played.

The Child Sets the Pace

The games must be read in a special way. Stop after every idea. The end of an idea is marked by a slant (/) or a paragraph. Do not read the next idea until the child signals that he wants to go on. Different children will have different ways of signaling. Some will say "Okay" or "Um-hm." Some will nod their heads. Some will look up expectantly. It does not matter how it is done, just so the message gets across. Some children may not signal at all. Then you will have to ask questions and work out a signal that is satisfactory to both players.

It is important not to confuse the child by going ahead with the next idea before he has completed the current one. Some children will play fast, others will play slow. Periods of silence are not a waste of time. The child is doing something. If you get bored waiting, make some images of your own.

Some children will play without saying much. Others will want to tell you just what is going on in their imaginations. Either way is all right. In fact, practically anything the child enjoys is all right. When you say, "Let us imagine a boy," the child may proceed to tell you a story about a boy. Let him tell it. While you are listening to the story, you can amuse yourself by making some images of it. When the story is finished, you can get back to the book.

In addition to the open-ended questions that are at the end of each game, other direct questions will be found here and there, in the short introductions and in the games themselves. The child may be asked, for example, what color he has made the girl's hat, or which teacher he is imagining. These direct questions may be answered as briefly or as fully as the child wishes. Even the silent player will usually answer them, and his answers will help you to know more about his feelings and his imagery.

When the games are played with groups of children, it will be helpful to work out a common signal for the completion of an idea, such as raising the hand. If there is much difference in speed among the players, it may be a good idea to assign them to fast and slow groups that can be conducted at different times or by different leaders.

When children in a group answer the direct questions in the games, you may not be able to take account of all their different answers, but the children will enjoy hearing and commenting on each other's ideas. Be sure to allow plenty of time for this exchange of ideas in the group. When you come to the open-ended questions at the end of each game, you can either select appealing images from those offered by the members of the group, or you can allow a period of individualized silent imagining.

Step-by-Step Achievement

In general, the book and the individual games progress from easy to difficult. This is in accordance with the principle of step-by-step achievement. When any difficulties are encountered, they can usually be overcome by applying the same principle.

For example, the first game, BOYS AND GIRLS, starts in the realm of possibility and progresses to actions that can occur only in a world of fantasy. First a boy is standing on the floor, next he is walking, then he is jumping. Finally he floats up to the ceiling.

Some players who are just starting out may have difficulty disregarding the rules of the real world, such as the law of gravity. A boy may seem too heavy to float up to the ceiling, even in imagination. If the child believes that his imagination must follow the rules of reality, he will say something like, "The boy is too heavy," or "He can't float up there."

Point out to the child that he does not have to follow the rules of reality when he is imagining things. Say, "If that were a real boy, he wouldn't be able to float to the ceiling, would he? But he is a pretend boy, an imaginary boy. In your imagination, he can float up to the ceiling, if you want him to."

A clear statement of the lack of constraints in the world of fantasy may be all that is needed to overcome the difficulty. If it is not — if the child continues to say that the boy cannot do this or that — then it is time to resort to step-by-step achievement.

In using the principle of step-by-step achievement, we make the following assumption: *For every imaginary event that is difficult to imagine because it contradicts the rules of reality there is a lesser, similar event that will present little or no difficulty.* If reality cannot be contradicted all at once, it can be contradicted by degrees.

If, for example, the child cannot get an imaginary chair to float up to the ceiling, perhaps he can get a balloon or a feather to do it. Once the first step is accomplished, succeeding steps usually follow easily. A balloon, a feather, a pencil, a ball, a book, a pillow, a suitcase, a chair, a bed, a car, a boat, a battleship, a mountain, a planet, the sun — all things may be accomplished. The trick is to find the first, easy step.

Some children, without asking for help, solve such problems by employing realistic aids and devices. When you say, "Change the color of the girl's hat," the child, without saying a thing, may imagine that a salesperson walks up to the girl, removes her hat, and replaces it with a new hat of a different color. The ingenuity of this solution bespeaks a clever child, but the solution itself is undesirable. Our purpose is not to compromise between reality and imagination but to distinguish them clearly and separate them effectively.

Check on this point. Ask the child, "How did the hat change color?" If he answers, "It just changed," or "I changed it," all is probably well. If he admits using realistic aids, like paint or new hats, ask him to change the color without using anything, just by imagining that the hat *is* a different color. Once you have given him the idea, he may be able to carry it out immediately, with no trouble at all.

The blue hat that stubbornly refuses to become a red one can be changed into a red one step by step. Ask the child to have just one red button on the hat. Then two red buttons. Then a lot. When, finally, the hat is completely covered with red buttons, it will be a red hat, of a sort. By that time, the child will probably be able to take away all the buttons and have the hat be red without any buttons. One or two repetitions of this procedure ought to give the child complete control of the hat and its color.

In the floating-chair exercise, you may learn by questioning the child that he is raising the chair with a hydraulic jack, or with the help of balloons or birds tied to the chair. Your job is to show him that he does not need such aids. One way is to go through the balloon-feather-pencil-ball kind of sequence. Another way is to diminish the aids gradually. Have the balloons or birds grow smaller or fewer, until they are no longer needed.

The method is not important, so long as it helps the child to distinguish reality from imagination and discover that he is master of his imagination.

An imaginary activity that may give some players trouble is seeing at a distance. When you ask the child to imagine something going on in the yard at his school, he may say, "It's too far away. I can't see it." This problem can be handled step by step.

An easy visualization is to look at the room in which the game is being played, then close the eyes and see a mental image of it. If the child can do that, then ask him to remember or imagine how the next room looks. Then another familiar room that is farther away — perhaps your garage, or a neighbor's or relative's living room. After that, more and more distant places can be visualized, until the school yard — or the North Pole — is within easy reach. Do not be concerned about the vividness of the images. The child only has to say that he imagines or remembers how a place looks. The brightness, completeness, or constancy of the mental image is unimportant.

If, after all methods have been tried, the child

says he simply cannot accomplish the requ task, ask him, "How do you feel about that?" low him to tell you how he feels, whether m or little, and to give you any reasons he has his failure. Accept his reasons or excuses, w ever they are and however illogical they seem, without criticism. Ask him what he wi to do about it.

If he is eager to go on with the game, t go on. If he wants to stop playing, then s But first try to interest him in playing HERE TOUCH for a few minutes, until he becomes ch ful. At the next opportunity, when both of feel like playing imagination games again, b play at the start of the game in which fai occurred. You may encounter no difficulty.

In group play, as with group instruction school, it will not always be convenient to individual players who report having difficul The group leader, like the teacher, will have decide how much attention can be given to dividual players. Difficulties should not be quent in groups, however, because the fact several other children are following the instr tions successfully will make the games seem ea to each individual group member.

Persistent Images

During one game or another, the child may tell you that a particular image is "still there," when the instructions have called for its metamorphosis or disappearance. For example, when a crowd of children have been imagined in the school yard and you say, "Look at the school yard and see that the children are all gone," the answer may be, "They are still there."

This is apt to occur when the child has a particular liking for or interest in the persistent image. He may feel that it is beautiful, valuable, or hard to replace. We might theorize, for instance, that a lonely child would be disinclined to give up a crowd of imaginary children in the school yard. A child raised in poverty might hang on to images of toys, money, or food. And so on.

Whatever the particular image, the remedy for persistence is to create more images of the same kind, increase the supply, alleviate the scarcity, and thus reduce the demand. You can see that this is a sort of supply-and-demand economics of mental images. The child who finds that he can create as many of the desired images as he wants, whenever he wants, will not be upset at temporarily giving them up for something else.

The persistence of images where change or

emptiness has been requested is counteracted, then, by the simple expedient of producing an oversupply of images. A typical solution of such a persistence problem might go as follows:

PARENT: Look at the school yard and see that there are no children there

CHILD: I see some children.

PARENT: Have them go home. / Now look and see that there are no children in the school yard.

CHILD: There still are some. They are playing ball.

PARENT: Do you want them to stay?

CHILD: No. I am telling them to go home, but they stay anyway.

PARENT: Have some more children in the school yard, then.

CHILD: All right.

PARENT: Have more. Fill the school yard up with them.

CHILD: It's all full now.

PARENT: Squeeze some more children in.

CHILD: There's no room to play ball or anything.

PARENT: Have one of the children go home.

CHILD: (*Slightly worried*) All right.

PARENT: Look all around the school yard for that

child and see that that child is not there anymore.

CHILD: The others are still there.

PARENT: Yes, the others are still there. Now look around for the one you sent home.

CHILD: (*Mild surprise*) He's gone. (*Satisfaction*) I sent him home.

PARENT: Send some more of them home. / Look around the school yard and see that they are gone.

CHILD: They're gone.

PARENT: Send some more home.

CHILD: It's almost empty now.

PARENT: Can you send all the rest of them home?

CHILD: Yes. They're all gone now.

PARENT: Do you want to bring them back?

CHILD: Yes.

PARENT: Bring them all back. Pack them in tight. / Send them all home again. / Bring them back. / Have them disappear. / Have them be there again. / Send them all home.

CHILD: I'm going to let them all stay home now. It's time for them to go to bed.

PARENT: Is the school yard empty?

CHILD: Yes. There is nobody there.

PARENT: Not even one person?

CHILD: No.
PARENT: Is that all right?
CHILD: Yes.
PARENT: What do you want to do now?
CHILD: Let's finish the game.

What Does This Game Do?

It would not be difficult to list the various meanings which the different games might have for children, or feelings which they might arouse. I could say, for example, that children sometimes worry about their parents' being hurt or getting lost, and that the game called PARENTS produces an oversupply of parental images and puts them through their paces until the child finally feels he has parental images to burn. This, in turn, could reduce any realistic concern he might feel about the safety or availability of his real parents.

No such list of psychological hypotheses or findings could guarantee, however, that any game would mean some particular thing to your individual child. Since it is your child you are interested in, and not some statistical trend among children, such theoretical speculations should be avoided while playing the games, lest they become an obstacle.

Suppose the child says he does not want to

imagine Mother on the roof because she might fall off and get killed. Do not become an amateur psychoanalyst and start to wonder about his dependency feelings or his ambivalence. Do not yourself confuse reality with imagination by assuring him that you are not afraid to be on the roof. Just handle the problem step by step. Whom can he have on the roof, if not Mother? How near the edge? Is a fence needed for a little while?

When several dozen assorted images have fallen off the roof, some shattering to bits, others bouncing, laughing, waving flags, the child will see that the activity is under his control and that he can afford to put Mother or anybody on the roof. It is mastery that counts, not explanations.

Parents' Imagination Games

There is no rule against exercise of the parent's imagination. Even before you have gone all the way through the book, you may find yourself inspired to make up some games of your own, or to modify the games in the book. Except for the rule that the child should go through the games the first time in the order given, you should feel free to improvise. In all improvisations, it will help to remember the principle of step-by-step achievement.

Some minor modifications may be in order the first time through. You will notice, for example, that I have frequently used the word *house*. "Have Mother go outside of the *house*." "Move all the beds in the *house*." "Throw those *houses* away." And so on. More and more people in our society are living in apartments and other non-houses, especially in the city. If you live in a non-house, you should feel free to change *house* to whatever word seems natural. On the other hand, *house* is a nice short word that tends to stand for almost any kind of dwelling, and so you may not feel that it is necessary to change it, even if you do not live in a house.

In the game called HOME, you will find an explicit opportunity to improvise. Since I do not know what your home looks like, how many rooms it has, or what the furnishings and decorations are, I have provided a paragraph with some blanks for you to fill. If you are living on a boat, you can work out some nautical adaptations — "Put your Captain on the ceiling. / Have the binnacle in the bunk," and so on.

In the last game, TOUCH, there are blanks for *real* objects.

Do not hesitate to make the games more enjoyable for your child by changing unfamiliar things to things that are familiar. In Boys and Girls, the song "Three Blind Mice" is mentioned. If your child does not know that song, change it to some other. In Being Things, the child is asked to imagine that he is Mother, Father, Brother, Sister, Aunt, and Uncle. You may wish to omit all but actual relatives. On the other hand, it will probably be easy for the child to imagine himself an uncle, even if he has no uncle.

If the child has no father, you can avoid awkwardness the first time or two the term *Father* is used by changing it to *a father* or *someone's father*. If the child's father is never called anything but Daddy, Pop, or Ralph, you may wish to substitute the more familiar name.

If the child is puzzled by the word *steamroller*, you will have to describe how a steamroller looks and what it does. Play it by ear. The act of imagining is the important thing — not any particular word or image.

Often you will find alternate words provided in the text — *boy (girl)*, *him (her)* — and you will have to decide which to use. The choice will sometimes be clear from what has just happened in the game, but when there is ambiguity it will usually be best to choose the same-sex word, so that boy players can imagine boys, and girl players can imagine girls. Examples of this will be found in *Manners* and *Baby*. In *Manners*, the whole game should be played using the same-sex word, even though *her* is usually omitted from the text. If the child wants to play *Manners* again, you can then use the opposite-sex word, for variety.

With mixed groups, *Manners* should be played twice, so as not to slight either sex. This procedure may elicit comments from the boys about the girls, and vice versa.

Now and then you will find a sequence like the following: "Have someone standing on the table. / Have him (her) jump off." If the child does not tell you who is standing on the table, you will not know which sex is correct. You can either ask, or use the conventional *him* until you are corrected by the child. When playing with groups, you will find it most practical in such cases to say "him or her."

In making up your own games, see that the rules of reality are broken as often as they are kept. Water should run uphill. Dogs should meow. Fish should fly. Outrageous flouting of the rules will help the child to distinguish reality from imagination.

Between your games, don't forget to touch

down to reality. A good way is to talk realistically about some of the ideas in the game. HERE and TOUCH will provide further contrast between what is real and what is not. Play them at the end.

Now that you have read through both of these introductory chapters, if there is anything that you are still puzzled about, don't worry. Your child will probably be able to explain it to you after a game or two.

THE
GAMES

Boys and Girls

You can put your clothes on or take them off. You can take off a red jacket at the store and put on a green one. But can you change a red jacket into a green one? Or change a cat into a dog? It's easy — in your imagination.

The name of this game is BOYS AND GIRLS.

Let us imagine that there is a boy standing in the corner of this room. / Let us give him a hat. What color would you like the hat to be? / Let us give him a jacket. What color jacket shall we give him? / Let us give him some trousers. What color do you want his trousers to be? / Let him have some shoes What color will you let him have?

Now change the color of his hat. / What color did you change it to? / Change it again. / What color this time? / Change it again. / What color? / Look at his jacket. What color is it? / Change it to another color. / Change it again. / Change it again. What color are his trousers now? / Change the color of his trousers. / Change them again. / Change them again. / What color are his shoes now? / Change them to another color. / Change them again. / Change them again. / What color are they now?

Have him stand on one foot and hold his other foot straight out in front of him. / Have him stand on the other foot. / Have him walk over to another corner of the room. / Have him go to another corner. / Have him sing a song. / Have him go to another corner.

Have him lie down and roll across the floor. / Have him run around on his hands and knees. / Have him stand on his hands. / Have him sing a song while he is standing on his hands. / Have him run around the room on his hands.

Have him stand on his feet. / Have him jump up into the air. / Have him jump up higher. / Have him jump up and touch the ceiling. / Have him sit in a chair. / Have the chair float up to the ceiling and stay there. / Have the boy sing something while he sits up there. / Have the chair come down. / Have the boy float up to the ceiling without the chair. / Have him float to a corner of the room up there. / Have him float to another corner. / Have him sing "Three Blind Mice." / Have him float to another corner. / Have him float to another corner.

Have him come down to the floor. / Have him say "Goodbye" and go out the door to visit a friend. / Look into one corner of the room and see that he is not in that corner. / Look into another corner and see that he is not there either. / Look into all the other corners, above and below, and find that he is not in any of them.

Put a girl in one corner of the room. / Give her a red hat. / Give her a blue sweater. / Give her a green skirt. / Give her brown shoes. / Now make her hat blue. / Make her sweater yellow. / Make her skirt purple. / Make her shoes black. / Change them to green. / Change them to yellow. / Change all her clothes to white. / Change them to black. / Change them to purple. / Change them to green.

Have her be in another corner of the room.

/ Have her be in another corner. / Have her sing a song. / Have her be in another corner.

Have her float up to the ceiling. / Have her turn upside down and stand on the ceiling. / Have her walk all around the ceiling, looking for the boy who was there before. / Have her look in all the corners up there and find that he is not in any of them.

Bring the boy back and put him on the ceiling with the girl. / Have them standing on the ceiling playing ball. / Put another boy and another girl on the ceiling with them, and have all four playing ball. / Put some more boys and girls on the ceiling, and have them all playing ball. / Turn them all right side up, and put them on the roof of the house. / Put them in the play yard at school. / Make twice as many of them, and have them all shouting.

Make a new crowd of boys and girls on the ceiling. / Put them on the roof. / Put them in the school yard. / Have all the children shouting and running around.

Look at the ceiling and see that there are no children there. / Put one boy there. / Put him in the school yard. / Put one girl on the ceiling. / Put her in the school yard.

Have no one on the ceiling. / Have it full of boys and girls. / Have it empty again. / Have no one on the roof. / Have it covered with boys and girls. / Have it empty again.

/ Have no one in the school yard. / Have it full of boys and girls. / Have it empty again.

Put one child in the school yard. / Is it a boy or a girl? / What color are his (her) clothes? / What would you like to do with him (her)? / All right, do it.

What is the name of the game we just played?

Animals

Have you ever seen a live elephant as small as a mouse? Are there any real elephants that small, in India or Africa, or at the zoo or the circus? I don't think so.

This game is called ANIMALS.

We are going to start with one little mouse, and see what we can do.

Let us imagine that there is a little mouse somewhere in the room. Where would you like to put him? / All right, have him sit up and wave to you. / Have him turn green. / Change his color again. / Change it again. / Have him stand on his hands. / Have him run over to the wall. / Have him run up the wall. / Have him sit upside down on the ceiling. / Turn him right side up and put him in a corner up there. / Put another mouse in another corner up there. / Put a mouse in each of the other two corners up there. / Put other mice in the four corners down below. / Are they all there? / Turn them all yellow. / Have them all say "Hello" at the same time. / Have them all say "How are you?" / Have them all promise to stay in their corners and watch the rest of the game.

Put a little dog right over there (*Pointing*). / Have him bark. / Have him sit up and laugh. / Give him the name Felix. / Ask him his name and have him answer Felix. / Have him grow bigger. / Have him grow smaller. / Have him grow much smaller. / Have him grow so small that he is no bigger than a pea. / Have him turn into a cat no bigger than a pea. / Have the cat grow as big as a potato. / Have it grow as big as your head. / Have it grow into a big, fat blue cat. / Have it turn into a horse but stay the same size.

Are the yellow mice all in their places? / Have them clap their hands because the cat turned into a little horse. / Have the little horse grow bigger. / Have him grow bigger still. / Have him grow very big. / Have him become little again. / Have him be as big as your head. / Have him be as big as your hand. / Have him be as big as your thumb.

Ask him his name and have him tell you George. / Change his name to Rudolph. / Ask him his name and have him tell you Rudolph. / Change his name to Harry. / Ask him his name and have him tell you

Harry. / Take away his name. / Ask him his name and have him shake his head. / Pick a good name for him and give it to him. / Ask him his name and have him tell you that name.

Is he as big as your thumb? / Change him into an elephant but keep him the same size. / Have him grow as big as a pumpkin. / Have him grow as big as your bed. / Have him grow as big as you want him to be. / How big is he?

Have him shrink until he is as small as your thumb. / Have him shrink until he is no bigger than a pea. / Have him be no bigger than a pinhead. / Have him shrink until there is nothing left of him at all.

Look at the place where he was and see that he is not there. / Have the yellow mice clap their hands in admiration. / Put a new elephant there. / Make him as big as a police dog. / Make him as big as a cat. / Make him as big as a mouse. / Make him as big as a pea. / Have him shrink away to nothing.

Look where he was and see that there is nothing there. / Have the yellow mice cheer and wave their arms and legs. / Put a new elephant where the other one was. / Make him as big as you want to make him. / Make him as small as you want to make him. / Have him shrink away to nothing.

Look where he was and see that there is no elephant there. / Have the yellow mice write letters home to their friends to tell what wonderful things you do with elephants.

Put a new elephant there. / Change him to a dog. / Change the dog to a cat. / Change the cat to a mouse. / Change the mouse to a pea. / Change the pea to nothing. / Look and see that there is no pea there.

Put a new pea there. / Have it not be there. / Have a dog there. / Have no dog there. / Have a cat there. / Have no cat there. / Have an elephant there. / Have no elephant there.

Have the yellow mice clap their hands. / Have them come to the place where the elephant was. / Have them grow smaller. / Have them grow smaller still. / Have no mice there. / Have some new mice there. / Make them blue. / Have no mice there.

Have one mouse there. / What color do you want it to be? / What do you want to do with it? / All right, do it.

What was the name of the game we just played?

Mother

Mother could climb up a ladder and touch the ceiling, couldn't she? I think so. But could she stand on the ceiling? I never heard of a mother doing that.

This game is called MOTHER.

Let us imagine that Mother is standing right there (*pointing*). / Let's give Mother a hat. What color hat will you give her? / What color dress will you give her? / What color shoes will you give her? / All right, change the color of her hat. / Change the color of her shoes. / Change the color of her dress. / Change the color of her hat again. / Change the color of her dress again. / Change the color of her shoes again.

Have her go to a different part of the room. / Have her go into another room. / Have her go outside the house. / Have her coming in the front door. / Have her cooking in the kitchen. / Have her setting the table. / Have her asleep in her bed. / Have her washing the dishes. / Have her making the bed. / Have her singing. / Have her talking on the telephone.

Have her standing on the roof. / Have her taking a bath in the bathroom. / Have her cooking dinner outdoors. / Have her sitting on top of a box. / Have her sitting on a ladder. / Have her sitting in a tree. / Have her cooking dinner up in a tree. / Have her taking a bath up in the tree. / Have her asleep in her bed up in the tree.

Have Mother at the store, buying things. / Have her buy something nice for you. / Have her come home and give it to you. / Have her walking through a forest. / Have her standing on top of a mountain. / Have her on a boat. / Have her swimming in a swimming pool. / Have her swimming in a lake. / Have her swimming in the ocean.

Have her riding a horse. / Have her riding a camel. / Have her riding an elephant. / Have her riding a tiger. / Have her riding a donkey. / Have her riding a hobbyhorse.

Have her riding a car. / Have her riding a bicycle. / Have her riding a motorcycle. / Have her flying in a plane. / Have her riding in a spaceship to the moon. / Have her cooking dinner on the moon. / Have her making beds on the moon. / Have her reading you a story on the moon.

Have Mother walking through a jungle. /

Have her riding across a desert. / Have her driving a sled through the snow. / Have her rounding up a herd of cattle. / Have her walking on the bottom of a lake, looking at the fish. / Have her walking on the bottom of the ocean. / Have her cooking dinner on the bottom of the ocean. / Have her making beds on the bottom of the ocean. / Have her doing the ironing on the bottom of the ocean. / Have her reading you a story on the bottom of the ocean.

Have Mother sitting in a chair at home, combing her hair. / Have her sweeping the floor. / Have her looking in her mirror. / Have her washing her face. / Have her sitting at dinner.

What would you like to have Mother do now? / All right, have her do that. / Have her do something else. / Have her do something else. / Have her do something else.

How does Mother feel now? / Have her feel happy. / Have her thank you for putting her in all those interesting places. / Is there anything else you would like to do with Mother? / All right, do it.

What was the name of the game we just played?

Father

I am sure Father has never ridden a rhinoceros. I suppose he could, if he didn't get scared — or if the rhinoceros didn't get scared of him.

This game is called FATHER.

Let us put Father right there (*pointing*). / Now give him a hat. What color will you give him? / What color suit will you give him? / What color shoes will you give him?

Change the color of his hat. / Change it again. / Change the color of his suit. / Change it again. / Change the color of his shoes. / Change it again.

Take away Father's hat. / Take away his shoes. / Take away his suit. / Have him dressed in a bathing suit. / Have him dressed in armor. / Have him dressed in black. / Have him dressed in white. / Have him dressed in red. / What would you like him to wear now? / All right, have him dressed in that.

Have Father go to a different part of the room. / Have him float up to the ceiling. / Have him come down again. / Have him go into another room. / Have him standing on the roof. / Have him sitting in a tree. / Have him taking a bath. / Have him asleep in his bed.

Have Father riding a horse. / Have him riding a camel. / Have him riding a tiger. / Have him riding an elephant. / Have him riding a giraffe. / Have him riding a rhinoceros. / Have the rhinoceros flying.

Have Father in the closet. / Have him rolled in the rug. / Have him sitting on the stove. / Have him under the bed. / Have him climbing up the side of the house. / Have him wearing your clothes. / Have him riding your wagon. / Have him driving a car. / Have him riding a motorcycle. / Have him flying a jet plane. / Have him piloting a spaceship to Mars. / Have him helping you with your schoolwork on Mars. / Have him helping you with your schoolwork at home in the kitchen.

Have Father sitting upside down on the ceiling. / Have him playing marbles upside down on the ceiling. / Have Mother playing marbles with him. / Have them playing marbles on the roof. / Have them playing marbles in the school yard.

Have Mother and Father walking down the street. / Have them riding on a train. /

Have them on a bus. / Have them on television. / Have them in the funny papers. / Have them in the park. / Have them at the seashore. / Have them in the kitchen.

Have Father sitting at the table for dinner. / Have him standing on the table. / Have him sitting under the table.

Have him up in that corner over there (*pointing*). / Have him in another corner up there. / Have him in another corner. / In another corner. / Have him in a corner down below. / Have him in another corner. / Have him in another corner. / In another corner. / Another.

What would you like to do with Father now? / All right, do it. / Is there anything else you would like to do with Father? / All right.

What was the name of the game we just played?

Home

We get used to the way things look, especially at home. We don't expect to see them changed. If we changed everything around in our house, do you think we could get used to it again? I suppose we could, after a while.

This game is called HOME.

Do you know just how Home looks? / Do you know how all the rooms look? / Do you know where all the things are in all the rooms? / Let us play a game of changing everything around.

Let us take the stove out of the kitchen and put it in some other room. What room would you like to put it in? / All right, now take the kitchen sink and put it with the stove. / How do they look together there? / Take something else out of the kitchen and put it with the stove and sink. / Take all the things that are left in the kitchen and pile them on the ceiling of the kitchen. / Turn the kitchen floor into glass. / Have some fish swimming under the floor. / Is there anything else you would like to do to the kitchen? / All right, do it.

Now change the bathroom all around. First, make it about twice as big. / Put the bathtub outside the window. / Have the toilet where the bathtub was. / Have the washbasin on the ceiling. / Have the medicine cabinet in the floor. / Have the toilet in the bathtub. / Have the door in the ceiling. / Is there anything else you would like to do to the bathroom? / All right, do it.

Now move all the beds in the house. Where would you like to put your bed? / Where would you like to put Mother's bed? / Are there any other beds you would like to move? / All right.

(The following may be used for the remaining rooms, and varied at the discretion of the reader.)

Now change the .... room around. Put the .... on the ceiling. / Have the .... hanging on the wall. / Have the .... hanging on another wall. / Throw the .... out the window. / Put the .... into another room. / Put the .... into the ground under the house. / Hide the .... in the .... / Roll the .... up in the .... / Is there anything else you would like to change? / All right.

Now, let's look at the house from the out-

Make the house bigger. / Make it smaller. / Make it any size you want it to be. / Is there anything else you would like to do with that house? / All right, do it.

What was the name of the game we just played?

I think it would be very hard for anybody to get along without his head. I don't think he could do it. I'm sure he couldn't. How would he know where to put his hat or his glasses? How would he blow his nose?

This game is called JUMBLY.

Let us imagine that we take you all apart and put you all back together again.

Take off one of your feet and put it on the other side of the room. / Take off the other foot and put it beside the first foot. / Take off one leg and put it on the first foot. / Take off the other leg and put it on the other foot. / Take off your middle and put it on the legs. / Take off your chest and put it on the middle. / Take off your arms and shoulders and put them on the chest. / Have your hands on the ends of your arms. / Put your neck on top of the shoulders. / Put your head over there on the top of the neck.

Make a new body for yourself over here. / How does that other body look over there?

Take the feet off this new body and put them over there on the other side of the room. / Put the legs over there, too. / Put the middle over there. / Put the chest and shoulders and arms and hands over there. / Put the neck and head over there. / Make a new body for yourself over here.

How do those two bodies look over there? /

Would you like to play Jumbly with them? / All right.

Switch the heads around. Take the head off the first body and put it on the second, and take the head off the second body and put it on the first. / Switch the necks. / Switch the shoulders and arms and hands. / Switch the chests. / Switch the middles. / Switch the legs. / Switch the feet.

How do they look now? / Would you like to jumble them even more? / All right.

Put the heads where the feet belong and put the feet where the heads belong. Do it with both bodies. / Have the legs where the arms belong and have the arms where the legs belong. / Have the necks where the stomachs belong and have the stomachs where the necks belong. / How do those bodies look now? / Pretty jumbly? / All right, throw them away and put two new bodies there.

/ Have them look ordinary.

Have the legs growing out of the tops of the heads. / Have the hands growing out of the feet. / Have the arms growing out of the hands. / Have the stomachs on top of the arms. / Have extra heads on top of the stomachs. / How do those bodies look now? / Very jumbly? / All right. Throw them away. / Put two new ones there.

Give the new bodies your name. / Ask them their names and have them tell you. / Now change their names to something else. / Ask them their names and have them tell you. / Change their names again. / Ask them their names and have them tell you. / What would you like to change their names to now? / All right, change them to that. / Ask them their names and have them tell you.

Have them grow smaller. / Have them grow bigger. / Have them grow thinner. / Have them grow fatter. / Have them grow smaller. / Have them grow much smaller. / Have them shrink away to nothing. / Put two new ones there. / Switch their heads. / Have them turn to each other and say "Thank you."

What would you like to do with them now? / All right, do it.

What was the name of the game we just played?

School

What would happen at school if you were the teacher? What would happen if parents went to school? Suppose monkeys went to school. Do you think they would learn to read and write? Would they do what they were told?

This game is called SCHOOL.

Let us imagine your school room. / Let us have it empty. / No one in the seats. No one at the teacher's desk. No one at the blackboard. / Look all around the school room and see that there is no one there.

Now, you be at the front of the room, teaching all the empty chairs. / Have books and pencils and papers at every place. / Have the pencils writing on the paper. / Have the pages of the books turning. / Have pieces of chalk writing on the blackboard. / Have the pieces of paper come up to the front of the room, to be graded. / Give some good marks and some bad marks. / Send them back to their places. / Tell all the empty places that school is out. / Have the books and pencils and papers rush out of the room.

Have a school room full of children. / You be teaching them. / Have one boy put up his hand and ask to leave the room. / Let him go. / Have the others write a spelling lesson on their papers. / Have them add some numbers. / Send some of them to the blackboard to draw pictures. / Have the others bring their papers to you to be graded. / Give some good marks and some bad marks. / Tell the children that school is out. / Have them pick up their books and papers and pencils and walk out the door.

Have a school room with big people sitting in all the chairs. / You be teaching them. / Have one of them stand up and spell a word. / Have another go to the blackboard and add some numbers. / Have another ask to leave the room. / Let him (her) go. / Have the other big people write on their papers about what they did during their vacations. / Have them bring the papers to you to be graded. / Give some good marks and some bad marks. / Tell the big people school is out. / Have them run out the door.

Have a school room full of teachers. / You be teaching them. / What would you like to have one of them do? / All right. / What would you like to have another do? / All right. / (*Continue asking the child what he would like to have the teachers do and have himself do in the scene, until he runs out of ideas.)*

Have another school room with no one in it. / You be the teacher. / Have the room full of monkeys, all jumping up and down. / Send them to the principal, to be scolded. / Have the room full of seals, all flapping their flippers. / Keep them in after school, as punishment. / Have the room full of lions, all roaring. / Send them to the blackboard to write, "I will not roar in school."

Have another school room. / Have it full of children. / You be one of the children. / Have a teacher at the front of the room. / Have the teacher walk up the wall and sit in a chair on the ceiling. / Have the teacher playing the trumpet up there. / Have the teacher skating on the ceiling. / Have the teacher fly out the window. / Have the children fly out after her (him). / Look all around the school room and see that it is empty.

What would you like to do with the school room now? / All right. / What else? / All right.

What was the name of the game we just played?

Parents

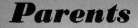

Parents need a lot of attention, don't they? — even one or two parents. Suppose you had a lot of parents. How would you keep track of them all?

This game is called PARENTS.

Let us have Father right over there (*pointing.*) / Let us have Mother over there with him. / Ask them who they are, and have them say "Mother" and "Father." / Ask them who they are again, and have them say "Parents." / Have two of each. Two

Mothers and two Fathers. / Have the two Mothers just alike. / Have the two Fathers just alike. / Ask them all who they are and have them say "Parents."

Have the parents grow smaller. / Have them all turn green. / Have them grow smaller still. / Have them turn blue. / Have them grow bigger. / Have them turn red. / Have them grow bigger still. / Have them turn yellow. / Have them shrink until they are no bigger than pumpkins. / Have them turn orange. / Have them turn black. / Have them turn white. / Have them turn any color you like.

Put the little parents up in that corner (*pointing*). / Put them all around in all the corners of the room, one corner after another. / Put them up on the roof. / Have them in a tree. / Have them on top of the tallest building in the world. / Have them down in the deepest mine in the world. /

Have them on top of the tallest mountain in the world. / Have them at the bottom of the deepest ocean. / Have them in the school yard.

Have the little parents walking down the street. / Have a big dog run up and bark at them. / Have him growl at them. / Have the parents grow up bigger than the dog. / Have the dog run away. / Have the parents grow little again. / Have the dog come back. / Have the parents grow big. / Have the dog run away. / Have the parents grow little.

Have a dragon come up and breathe fire at the little parents. / Have the parents grow big and breathe fire back at the dragon. / Have the dragon put his tail between his legs and yelp and run away, scattering sparks as he runs.

Have the parents grow little again. / Have

them walking down the middle of the street. / Have them lie down in the street. / Have them become as flat as pancakes in the middle of the street. / Have them jump up and run around the street, still as flat as pancakes. / Have a steamroller standing in the middle of the street. / Have the pancake parents run and jump under the roller of the steamroller. / Have them fit nicely under there because they are so flat. / Have them feeling comfortable under there. / Have them suddenly grow big and fat and upset the steamroller.

Have another steamroller come down the street. / Have the parents get little again, and thin like pancakes. / Have them lie down in front of the steamroller. / Have it roll on them. / Have them suddenly get big and fat and upset the steamroller.

Have the parents run around on the street, laughing at the two upset steamrollers. /

Have the steamrollers jump up and chase the parents. / Have the steamrollers run over the parents and flatten them out like pancakes on the street. / Have the steamrollers run around laughing at the flat parents.

Have the steamrollers run over the flat parents. / Have the parents suddenly get big and fat and upset the steamrollers again. / Have the steamrollers burst into tears. / Have the parents run around laughing at the steamrollers and calling them crybabies. / Have the steamrollers jump up and run away, still crying.

Have the four parents standing in the middle of the street. / Double the number, so that there are eight parents standing in the street. / Have the eight parents standing on a mountain. / Have them flying through the air. / Have them walking on the bottom of the ocean.

Have them swimming in the ocean. / Have a shark swim up and eat two of the eight parents. / Have the shark swim away. / Make two new parents there, to take the places of the ones that were eaten up. / Have another shark come up and eat two more of the parents. / Have the shark swim away. / Make two new parents to take the places of those that were eaten by the second shark.

Have another shark swim up to the parents. / Have him open his mouth to eat all the parents. / Have the parents grow much bigger. / Have them catch the shark and eat him all up. / Have them all say, "Mmm. That was good!"

Have the eight parents standing in the school yard. / Have four of them shrink until they are no bigger than pumpkins. / Have the same four be no bigger than peas. / Have the same four shrink away to nothing. / Have two more shrink away to nothing.

Have the two parents who are left turn blue. / Have them on the roof. / Have them in this room. / Make them any color you like. / Have them be little. / Put them in all the corners of the room, one corner after another. / Have them shrink away to nothing.

Have two new parents right there (*pointing*). / Have no parents there. / Have two parents there. / Have them wink at you. / What would you like to do with them now? / All right, do it.

What was the name of the game we just played?

Party

Sometimes other children get together and don't let you in. They might even have a party and not invite you. Would you feel unhappy? I would. But it happens to everybody sometimes.

This game is called PARTY.

Let us imagine that there is a big party of boys and girls in the school yard. / Would you like to be at the party with them? / All right, be there with them.

Have all the children singing songs. / Are

you singing too? / Have all the children playing with a big ball. / Have them sitting at a big table. / Have them eating good things. / Have them standing on the table. / Have them pick up the table and carry it around the school yard. / Have them take it to a secret place and hide it. / Have them all go home. / Have the school yard empty.

Have one of your friends give a party. / Have the children you know go to the party. / You go to the party, too. / Have the party be over. / Have everyone go home.

Have the same friend give another party but not ask you to come. / Have all the children go to the party without you. / Go and stand outside the door of the house and ask them to let you in. / Have them let you in. / Have the party be a lot of fun. / Have the party be over. / Have everyone go home.

Have the same friends give another party

and tell you that you can't come. / Go and stand outside the door of the house and ask to come in. / Have them tell you that you can't come in. / Shout at them that you want to come in. / Have them say "No." / Tell them you will blow the door down if they don't let you in. / Have them put their hands over their ears.

Take a deep breath and blow on the door of the house. / Have it fall in with a crash. / Go right into the house and join the party. / Have carpenters come and put the door back up. / Have everyone say you are a wonderfully strong blower. / Have the party be a lot of fun. / Have everyone go home.

Now you give a party, and invite everyone except the friend who kept you out. / Have all the others come. / Have your friend come and stand outside the door and ask to be let in. / Tell him (her) to stay out. / Have him (her) take a deep breath and blow the door down. / Have him (her) come in and join the party. / Have the party be a lot of fun. / Have everyone except your friend go home.

Give your friend a spanking for blowing down the door. / Have your friend crying. / Make your friend put the door back up. / Have your friend ask if he (she) may blow down the door again. / Let him (her) blow down the door once more. / Have him (her) put it back up again. / Shake hands with him (her). / Have your friend go home.

Give a party and invite everyone in the whole world. / Have them all come. / Have the party be a lot of fun. / Have the party be over. / Have them all go home.

Give a party and invite nobody. / Have nobody come. / Have the party be a lot of fun. / Have the party be over. / Have nobody go home.

Give a party and invite nobody. / Have the whole world come. / Have the party be a lot of fun. / Have everyone go home.

Give a party and invite everyone in the world. / Have nobody come. / Have the party be fun. / Have the party be over. / Have nobody go home.

Give a party and invite nobody. / Have nobody come. / Have the party be fun. / Even though nobody came to the party, have the whole world go home from the party.

Give a party and have nobody come. / Have the whole world go home. / Have nobody come again. / Have the whole world go home.

Give a party and invite another you. / Have you come. / Have you go home. / Have a lot of yous come to the party. / Have them all go home. / Wave goodbye to them from the door.

What kind of a party would you like to give now? / All right, give it.

What was the name of the game we just played?

Helping

Sometimes you do things to help Mother and Father, but they don't like what you do. It's hard not to make mistakes. And it's hard to find things that really help. Does anyone ask you to help by keeping your room neat, or by being a good boy (girl)? That's not much fun, is it?

This game is called HELPING.

Let us imagine that you are in the kitchen, helping Mother. / Wash the dishes. / Cook something. / Scrub the floor. / Set the table. / Break something. / Pick it up and put it back together again. / Have it be as good as new.

Wash all the windows in the house. / Break one. / Go to the store and buy a new piece of glass for the window. / Put the new piece in the window.

Have your toys and possessions all around the house, making it untidy. / Have Mother and Father trip and fall over your things. / Have guests come and say, "What a messy house!" Have Mother and Father feeling sad because the house is messy. / Have them angry. / Have them go out for a walk. / Pick up your possessions and put them away. / Have new guests come and say, "What a neat and orderly house!" Have Mother and Father come home and be happy because the house is so neat.

Bring home a good report card from school and show it to Mother and Father. / Have them happy. / Bring home a bad report card and show it to them. / Have them sad. / Bring home a good report card. / Have them laughing.

Have Mother and Father catch the measles. / Take care of them while they are sick. / Make them stay in bed. / Read to them. / Cook for them. / Take them to the bathroom. / Take their temperatures. / Call the doctor. / Give Mother and Father lots and lots of medicine. / How does it taste to them? / Have them be well again. / Have them thank you for taking care of them.

Go out and get a job. / Come home from work and give Father a lot of money. / Give Mother some big packages of things to eat. / Buy some new clothes for yourself. / What kind will you buy? / Buy a new car for yourself. / Buy a new car for Mother and Father. / Buy another and keep it in your room.

Have the wind blow off the roof of the house. / Go up there and put a new roof on. / Have water leak into the house. / Get a bucket and carry the water out of the house. / Have some mosquitoes in the house. / Go around with a swatter and swat them. / Have Mother and Father thank you.

Ask Mother and Father to give you some more work to do around the house. / Have them say there is no work for you. / Make them stay indoors until they have some work for you. / Have them give you some work. / Have them thank you for doing the work.

Ask them for some more work. / Have them tell you that they will do everything themselves. / Get a long rope and tie them in their chairs. / Give them nothing to eat but bread and water. / Tell them to give you some more work. / Have them give you some. / Have them thank you for doing the work.

Have Mother and Father come to you and ask you what they can do to help you around the house. / Tell them there is nothing for them to do. / Tell them that you have a job and will buy everything for everybody. / Tell them that you will do all the cooking and cleaning. / Have them burst into tears because there is nothing for them to do. / Tell them they can help you by keeping their rooms neat. / Tell them they can help you by being good parents and not fighting or being rude. / Tell them they can help you by washing their faces and hands before meals and after meals without being told each time. / Have them thank you for letting them help you by doing these things.

What would you like to let them do now? / All right. / Anything else? / All right.

What was the name of the game we just played?

Theater

In the theater, the person on the stage does things, and the people in the audience watch. The person on the stage is called the performer. The performer hopes the audience will clap their hands or even cheer. If they don't even smile, the performer feels unhappy.

This game is called THEATER.

Let us imagine that we have a theater. / Make it a big theater, with lots of seats. / Have a red curtain hanging at the front of the stage. / Turn the curtain green. /

Have a lot of people in the seats, looking at the curtain. / You be one of the people sitting in the seats.

Have the curtain go up. / Have a girl walk out to the center of the stage. / Have the people in the audience clap. / Have the girl sing a song. / Have the audience clap again. / Have the girl leave the stage.

Have a man walk out and recite poetry. / Have the audience all nod their heads. / Have the man leave the stage.

Have a boy walk out and sing and recite. / Have the people clap. / Have a girl walk out and sing and recite. / Have the people clap again. / Have the boy and girl leave the stage.

Be up on the stage, looking out at the audience. / See all the bright lights shining toward you. / Say "Gobble-gobble-gobble," to the audience. / Have them clap. / Sing a song to them. / Have them cheer. / Have them go on clapping for a long time. / Do you like the way their clapping sounds?

Have them quiet again. / Be telling them a long story. / Have them listening very carefully. / Have them enjoying the story. / Have them hoping they can remember it, to tell their friends when they get home.

Be one of the people who are sitting in the audience. / See yourself up on the stage. / Hear yourself telling the story. / Lean over to the person who is sitting next to you in the audience and whisper in his ear. Say, "He (she) is telling a very good story." / Have that other person nod his head. / Have the story end. / Have the audience clap. / Be in the audience clapping for yourself up on the stage.

Be up on the stage, telling another story. / Finish the story. / Hear all the people applauding. / Stand on the stage and listen to the cheers and clapping for a long time. / Bow to the audience and walk off the stage.

Be out in the audience. / See yourself up on the stage. / See yourself bow to the audience. / See yourself walk off the stage. / Have the curtain go down. / Have the curtain go up.

Be up on the stage. / Bow to the audience. / Have them clap. / Whistle a tune for them. / Have them clap. / Sing a song for them. / Have them cheer. / Run around the stage and turn handsprings for them. / Have them stamp their feet and cheer. / Whistle another tune for them. / Have them tell you to stop. / Sing them another song. / Have them tell you to go away. / Turn handsprings for them. / Have them all walk out of the theater.

Have new people there. / Recite for them. / Have them all walk out of the theater. / Whistle at them. / Have all the people come running back and sit down in the seats. / Say "Gobble-gobble-gobble!" to them. / Have them clap and cheer and stamp their feet and tell each other that you are wonderful.

What would you like to do for them now? / All right. / Is there anything else you would like to do? / All right. / Is there anything else you would like the audience to do? / All right.

What was the name of the game we just played?

Captive

People like to move around when they want to. They like to feel free. They don't want to be tied up, or locked up, or sat on. Sometimes they don't even want to sit still in a chair. Do you feel like that sometimes? I feel like that sometimes.

This game is called CAPTIVE.

Let us imagine that we have a canary in a cage. / Turn him green. / Turn him blue. / Have him jumping around inside the cage. / Have him wishing he could fly outside. / Have him open the door of the cage and fly out. / Have him fly around the room. / Have him be glad to be outside. / Have him fly back into the cage. / Have him shut the door.

Put a lock on the door. / Have the canary try to open the door. / Have him stay in the cage, crying. / Have him stamp and shout. / Have him roll on the floor of the cage because he is so angry. / Have him jump up and bend the bars of the cage apart. / Have him fly out into the room. / Have him fly around the room, singing. / Have him fly back into the cage. / Have him bend the bars back into place again.

Now you be inside the cage instead of the canary. / Jump around inside the cage. / Try to get out of the cage. / Bend the bars of the cage and jump out. / Grow bigger. / Take the cage apart and throw the pieces away.

Have a new cage, big enough for you. / Be

inside it. / Bend the bars and jump out. / Grow even bigger. / Take the new cage apart and throw the pieces away.

Be inside an old castle. / Be locked in a dungeon at the bottom of the castle. / Have the dungeon made of stone, with iron bars. / Wish that you could be outside. / Put your hand against the wall of the dungeon and push the wall out into the moat. / Jump out of the dungeon. / Put your hand against the castle wall and push just a little. / Have the whole castle fall down with a great crash. / Put a new castle there. / Take a deep breath and blow the new castle down. / Blow all the pieces away. / Put a new castle there. / Put nothing there. / Look all around and see that there is no castle there.

Be in a cave. / Have many big rocks fall down outside and cover up the entrance of the cave. / Walk all around the cave and find that there is no way out. / Take a little breath and puff all the rocks away from the entrance of the cave. / Put new rocks there. / Put no rocks there. / Look at the entrance of the cave and see that there are no rocks there. / Walk out of the cave into the sunlight. / Look back at the cave. / Frown at the cave. / Have the cave fall flat. / Have flowers grow up out of the flat cave.

Be all tied up with thick ropes. / Have them around your wrists, and arms, and legs, and stomach, and feet. / Have them tight. / Lie there for a long time, all tied up. / Wonder if anyone is going to come and set you free. / Decide that no one is going to come. / Take a deep breath and break all the ropes. / Burn the ropes in a furnace. / Have new ropes lying on the ground. / Burn them, too. / Have new ropes. / Have them get old and fall apart. / Have no ropes. / Look around and see that there are no ropes.

Be sitting in a chair. / Have iron bands

holding you in the chair. / Have them around your wrists, and ankles, and chest, and neck. / Have someone telling you that you have to sit in that chair forever. / Yawn a great big yawn, and have the iron bands fall off. / Get up out of the chair. / Have the other person be very angry. / Take the chair apart and throw the pieces away. / Have the other person jump up and down in a rage.

Have another chair with iron bands. / Put that other person in it and fasten the iron bands. / Tell the other person to sit there for a week. / Have him (her) do it. / Unfasten the iron bands. / Let him (her) go free. / Take the chair apart and throw away the pieces. / Put a new chair there. / Have it get old and fall apart. / Throw away the pieces. / Put a new chair there. / Have no chair there at all. / Look around and see that there is no chair.

Where would you like to be now? / All right, be there. / Where now? / All right. / Where now? / All right.

Look up in that corner of the room (*pointing*) and see that you are not up there. / Look in another place and see that you are not there. / Another place. / Another place. / Another place. / Another place. / Another place.

What was the name of the game we just played?

Would you be unhappy if you were hungry and had nothing at all to eat? I would. Would you like it if someone told you that you had to eat, when you were not hungry? I wouldn't. The best thing is to have just enough, isn't it?

This game is called HUNGRY.

Let us imagine some things about being hungry and being not-hungry.

Let us imagine that we have a plate full of good things to eat. / Let us have a child looking at the plate. / You be the child. /

Be hungry and want to eat the food. / Eat the food. / Throw away the plate. / Have another plate of food. / Want to eat it. / Eat the food. / Throw the plate away. / Have another plate of food. / Be not-hungry. / Throw away the plate and the food. / Have another plate of food. / Be not-hungry. / Throw it all away.

Have an empty plate. / Be hungry. / Put the empty plate in a safe place. / Have a plate with one bean on it. / Be hungry. / Eat the one bean. / Have another bean there. / Be very hungry. / Eat the bean. / Have another bean there. / Be starving. / Eat the bean. / Be not-hungry. / Throw away the plate.

Have a whole room full of food. / Be not-hungry. / Begin to eat the food. / Get hungrier as you eat. / When you have eaten up all the food, be the most hungry. / Have one bean. / Eat it. / Be not-hungry. / Have a whole mountain of food. / Be not-hungry. / Begin to eat it. / Get hungrier and hungrier as you eat it. / When it is all gone, be the most hungry. / Have one grain of rice. / Eat the rice. / Be not-hungry.

Be at the table with Mother and Father. / Have three plates full of food. / Eat your food. / Eat Mother's food. / Eat Father's food. / Have Mother and Father be very hungry. / Throw away the plates and tell them there is no food.

Be at the table with them again. Eat up all their food. / Tell them there is no more food. / Have them begin to cry.

Be at the table with them again. / Have them be not-hungry. / Tell them to eat their food. / Have them eat it. / Give them new plates of food. / Tell them to eat it. / Have them eat it. / Have them say they are really not-hungry now. / Give them new plates of food. / Have them eat it. / Have them swell up because of all the food they have eaten. / Have them say they cannot eat another bite. / Give them new plates of food. / Have them eat it. / Have them swell up as big as elephants. / Give them new plates. / Have them eat. / Have them swell up as big as a house. / Give them new plates. / Have them eat. / Have them swell up as big as a mountain. / Give them new plates. / Have them eat. / Have them swell up as big as the whole world. / Tell them they are a good Mother and Father for eating all their food.

Have them be thin again. / Have them be hungry. / Have a whole room full of food, with good things to eat on one side, and things they do not like on the other side. / You eat up all the good things. / Have Mother and Father eat up all the other things.

Have another room full of food. / Open the window and throw all the food out. / Have Mother and Father come in and ask for something to eat. / Tell them the food is all gone.

Have a room full of food. / Be very fat. / Eat up all the food and grow thin. / Have no food. / Go a whole year without eating, and get fatter and fatter all the time.

Be very hungry. / Eat up all the food in the house. / Eat up all the suits and hats. / Eat up all the shoes and underwear. / Eat up all the furniture. / Eat up all the books. / Eat up all the windows and doors. / Eat up the roof. / Eat up the walls. / Eat up the floors. / Eat up all the trees around the house. / Eat up all the other houses. / Eat up all the mountains. / Eat up all the rivers. / Eat up all the oceans. / Eat up the whole world. / Be hungry still.

Have the whole world new again. / Eat it all up again. / Have it new again. / Eat it up again. / Have it new again. / Eat it up again.

What would you like to do about that now? / All right.

What was the name of the game we just played?

Mirror

When you look straight into a mirror, you see your reflection. Your reflection looks just like you. What would it be like if your reflection looked bigger than you, or smaller, or looked like somebody else?

This game is called MIRROR.

Imagine that you are standing in front of a big mirror. / You are looking at your reflection, and it is looking at you. / You smile at it, and it smiles at you. / You frown at it, and it frowns at you. / You nod your head at it, and it nods its head at you.

Now you smile at your reflection, but it frowns at you. / You frown at it, and it smiles at you. / You nod your head at it, and it shakes its head at you.

Have your reflection grow bigger, while you stay the way you are. / You grow as big as your reflection. / Have your reflection grow smaller, while you stay the way you are. / You grow as small as your reflection. / Be your regular size, but have your reflection be smaller than you. / Have your reflection say, "I wish I could be as big as you are." / Tell your reflection to get bigger. / Have it grow as big as you are.

Look away from the mirror. / Look back and see that your reflection has the head of a bear. / Look away. / Look back and see that it is a whole bear. / Have it turn into a girl (boy) (*opposite sex*). / Have it turn into a boy (girl) (*same sex*). / Have your reflection look like you. / Have it look like somebody else. / Whom does it look like?

Have it look like Father. / Have it look like Mother. / Have it look like a teacher. / Which teacher does it look like? / Have it look like an animal. / What animal does it look like? / Have it look like a tree. / Have it look like a rock. / Have it look like a chair.

Have it look like some clothes standing there with nobody in them. / Have somebody in them. / Who is it? / Have your reflection look like you.

What would you like to have your reflection do now? / All right. / What now? / All right. / (*Continue until the child runs out of ideas.*)

What was the name of the game we just played?

Manners

Parents try to teach children good manners, but there are still a lot of bad manners around. Where do they come from? Do you suppose there is someone who is teaching the children bad manners? Who could it be?

This game is called MANNERS.

Let us have a boy (girl) who has very bad manners. / Have him (her) teach his (her) parents to have bad manners. / Have him teach them to slam doors. / Have him teach them to break windows. / Have him teach them to shout at the dinner table. / Have him teach them to throw butter at each other. / Have him teach them to spill their milk. / Have him teach them to eat with their fingers. / Have him teach them to roll under the table. / Have him teach them to jump on top of the table and dance.

Have him teach them to interrupt each other. / Have him teach them to shout at guests. / Have him teach them to take the biggest piece of pie before anyone else can get it. / Have him teach them to do something else which is bad manners. / Have him teach them to do something else which is bad manners. / Something else which is bad manners. / Something else. / Something else.

Have a boy (girl) who has good manners. / Have him (her) teach his (her) parents to have good manners. / Have him teach them to close doors quietly. / Have him teach them to take good care of windows. / Have him teach them to speak softly at the table. / Have him teach them to use butter only as food. / Have him teach them to handle things without spilling them. / Have him teach them to eat with their forks and spoons. / Have him teach them to keep their napkins in their laps. / Have him teach them to stay in their chairs.

Have him teach them to listen to each other without interrupting. / Have him teach them to treat guests nicely. / Have him teach them to share good things fairly. / Have him teach them to do something else which is good manners. / Have him teach them to do something else which is good manners. / Something else which is good manners. / Something else. / Something else.

What would you like him (her) to teach them about manners now? / All right. /

What now? / Is there anything else? / All right. / Is there anything you want to say about manners?

What was the name of the game we just played?

Breathing

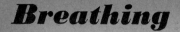

When we breathe — like this (demonstrate, in and out, mouth closed) — *the air goes in and out. If there is dust floating in the air, it goes in, too. Most of it sticks in your nose. If you get too much, you sneeze, or cough, or blow your nose.*

This game is called BREATHING.

Let us imagine that we have a goldfish in front of us. / Have the fish swim around. / Have the fish swim into your mouth. / Take a deep breath and have the fish go down into your lungs, into your chest. / Have the fish swim around in there. / Let out your breath and have the fish swim out into the room again.

Now breathe in a lot of tiny goldfish. / Have them swim around in your chest. / Breathe them all out again.

Let's see what kind of things you can breathe in and out of your chest. / Breathe in a lot of rose petals. / Breathe them out again. / Breathe in a lot of water. / Have it gurgling in your chest. / Breathe it out again. / Breathe in a lot of dry leaves. / Have them blowing around in your chest. / Breathe them out again. / Breathe in a lot of raindrops. / Have them pattering in your chest. / Breathe them out again. / Breathe in a lot of sand. / Have it blowing around in your chest. / Breathe it out again. / Breathe in a lot of little firecrackers. / Have them all popping in your chest. / Breathe out the smoke and bits of them that are left. / Breathe in a lot of little lions. / Have them all roaring in your chest. / Breathe them out again.

Breathe in some fire. / Have it burning and crackling in your chest. / Breathe it out again. / Breathe in some logs of wood. / Set fire to them in your chest. / Have them roaring as they burn up. / Breathe out the smoke and ashes.

Have a big tree in front of you. / Breathe fire on the tree and burn it all up. / Have an old castle in front of you. / Breathe fire on the castle and have it fall down. / Have an ocean in front of you. / Breathe fire on the ocean and dry it up.

What would you like to breathe in now? / All right. / Now what? / All right. / What would you like to burn up by breathing fire on it? / All right. / (*Continue these until the child runs out of ideas.*)

Be a fish. / Be in the ocean. / Breathe the water of the ocean, in and out. / How do you like that? / Be a bird. / Be high in the air. / Breathe the cold air, in and out. / How do you like that? / Be a camel. / Be on the desert. / Breathe the hot wind of the desert, in and out. / How does that feel? / Be an old-fashioned steam locomotive. / Breathe out steam and smoke all over everything. / How is that? / Be a stone. / Don't breathe. / How do you like that? / Be a boy (girl). / Breathe the air of this room in and out. / How do you like that?

What is the name of this game?

Do you know where your heart is? Yes. It beats all the time. It works like a pump. It makes the blood go. Sometimes fast. Sometimes slow. Most of the time we forget all about it.

This game is called TICK-TOCK.

Let us imagine that you have a clock in your chest. / Let us hear it going "tick-tock." / Have it on the right side. / Have it on the left. / Have it in the middle. / Have it right there (*pointing to the heart*).

Have the clock right where your heart is. /
Have it in your head. / Have it in your foot.
/ Have it out in the yard. / Have it in a
clock shop. / Leave it there. / Turn your
heart into a clock. / Have it go "tick-tock."
/ Have it run fast. / Have it run slow. /
Have it run just right. / Throw it away. /
Have a little sewing machine there, instead.
/ Have it run fast. / Have it run slow. /
Have it run just right. / Throw it away. /
Have a water pump there. / Have it pump
fast. / Have it pump slow. / Have it pump
at just the right speed. / Throw it away. /
Have an oil pump there. / Have it pump
fast. / Have it pump slow. / Have it pump
just right. / Throw it away.

Have a balloon there. / Have it get bigger
and bigger. / Have it pop. / Have a football there. / Have it get bigger. / Have it
pop, too. / Have a firecracker there. / Light
it. / Have it explode. / Have a light bulb

there. / Light it. / Have it get hotter and hotter. / Have it melt. / Have a bomb there. / Have it explode.

Have your heart there. / Have it pump fast. / Have it pump slow. / Have it pump just right.

Have a lot of green dogs running around in your chest. / Have them running through your heart. / Have them turn yellow. / Throw them away. / Have a lot of men on horseback riding around in your chest. / Have them swinging swords. / Have them ride through your heart. / Have them slice it all up with their swords. / Throw away the horsemen. / Throw away the pieces of your heart. / Have a new heart.

Have it turn to gold. / Have it feel happy. / Have it turn to lead. / Have it feel sad. / Have it turn to wood. / Have it feel angry. / Have it turn to stone. / Have it feel cold. /

Have it turn into a potato. / Have it turn to glass. / Have it turn into a piece of ice. / Throw it away. / Have a new heart.

Have it beat fast. / Have it beat slow. / Have it go just right. / What are you going to do with it now? / All right.

What was the name of this game?

Camera

Your head is something like a camera. The light goes into it at the front. The pictures are at the back. A camera is mostly empty, but your head isn't. A camera doesn't think, but you do. You know when you are looking at a camera, but a camera doesn't know when it is looking at you.

This game is called CAMERA.

Let us imagine that your head is a camera, with two glass lenses in front, for eyes. / Open the lenses. / Close them. / Open them again. / Throw them away. / Have two new lenses. / Close them. / Open them. / Throw them away. / Have two new lenses.

Throw the lenses on the ground and stamp on them. / Have two new ones. / Throw those into the ocean. / Have two new ones. / Throw those into the fire. / Have two new ones. / Close them. / Open them.

Turn the camera into a head. / Have two eyes in front. / Close them. / Open them. / Throw them away. / Have two new ones. / Throw them on the ground and stamp on them. / Have two new ones. / Throw them into boiling water. / Have two new ones. / Throw them into the fire. / Have two new ones. / Make them beautiful. / Open them. / Close them.

Have your eyes turn to stone. / Have them turn to ice. / Have them be glowing coals. / Have them be glass. / Throw them away. / Have new ones.

Have two little automobiles out in front of you. / Have them drive into your eyes. /

Have two moons. / Push them into your eyes. / Have two suns. / Push them into your eyes. / Have two more suns. / Push them into your eyes. / Have two very big and very bright suns. / Push them into your eyes, too.

Have two new eyes. / Make them beautiful. / Close them. / Open them. / Blink them. / Have them feel happy.

Have two new eyes. / Have everything look green through them. / Have everything look yellow. / Have everything look dim, so that you cannot see things very well. / Have everything look bright and clear, so that you can see things perfectly. / Have everything look upside down. / Have everything look right side up again.

Have a man who is blind. / Give him two new eyes. / Have a woman who is blind. /

Give her two new eyes. / Have a boy who is blind. / Give him new eyes. / Have a girl who is blind. / Give her new eyes. / Have a baby whose eyes hurt. / Give the baby new eyes. / Is there anyone else you would like to give new eyes to? / All right. / Anyone else? / All right.

What would you like to do about eyes now? / All right.

What was the name of this game?

All Over

When do you think about your stomach? Most of us think about our stomachs only when they hurt. Is that fair? Suppose you were a stomach, and nobody thought about you unless you hurt. Let's make up for that right now.

The name of this game is ALL OVER.

Fill your head full of water. / Have the water spray out of your ears. / Have it spray out of your nose. / Have it spray out of your eyes. / Have it spray out of your mouth. / Have the water go back into your ears. /

Have it go back into your nose. / Have it go back into your eyes. / Have it go back into your mouth. / Have it spray out of all those places again. / Have it go in again. / What do you want it to do now? / All right.

Have a fire in your stomach. / Have your stomach full of ice. / Have it full of hot cereal. / Have it full of water. / Have it full of nothing. / Have it full of ice cream. / Have it full of sand. / Have nothing in it at all. / Have no stomach. / Have a new stomach. / What do you want to do about your stomach now? / All right.

Have your backbone get hot. / Have it get cold. / Have it get soft. / Have it get hard. / Have it turn blue. / Have it turn white. / Have it turn any color you like. / Take it out and throw it away. / Have a new backbone. / Have it crooked. / Have it straight. / Take it out. / Tie it in a bow. / Throw it away. / Have a new one. / Have it come apart and fall on the floor in pieces. / Have a new backbone. / What do you want to do with it? / All right.

Have your skin be cold. / Have it be hot. / Have it turn blue. / Have it turn green. / Have it turn to wood. / Have it get furry. / Have it grow scales like a fish. / Have it grow feathers. / Have it get smooth. / Have it be beautiful. / Have it get sores all over. / Have it be smooth again. / Have it feel good. / Have it itch. / Have it burning with fire all over. / Have it all burn up. / Have new skin. / Have it soft and smooth. / Have it tough as leather. / Have it hard as rock. / Have it soft and smooth. / How do you want it now? / All right.

What was this game called?

Boo!

Most children are a little bit afraid of the dark. I was afraid of the dark when I was a child. Children think that something may be hiding in the dark, when nothing is really there. Or they think the chair is a bear, when it is really a chair. Sometimes even grownups feel that way, but not so often as children do.

This game is called BOO!

Be asleep. / Be awake. / Be pretending to be asleep. / Be asleep. / Be awake. / Be asleep.

Be afraid of me. / Be not-afraid of me. / Be afraid of the table. / Be not-afraid of the table.

Is there something else you want to be afraid of? / All right, be afraid of it. / Now be not-afraid of it. (*Continue with this, until the child runs out of ideas.*)

Have a closet with the door shut. / Be outside the closet. / Have something big and black in the closet. / Open the door and shout "Boo!" at the thing. / Have the thing be afraid of you. / Have it run away. / Have another closet. / Have a big black thing in it. / Open the door and shout "Boo!" / Have the thing run away.

Would you like to scare something else? (*If the answer is No, repeat the above paragraph. Then, skip this paragraph. If the answer is Yes, continue.*) What would you like to scare? / All right. / What else? / All right. (*Continue until the child runs out of ideas.*)

What would you like to do about scaring now? / All right.

What is this game called?

Squeeze

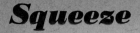

A *thimble is a little metal cap that goes on your finger. When you are sewing, you use the thimble to push the needle through the cloth. If you look inside a thimble, you can see that it is not big enough to hold very much.*

This game is called SQUEEZE.

Have a thimble. / Take a big automobile and squeeze it into the thimble. / Take a tree and squeeze it into the thimble, too. / Squeeze a house into the thimble. / Squeeze a mountain in, with all the other things. /

How is the thimble? Not full yet? / Squeeze the moon into the thimble. / Squeeze the sun into the thimble. / Squeeze the stars into the thimble. / How is it? Is it full now? / Do you want to squeeze anything else into it? / All right.

Take a horse and put him in your closet. / Have an elephant in your bed. / Have a steamroller in the bathroom. / Have a giraffe in a milk bottle. / Have a lion in a matchbox.

Have a battleship in your pocket. / Have a thimble in your hand. / Have everything in the whole world in the thimble. / Squeeze it.

What would you like to put into anything now? / All right. / Anything else? / All right.

What is this game called?

Being Things

If you have bad manners, you may eat like a pig, but you can't really be a pig. You can't know how a pig feels. The best way to imagine how a pig feels is to imagine that you are a pig. You can say, "Now I am a pig." There is nothing you can't be, in your imagination.

Would you like to be some things? / All right, this game is called BEING THINGS.

Be a bird. / Be a dog. / Be a pig. / Be an eagle. / Be a duck. / Be a tiger. / Be a lizard. / Be a shark. / Be a giraffe. / Be a chicken. / Be a mosquito. / Be a tarantula. / Be a rattlesnake. / Be an octopus. / Be a whale. / Be a goldfish in a bowl. / Be a cat. / Be a horse. / Be an ant. / Be a bee. / Be a butterfly. / Be a black widow spider. / Be a tree. / Be a squirrel. / Be a rabbit. / Be a wolf. / Be a hawk. / Be a pelican.

What is the most awful thing to be that you can think of? / All right, be that. / Now be the nicest thing you can think of. / Be something else. / Be something else. / Something else. / Something else.

Be something standing still. / Be something moving. / Be something walking. / Be something swimming. / Be something flying. / Be something lying down. / Be something standing up.

Be something hot. / Be something cold. / Be a mountain. / Be a person. / Be young.

/ Be old. / Be a tree. / Be a house. / Be a stone. / Be an animal. / Be a fish. / Be a snake. / Be a bird. / Be an insect. / Be water. / Be earth. / Be fire. / Be air. / Be wind, blowing. / Be a doughnut. / Be the hole in the doughnut. / Be an empty bottle. / Be the space in the bottle. / Be a balloon. / Be the air in the balloon.

Be Mother. / Be yourself. / Be Father. / Be yourself . / Be Brother. / Be yourself. / Be Sister . / Be yourself. / Be Uncle. / Be yourself. / Be Aunt. / Be yourself. / Be a doctor. / Be yourself. / Be a nurse. / Be yourself. / Be a policeman. / Be yourself. / Be someone else. / Be yourself.

Who would you like to be now? / All right. / Anyone else? / All right.

Be a rock. / Be a mountain. / Be the moon. / Be the sun. / Be a star. / Be an airplane, flying. / Be an automobile. / Be a boat. /

Be a telephone. / Be a letter. / Be a volcano. / Be a white cloud. / Be a black cloud. / Be yourself. / Be something no one has ever been before. / What is it?

Be nothing. / Be something. / Be nothing. / Be something.

What would you like to be now? / All right.

What is this game called?

Heavy

If you throw a baseball or a stone back over your shoulder, will it break a window? Or hit somebody? It might. It would be dangerous to throw an automobile back over your shoulder. Better not do that. Not a real one.

This game is called HEAVY.

Let us imagine that you are walking down the street. / Lean down and pick up a penny. / Throw it over your shoulder. / Pick up a baseball. / Throw it over your shoulder. / Pick up a watermelon and throw it over your shoulder. / Hear it break when it hits the street. / Look back and see the seeds scattered all over.

Pick up a suitcase and throw it over your shoulder. / Pick up a horse that is standing there and throw it over your shoulder. / Pick up an automobile and throw it over your shoulder. / Pick up a truck and throw it over your shoulder.

Walk up to an office building, ten stories high. / Take hold of the handles of the front door. / Pick the whole building up by its door handles. / Throw it over your shoulder.

Lean down and try to pick up a toy dog. / Have the dog be too heavy to pick up. / Have two big men trying to pick the dog up, but have it be too heavy. / Have a machine trying to pick the dog up, but have it be too heavy. / You pick up the dog. / Have the dog kiss you.

Now, walk up to Father and pick him up with one hand. / Pick Mother up with the other hand. / While you are holding them, have Father pick up a policeman. / Have Mother pick up a nurse. / You walk around, holding them all up. / Have them say, "Put us down. Put us down." / Put them down. / Have them say, "Thank you."

What would you like to pick up now? / All right. / What now? / All right.

What was the name of the game we just played?

Baby

Babies have a pretty good time. People are always picking them up and carrying them around. Or giving them baths and changing their diapers. Or feeding them. Or kissing them and rocking them to sleep. Suppose there were a very big baby who could pick people up.

This game is called BABY.

Be a baby. / Have Mother holding you in her arms. / Have Father come up and say, "Let me hold the baby." / Have Mother say, "No, the baby belongs to me." / Have

Father say, "Please let me hold the baby." /
Have Mother give you to Father to hold.

Have Father rock you in his arms and sing
you a song. / Have Mother come up and
say, "Please let me hold the baby." / Have
Father say, "Do I have to?" / Have Mother
say, "Yes, I want the baby." / Have Father
give you to Mother to hold.

Have a big baby who is holding Mother
and Father in his (her) arms. / Have him
(her) rock them and sing them a song. /
Have the baby tell them that he (she) loves
them. / Have the baby tell them to go to
sleep. / Have them go to sleep.

What would you like to do about the baby
now? / All right. / What now? / All right.
(*Continue until the child runs out of ideas.*)

What was the name of the game we just
played?

Hard

When we walk around, we are walking through air. You can't see it, but if you swing your hand around, you can feel it. Air is easy to walk through. At the beach or in a swimming pool you can walk through water. Water is harder to walk through than air. Trees or bricks or rocks are too hard to walk through, except in your imagination.

This game is called HARD.

Be outdoors, walking. / Walk through some tall grass. / Walk through some bushes. / Walk up to a thick hedge. / Walk right through it. / Walk up to a big tree trunk. / Walk right through it.

Find a big rock. / Walk into the middle of it and look around inside it. / Have it look rocky in there. / Walk out on the other side of the rock. / Walk up to a brick wall. / Walk through it. / Walk through a stone wall. / Walk through an automobile. / Walk through a railroad engine.

Be up in an airplane, flying around the world. / Jump out of the airplane. / Start to fall down to the ground. / Wonder whether you are going to hit hard when you land. / Be afraid. / Decide that you are going to fall right through the world. / When you get to the ground, fall right through the world and come out the other side. / Now fall back to the ground on the other side of the world. / This time, hit hard when you land. / Have the world say, "Ouch!" / Say,

"I'm sorry." / Have the world say, "That's all right."

Be walking along by the side of a road. / Have your feet start to sink into the ground. / Sink in up to your knees, but keep on walking. / Sink in up to your waist. / Sink in up to your chest, and keep on walking. / Sink in up to your chin. / Sink all the way in. / Keep on walking.

Walk by some big rocks, under the ground. / Walk by some water pipes down there. / Look at them and see how rusty they are. / Walk under the road. / Listen to the cars rumbling along, up above you.

Walk away from the road until you are under a grassy field. / Walk by the roots of a big tree. / Listen to a gopher working in his burrow. Hear him go *scratch, scratch, scratch.* / Poke a hole in his burrow, so that you can talk to him. / Say, "Hello, gopher."

/ Have the gopher say, "What are you doing down here?" / Tell him you are exploring. / Have him say, "Okay."

Walk under a hill. / Find a big cave. / Walk into the cave. / Walk toward the mouth of the cave. / Walk out of the cave onto the grassy field. / Look all around at the trees and bushes. / Dust your clothes off. / Take a deep breath. / Have the air smell good. / Notice that the gopher is looking at you out of his hole. / Say, "Goodbye, gopher." / Have him say goodbye.

What would you like to do about those things now? / All right.

What was the name of the game we just played?

Seeing

When you lose something, do you run all around looking for it? That is one way to find it. Another way is to stay where you are and look into all the places where it might be. You are not looking with your eyes but with your memory and your imagination. Often you can find what you have lost right away. Of course, it doesn't always work — but then running all around doesn't always work, either.

This game is called SEEING.

Let us imagine that you can see anywhere. / Look into the next room and see what is in there. / Look into the next house. / What do you see? / Look into another house. / What do you see? / Look into a store. / What do you see? / Look into another store. / What do you see?

Look inside a clock. / See the wheels going around. / Look under a bed. / See someone's shoe that is lost under there. / Look into a dark closet. / See the clothes hanging there. / Look into the ocean. / See the fish swimming there. / Look into the sand at the beach. / See a box buried there. / Look into the box. / See gold coins and pearls and rubies and diamonds and emeralds and candy inside the box.

Be in your bed at night. / Have the room be all dark. / Look at everything in the room. / Have it easy to see all the things in the room, even though the room is dark. / What do you see in your dark room? / What else? / What else? (*Continue until the child runs out of ideas.*)

Look into a can of beans that Mother has left in your dark room by mistake. / Have the beans say, "Shhh!" / Ask them, "What are you doing in my dark room?" / Have them say, "Sleeping, silly."

What would you like to do about seeing now? / All right. / What now? / All right.

What was the name of the game we just played?

Ouch!

When you go to the doctor and he says, "This won't hurt," what usually happens? Sometimes he says, "This may hurt a little bit." Then what happens? Sometimes when we think we are going to be hurt, we say "Ouch!" before anything hurts us. Have you done that? I've done that.

This game is called OUCH!

Imagine that you are running after a ball. / Fall down and bump your knee. / Have it hurt. / Say "Ouch!" / Now run again, but don't fall down. / Have your knee hurt anyway. / Say "Ouch!" / Run again, fall down, and bump your knee. / Have it not hurt at all. / Say "Ouch!"

Have another boy (girl) who is running after a ball. / Have him (her) fall down and bump his (her) knee. / Feel the hurt in your own knee. / Say "Ouch!"

(Repeat this paragraph twice, using first the opposite sex, then the same sex.)

Now be at the doctor's office. / Have the doctor say he is going to give you a shot. / Have him say, "This won't hurt." / Have him give you the shot. / Have it hurt. / Say "Ouch!" / Have the doctor say, "That didn't hurt."

Tell the doctor you are going to give him a shot. / Tell him it won't hurt. / Give him the shot. / Have it hurt him. / Have him say "Ouch!" / Tell him it didn't hurt *you*. / Have him say, "But it hurt *me*."

Be at school. / Tell the teacher about your shot. / Show the place to the teacher. / Have the place hurt. / Say "Ouch!" / Have the teacher ask, "Why did you say 'Ouch'?" / Say, "Because my shot hurt."

Now I want you to do something really. Put your hand on your head and say "Ouch!" / Very good. / Now put your hand on your knee and say "Ouch!" / Now the other knee. / Good.

Each thing I name, you put your hand on it and say "Ouch!" / Ready? Here we go.

Your head. / Your knee. / Your other knee. / Your other hand. / Your shoulder. / Your nose. / Your ear. / Your other ear. / The back of your neck. / The top of your head. / Your chin. / Your chest. / Your stomach. / Your leg. / Your other leg. / Your knee. / Your other knee. / Your foot. / Your other foot. / Your back. / All right.

What would you like to say "Ouch!" about now? / (*Let the child say "Ouch!" or talk about* ouches *until he runs out of ideas.*)

What was the name of the game we just played?

Bed

We don't like to feel sick, but sometimes we like to stay in bed to read a book, or sleep, or watch television, or do something else. Sometimes we like to stay in bed because we don't feel like going to school. After a while, we get tired of staying in bed, and we want to get up.

This game is called BED.

Let us imagine that you are staying home from school and are in bed for the day. / Have Mother come in and ask how you are feeling. / Tell her you feel fine. / Have her take your temperature. / Have her say,

"Your temperature is normal." / Have her give you some good medicine. / Have her bring you all the things you want to eat and drink. / Have her read to you. / Have her play games with you. / Tell her you want to get up. / Have her say, "If you can get up, you can go to school." / Tell her you will stay in bed and not go to school.

Have Mother take you to see the doctor. / Have the doctor look into your ears. / Have him put a cold stethoscope on your chest and listen to your breathing. / Have him look into your throat. / Have him push your tongue down with a stick. / When he does that, you say, "Aggle, aggle, aggle!" / Have him say, "This child is not sick." / Have Mother take you toward school. / Tell her you would rather go home to bed. / Have her take you home and put you to bed. / Say ,"Thank you, Mother." / Have her say, "That is all right."

How long are you going to stay in bed like that? / What do you want to do there? / What else? (*Continue until the child runs out of ideas.*) / Do you want to get up now? / All right.

What was the name of the game we just played?

I am going to ask you where some things are. I want you to point to each thing as I ask about it.

Where is your head? / Where is your foot? / Where is your hand? / Where is your stomach? / Where am I? / Where is the floor? / Where is the ceiling? / Where is the wall? / Where is your ear?

Where is your fist? / Where is your elbow? / Where is your shoulder? / Where is your chair?

Shake your head. / Move your foot. / Nod your head. / Move your other foot. / Clap your hands. / All right.

(*Optional.*) Stand up. / Reach for the ceiling. / Put your arms down. / Walk around your chair. / Sit down. / What would you like to do now?

Now I am going to ask you to touch some things. Put your finger on each thing when I tell you.

Touch the floor. / Touch the wall. / Touch the chair. / Touch the table. / Touch the bed (*or other object*). / Touch the glass. / Touch the .... / Touch the .... / Touch the ....

Touch the window. / Touch the other side of the door.

What do you want to touch now? / All right.